D1616232

Studies in Organic Chemistry 5

COMPREHENSIVE CARBANION CHEMISTRY

PART A

Studies in Organic Chemistry

Studies in Organic Chemistry 5

COMPREHENSIVE CARBANION CHEMISTRY

Edited by

E. Buncel
Department of Chemistry, Queen's University, Kingston, Ontario, Canada K7L 3N6

T. Durst
Department of Chemistry, University of Ottawa, Ottawa, Ontario, Canada K1N 6N5

PART A
STRUCTURE AND REACTIVITY

ELSEVIER SCIENTIFIC PUBLISHING COMPANY
Amsterdam — Oxford — New York   1980

ELSEVIER SCIENTIFIC PUBLISHING COMPANY
335 Jan van Galenstraat
P.O. Box 211, 1000 AE Amsterdam, The Netherlands

Distributors for the United States and Canada:

ELSEVIER/NORTH-HOLLAND INC.
52, Vanderbilt Avenue
New York, N.Y. 10017

ISBN 0-444-41913-6 (Vol. 5A)
ISBN 0-444-41737-0 (Series)

Printed in The Netherlands

FOREWORD

The impetus to the study of the structure, stability and reactivity of carbanions was provided to a large extent by Professor Donald J. Cram, through his own work, and in the publication in 1965 of the classic monograph "Fundamentals of Carbanion Chemistry". Since that time, the study of carbanion chemistry has intensified, in part as new techniques such as ^{13}C and hetero-nuclear magnetic resonance spectroscopy have become available, and in part as new theoretical concepts have come to light. A particularly interesting development is that of ion cyclotron resonance and related techniques for the gas phase investigation of carbanion reactivity. Such studies have heightened our awareness of medium effects and have caused a re-evaluation of the theoretical bases of structural and electronic effects.

Carbanion chemistry plays a central role in modern synthetic organic chemistry. This relationship has developed at an extremely rapid pace since the 1960's, due to the commercial availability of a variety of alkyllithiums, and the development of a number of potent non-nucleophilic bases such as lithium diisopropylamide, lithium 2,2,6,6-tetramethylpiperidide and sodium hexamethyldisilazane. The availability of these reagents has made accessible many structural types of carbanions which are extremely valuable as synthetic units since they generally undergo very efficient carbon-carbon bond formation with typical electrophiles.

In this series, which has been entitled "Comprehensive Carbanion Chemistry", it is hoped to discuss in detail key aspects of carbanion chemistry, via contributed chapters written by active investigators in the field. Several volumes are currently planned, each devoted to related aspects of carbanion chemistry. Thus Part A is concerned with the physical aspects of carbanions, namely the acidity of carbon acids both in solution and in the gas phase, the structure of mono- and dianions as determined by proton and carbon nuclear magnetic resonance, ultraviolet, infrared and Raman spectroscopy, and, the involvement of electron transfer processes in carbanion reactions. Subsequent volumes will deal with general aspects of carbon-carbon bond formation, including problems of stereo- and regiochemistry, and finally the generation and synthetic applications of various structural types of carbanions, e.g. silicon or sulfur stabilized, etc.

We would like to thank the authors of the individual chapters in the present volume for their excellent contributions and the extra effort which they undertook in preparing camera-ready copy manuscripts.

April, 1980

E.B.

T.D.

CONTENTS

CHAPTER 1

DIANIONS AND POLYANIONS

R.B. BATES

Department of Chemistry, University of Arizona, Tucson, Arizona 85721, USA

CONTENTS

I.   INTRODUCTION

A great variety of dianions and some higher anions with at least one carbon atom bearing charge have been reported, with no doubt many more to follow. They are often prepared easily and converted in good yield to many other substances, making them valuable intermediates in synthesis.

Dianions in which the negative charges are on two independent π (or other) systems have been largely omitted from this chapter as their structures, preparations, and reactions differ so little from those of mono-anions covered in other chapters. Examples are the dimer (1) of 1,1-di-phenylethylene anion radical,[1] the dianion (2) formed by dimetalating di-phenylmethane and related species,[2,3] and some highly lithiated compounds.[4] A few species (e.g., (3)[5]) have been included which might have been expect-ed to contain a single π system bearing two negative charges but which (usually for steric reasons) prefer a twisted arrangement with little or no overlap.

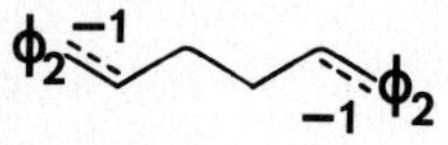

(1) 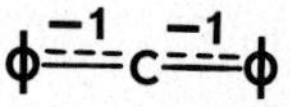   (2) 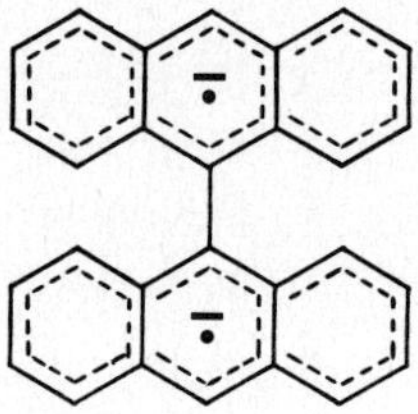   (3)

Before surveying the di- and higher anions that have been described, some generalizations will be made regarding their structures, preparations, and reactions.

A. Structures

Most of these substances have been only poorly characterized, due in part to their instability in air. In most cases, the only evidence that a dianion has been obtained comes from the products it gives with two equivalents of electrophile. In some cases, ^{1}H and/or ^{13}C nuclear mag-netic resonance (NMR) spectra have been obtained on the dianion in

solution, and in a few cases X-ray studies on suitable salts have shown
the molecular geometry in the solid state. Thus, for most of the
structures in this chapter, the geometry depicted is only a guess.

   Many structural principles familiar from hydrocarbon and monoanion
chemistry carry over without change. Alkyl substitution destabilizes
carbanions, i.e., the stability order is primary>secondary>tertiary.
Aromaticity is observed in many closed monocyclic systems with 4n+2 πe;
e.g. (4), where n=2, is readily prepared and relatively stable,[6] as are
many aromatic dianions with larger rings. It has been suggested[7] that in
(5), with n=1, which has been prepared[8] but may not be especially stable,
coulombic repulsion essentially balances the expected stabilization; the
corresponding dication, however, would appear from the spectral properties
of its mono- and dibenzo derivatives to be aromatic.[9] Steric inhibition
of resonance is also observed with dianions, an example being (3), shown
by ESR to have a triplet ground state with the two conjugated systems
essentially perpendicular.[5] Approximate electron densities on carbon
atoms can be deduced from ^{13}C and ^1H NMR shifts, with expected upfield
shifts of about 160 ppm/electron in the former and 10 ppm/electron in the
latter.[7] Anti-aromaticity is expected to destabilize the unobserved
benzene dianion (6).

      (4)   (5)   (6)

   Di- and higher anions have a few special features. The general
tendency of linearly conjugated systems to possess greater stabilization
than isomeric cross-conjugated systems is frequently reversed; e.g., (7)
is calculated and observed to be more stable than (8).[10] And unlike most
substances, many of these multiply charged anions have one or more filled
antibonding orbitals; fortunately, this destabilizing influence does not
preclude their preparation.

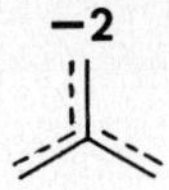

4

(7)

(8)

B. Preparations

The majority of the di- and higher anions in this chapter were prepared simply by dimetalation of a neutral (often readily available) species, e.g., (7) from isobutylene (9).

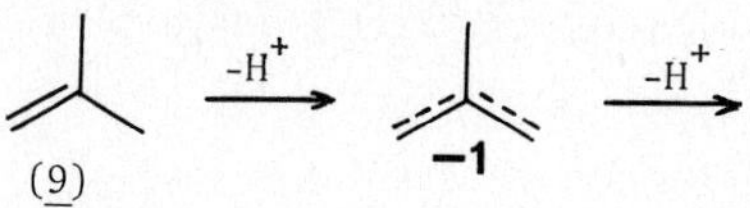

(Ref. 11)

Dimetalation of hydrocarbons is usually done with the very strong base n-butyllithium, with either tetramethylethylenediamine (TMEDA)[10] or potassium t-butoxide.[12] If one or more electronegative atoms such as oxygen will be bearing part of the negative charge in the substrate, weaker base systems may suffice, as in the preparations depicted for dianions (10)- (13).

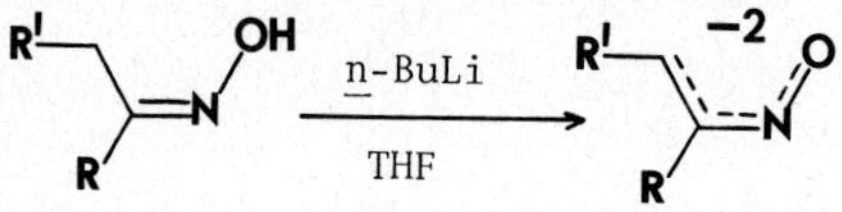

(Ref. 13)

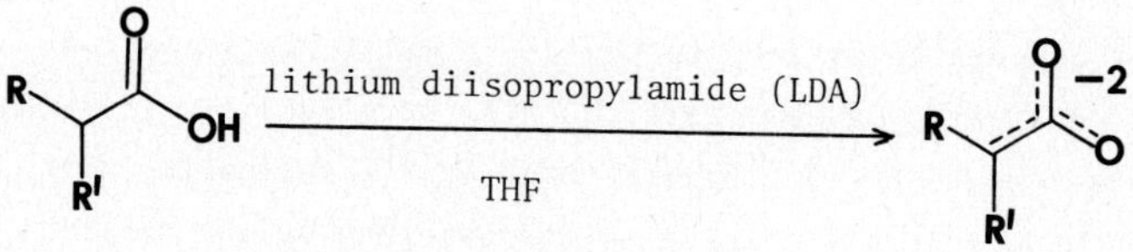

(10)

(Ref. 14)

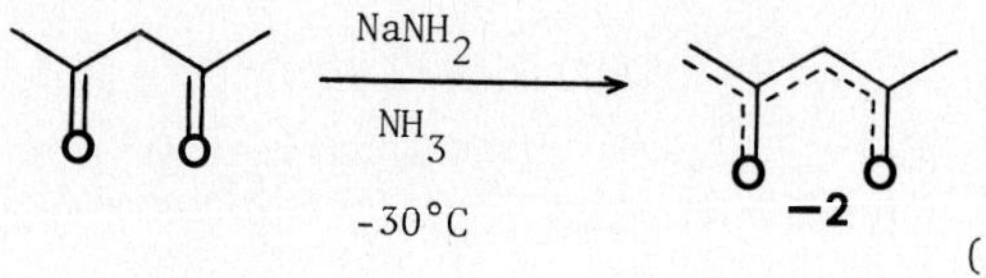

(11)

(Ref. 15)

(12)

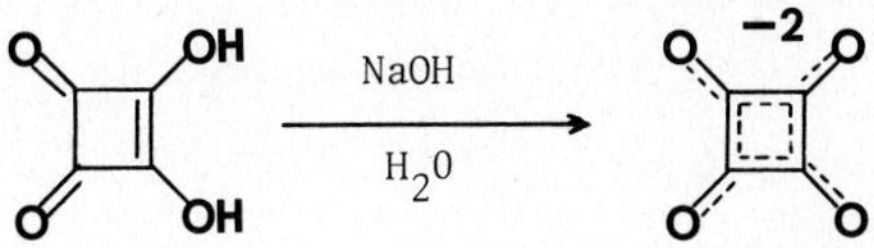

(Ref. 16)

(13)

In some cases no single base system will work because it will be either too weak to abstract the second proton or will react by addition rather than abstraction of the first proton. In such cases, it may be possible to obtain dianion by successive treatment with two different bases, e.g., as shown for (14).

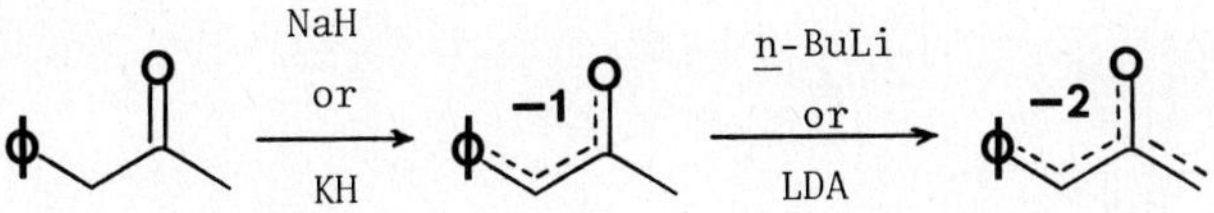

(Ref. 17)

(14)

The second most important method of preparation is by two-electron reduction of the corresponding neutral species electrochemically or with a metal, as shown for (4), (15), and (16).

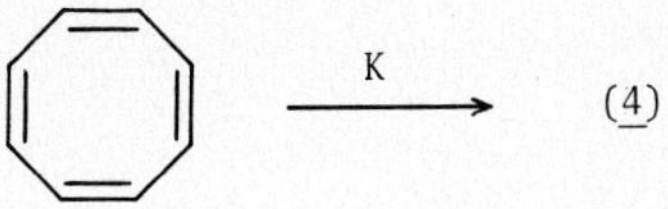

(4)

(Refs. 6,18)

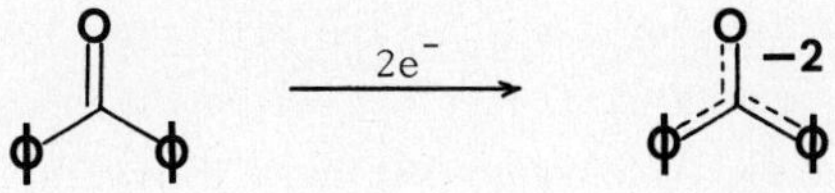

(15)

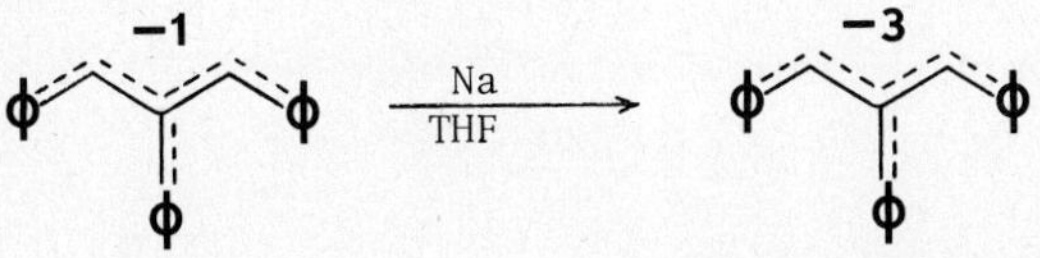

(Ref. 19)

(16)

(Ref. 20)

6

While overall a halogen-metal exchange, the preparation of (5) shown
is postulated to proceed by two-electron reduction of intermediate cyclobutadiene.

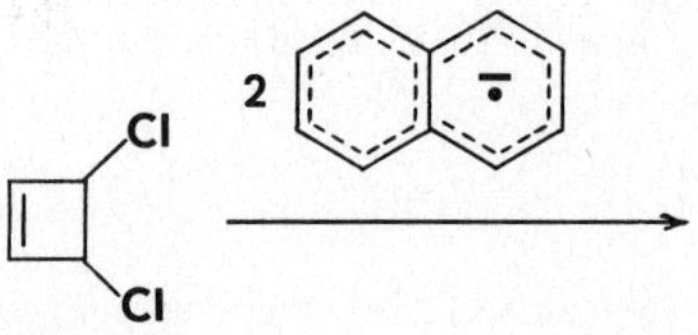

(5)   (Ref. 8)

When direct dimetalation fails to produce a dianion due to side
reactions,[21] an indirect route may succeed, e.g., in the synthesis depicted
for water-stable dianion (17), a vinylog of carbonate ion.

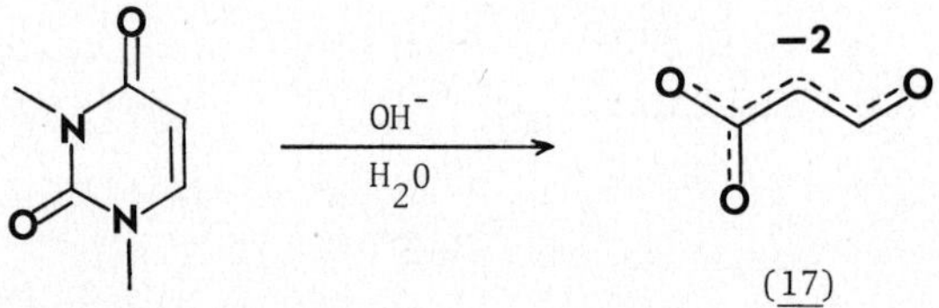

(Ref. 22)

(17)

The cation can be readily changed in some cases in which it is not
easy to prepare the desired salt directly, e.g., as shown for dianion (14).

$$(14) \ K^+Li^+ \ \xrightarrow[\text{THF}]{\text{LiBr}} \ (14) \ 2 \ Li^+ \qquad \text{(Ref. 17)}$$

C. Reactions

The most important reactions of dianions are with two electrophiles,
E_1 and E_2, which may or may not be different. Electrophiles used include
alkyl halides, dialkyl sulfates, aldehydes, ketones, epoxides, nitriles,
esters, carbon dioxide, and protonating agents. In many cases, the first
electrophile reacts at the last site of proton removal, e.g., as shown
for anions (12), (11), (18), and (19). The last three of these represent
possible improvements on the classical malonic ester synthesis involving
monoanions.

(12) $\xrightarrow[\text{(2) H}^+]{\text{(1) RX}}$ R$\diagup\diagdown\diagup\diagdown$ (O, O)   (Ref. 23)

(11) $\xrightarrow[\text{(2) H}^+]{\text{(1) R''X}}$ RR'R''CCO$_2$H   (Ref. 24)

(18) $\xrightarrow[\text{(2) H}^+]{\text{(1) RX}}$ RCH$_2$CO$_2$Et   (Ref. 25)

(19) $\xrightarrow[\text{(2) H}^+]{\text{(1) RX}}$ RMeCHCO$_2$H   (Ref. 26)

That the situation is not always as straightforward as these examples might indicate is illustrated by the cases of (14) and (20), which react as shown.

(14) $\xrightarrow[\text{(2) H}^+]{\text{(1) RX}}$ φ (structure with R, O, Me)   (Ref. 27)

(20)   (Ref. 28)

In many cases, the carbon initially attacked by an electrophile is the one with the highest electron density, though steric factors can enter as well.[27] Good agreement has been noted between protonation sites of dianions from aromatics and sites of highest electron density from molecular orbital calculations.[29] For some especially stable dianions, e.g. (7), reaction with two different electrophiles is unsatisfactory due to the monoanion from the first reaction competing successfully with the dianion for the first electrophile.[30] A further complication arises if proton exchange occurs between the dianion and the monoanion, as with the dipotassium salt of (14); this exchange was avoided by using the disodium or especially the dilithium salt.[31]

When both electrophiles are in the same molecule, a ring may be formed, e.g., in the synthesis depicted for (21). Sometimes a cyclization follows the reaction of the second electrophile, as in the preparations shown for (21)-(23).

$$(7) \xrightarrow[90\%]{Br(CH_2)_3Br}$$

(21)   (Ref. 32)

$$(7) \xrightarrow[80\%]{2\ \phi CN}$$

(22)   (Ref. 30)

$$(10) \xrightarrow{R''(CO)Y} \cdots \xrightarrow{H^+}$$

(23)   (Refs. 33,34)

Not surprisingly, some of these multiply charged anions react with certain alkyl halides by elimination rather than substitution.[35] Nevertheless, it was possible to effect substitution on t-butyl chloride with dianion (24) to produce (25), presumably by a single electron transfer mechanism.

(Ref. 36)

(24)   (25)

Loss of two electrons from a dianion may be smoothly accomplished with 1,2-dibromoethane, which allows a two-step dehydrogenation of a molecule like biallyl (26). In cases where a double bond cannot be formed in this sort of reaction, a ring forms, as with isobutylene (9)→(28).

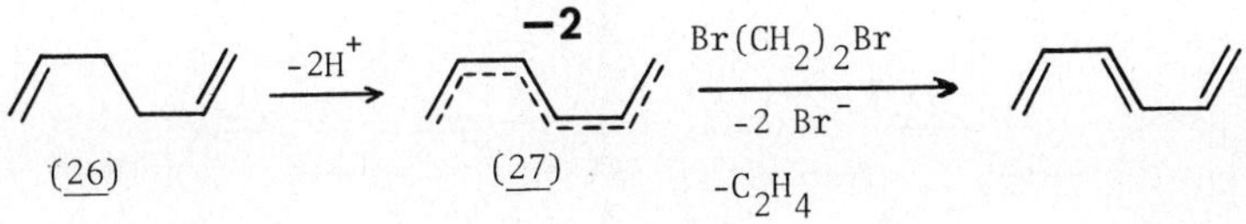

(Ref. 32)

(26)   (27)

(9) ⟶ (7) ⟶   (Ref. 32)

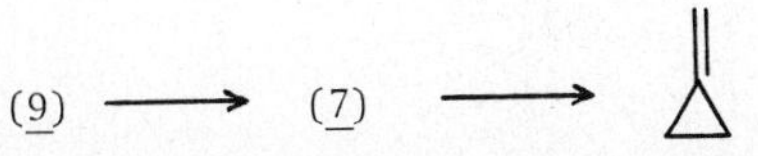

(28)

Some of these dianions, notably cyclooctatetraene dianion (4)[37,19] and (29),[38] form complexes readily with a variety of transition metals.

(29)

In a few cases dianions appear to form products, e.g., (32), (35), and (37), via initial electrocyclization.

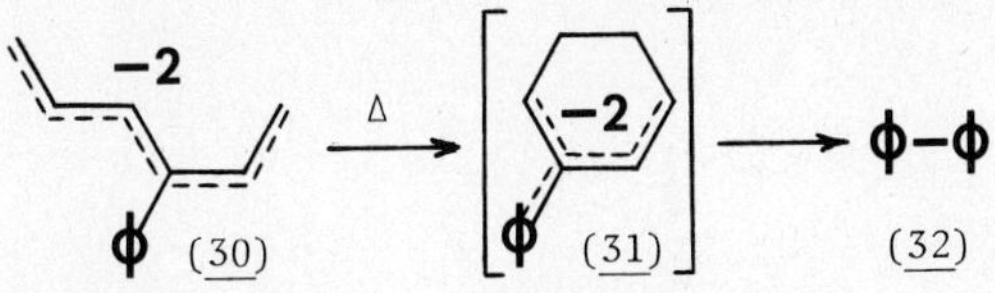

(Ref. 39)

(30)   (31)   (32)

(Ref. 40)

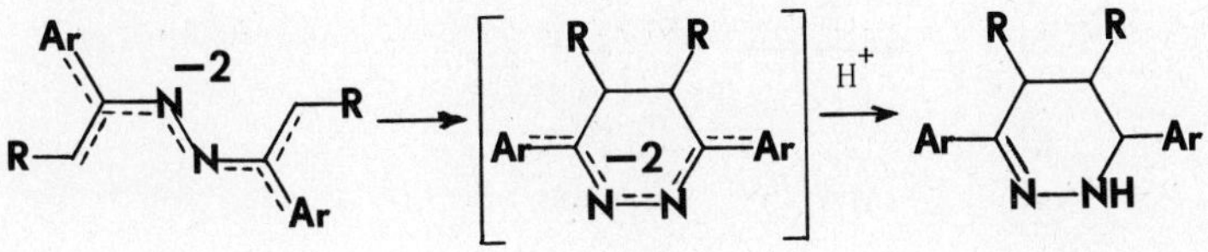

(33)   (34)   (35)

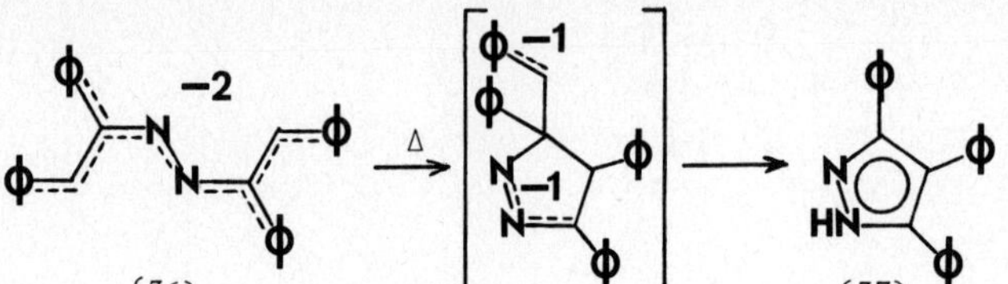

(36)   (37)   (Ref. 40)

A few dianions fragment, with varying consequences, e.g., (38) and (34) to give divinyl anions (39) and (40), and (42) to give vinyl anion (43). The latter example is part of the "Shapiro reaction" sequence (41)→(44).

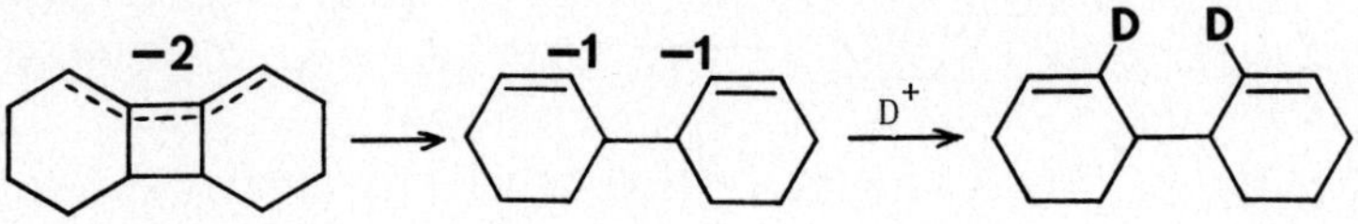

(38)   (39)   (Ref. 41)

(34)   (40)   (Ref. 40)

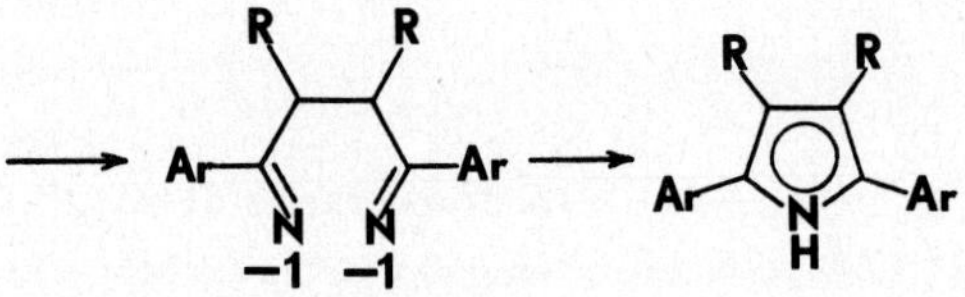

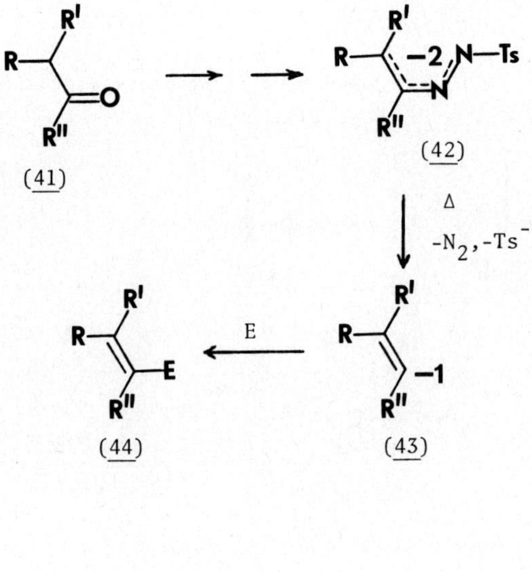

(41)   (42) Δ $-N_2, -Ts^-$ (43)   (44)   E   (Refs. 42-44)

II. DIANIONS

In this survey, dianions are presented according to the number of
atoms in the negatively charged π system (single heteroatoms such as
oxygen in a methoxyl group do not extend the conjugated system very
effectively and are arbitrarily not counted as being in the π system).
Counterions are not usually mentioned, but are generally Li^+, Na^+, or K^+,
with strong ion pairing in many cases.

A.   2-Carbon Dianions

With a predicted π bond energy of zero (simple Hückel MO calculations)
and electrostatic repulsion between like-charged atoms, ethylene dianion
(45) should be relatively difficult to prepare. Although the parent
species has apparently not yet been reported, measurements on some phenyl-
substituted derivatives (in which the charges are of course partially delocalized over the rings) are revealing: Angles of twist about the
central bond in (46), (47), and (48) are 30-90° (^{1}H NMR and electronic
spectra),[45,46] 48° (X-ray),[47] and 0° (X-ray),[48] respectively; central
bond lengths in the last two structures are 1.49 ± 0.05 and 1.42 ± 0.05 Å,
respectively. This willingness to twist and lengthening of the central
bonds as compared to the corresponding alkenes are consistent with
calculated lower π bond orders for the central bonds in the dianions.

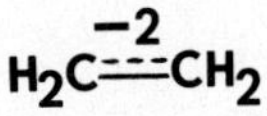

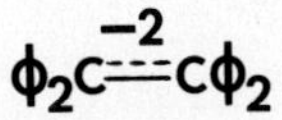

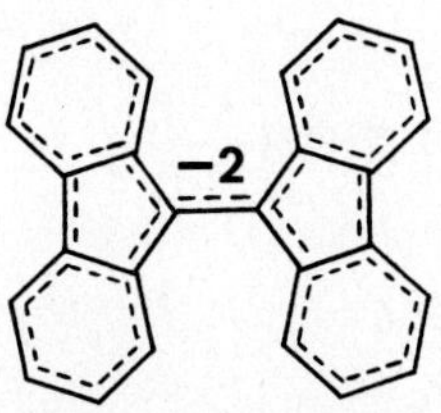

Several heteroatom derivatives of (45) have been prepared. The most
intriguing of these is a pentane-soluble substance which reacts as if it
were the dilithium salt of (49);[49] it was suggested that this dilithium
salt is a reaction intermediate, but that the pentane-soluble substance
may be a complex with a tetraalkyltin. Phenyl-substituted heteroatom
derivatives such as (50)[50] and (51)[51] have also been prepared.

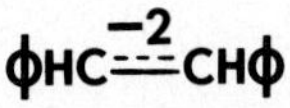

12

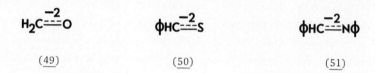

$$H_2C\overset{-2}{=\!=\!=}O$$ $$\phi HC\overset{-2}{=\!=\!=}S$$ $$\phi HC\overset{-2}{=\!=\!=}N\phi$$

(49)   (50)   (51)

B. 4-Carbon Dianions

Butadiene dianion (8) has been prepared as a crystalline red or orange dilithium salt solvated by TMEDA (tetramethylethylenediamine)[10,32] and as an analytically pure white magnesium salt solvated by two THF (tetrahydrofuran) molecules.[52] An unsolvated version of the dilithium salt may also have been prepared by a metal atom route.[53] The dilithium salt in solution had methylene absorption at $\delta 0.0$ and methinyl absorption at $\delta 4.8$ in its ^{1}H NMR spectrum.[10] Absorptions at 1604 and 1575 cm^{-1} in the infrared spectrum of the magnesium salt were interpreted as due to trans and cis double bonds, and their relative intensities suggested a cis/trans ratio of 15.5.[52] Structures (52) and (53) were suggested, with the latter favored due to the very low solubility of the salt in THF.

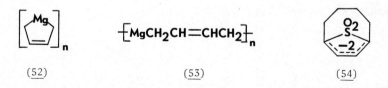

(52)   (53)   (54)

Though the structural information available to date on the above compounds leaves much to be desired, it is worth noting that it is in accord with the expectation, based on compounds with the same π system such as the 1,2-dihaloethenes and analogy with hexatriene dianion (27)[54] that the cis isomer is more stable than the trans. The reason for this preference is probably favorable 1,4-overlap, though other explanations have been offered.[55]

Magnesium derivatives analogous to that above have also been prepared from isoprene[56] and myrcene.[57] The latter derivative was dark,
highly viscous, and apparently polymeric. Sulfone-stabilized dianion (54)
has recently been made.[58] Strained butadiene dianion derivative (38) is
unstable and fragments at room temperature to give two vinyl anions.[41]

Many heteroatom derivatives of butadiene dianion have been prepared:
A series of acrolein dianions (55) with stabilization from phosphorus
groupings;[59] thioacrolein dianion (20),[60,28] which gives over 95% of Z
products on reaction with an electrophile at each end of the π system;
hydrazone-derived dianions (56)[61] and (42);[42,44] oxime-derived dianions
(10) and (57);[13,33,62] acyloin-derived dianions (58);[63,64,14] and dithiene
dianions (29).[38] The stereochemistry shown for most of these dianions is
inferred rather than demonstrated except for the oxime-derived dianions
(10), for which strong preference for syn-dianion is shown by the finding
of only syn-dianion (10, R=Me, R' = H) when acetone oxime is dimetalated,
and only syn-dianion (10, R = R' = Me) when syn-butanone oxime is dimetalated. There is a limit to the preference for syn-dianion, as demonstrated
by the loss of a methyl hydrogen from syn-methyl isopropyl ketone oxime
to give anti-dianion (57) rather than loss of a methinyl hydrogen to give
the syn-dianion. No syn-anti equilibrium was observed in these dianions
even on refluxing in THF for 1 hour.

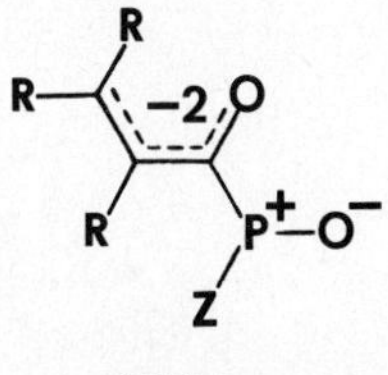

(55)

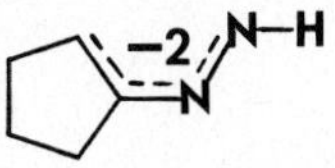

(56)

R = H or Me
Z = NMe$_2$, NEt$_2$, or OEt

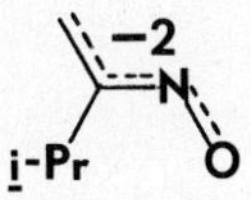

(57)

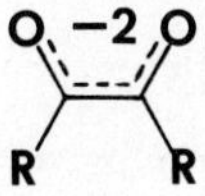

(58)

The dilithium salt of the simplest cross-conjugated dianion, 2-methyleneallyl dianion (7) has been prepared in solution[11] and as a solid solvated by TMEDA.[32] It has been pointed out that this system has the same degeneracy of the second and third π orbitals which characterizes benzene, and the term "Y-aromaticity" was suggested for such substances.[65] It is presumably planar. Its large resonance energy is reflected in its ease of preparation as compared to its linearly conjugated isomer (8). Alkylated analog (59) has also been prepared.[66]

(59)

Sulfur- and phosphorus-substituted derivatives of the mono-oxygen analog of (7) have been prepared: (60)[67-69] and (61)[70,71] with R and R' = H or alkyl and (62).[72] In none of these cases was the geometry determined.

(60)   (61)   (62)

The dioxygen analog of (7), i.e. (11, R = R' = H),[73] and many alkyl substituted derivatives[74,24,75-80] have been prepared by treating carboxylic acids with strong bases. Again, derivatives substituted with hetero-atoms were made: (11, R = NMe$_2$ or -NEt$_2$,[81,82] -Oϕ,[83] -SiMe$_3$,[84] and

-SMe[85] or -Sϕ[86]). Disulfur analogs (63, R, R' = H, alkyl) have been prepared similarly.[87]

(63)

Cyclobutadiene dianion (5) should be an aromatic system, but has proven difficult to prepare; it is believed to have been prepared as the disodium salt in THF at -40°, but unfortunately no spectral parameters were obtained on it.[8]

C. 6-Carbon Dianions

An X-ray study has been performed on the red dilithium salt of hexatriene dianion (27) solvated by two TMEDA molecules.[54] The shape of the dianion is as shown; this shape, earlier predicted from MO calculations to be the most stable one,[88] also is favored in solution as evidenced by the small (7 Hz) coupling constant between the protons on C2 and C3.[10] The basis for favoring this shape over the fully extended one is presumably some composite of the favorable 1,4 overlap and additional coordination of lithium to a fourth carbon atom which occur in the observed shape. There is a lithium above one group of four carbons and one below the other related through a center of symmetry; Li-C distances are 2.27, 2.21, 2.26, and 2.40 Å to carbons 1-4, respectively.

As expected from MO calculations, the C1-C2 and C2-C3 bonds are about equally long (1.36 and 1.38 ± 0.05 Å) and are shorter than the central bond (1.46 ± 0.05 Å). The dianion can thus be approximated as two allyl anions attached by a single bond, a situation reminiscent of butadiene (central bond, 1.483 Å). As in butadiene, some delocalization energy is very likely gained in (27) by having the two π systems coplanar.

Sulfone-stabilized derivatives (64) and (65) have been made,[58] but it is not clear how much overlap occurs around the π system. Heteratom-substituted derivatives of (27) include: (66);[33] (67), a proposed intermediate in a reaction of a penicillin derivative;[89] and (68, R = H, Me).[90]

16

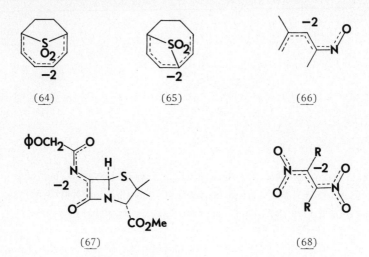

(64)   (65)   (66)

(67)   (68)

Branched-chain dianion (69) can be thought of as two allyl anions joined in a different way. It is calculated to be more stable than linear isomer (27),[10] and it is indeed easily prepared as the red crystalline dilithium salt solvated by TMEDA. The relatively large value (11.5 Hz) of the critical coupling constant indicates that (presumably for steric reasons) it adopts the planar shape depicted. The protons within each methylene group were equivalent on the NMR time scale, indicating low rotation barriers about the adjacent carbon-carbon bonds.

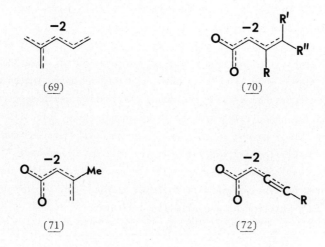

(69)   (70)

(71)   (72)

Several dioxygen analogs of the type (70) are known, including the simplest such compound (R = R' = R" = H).[75,91] (70, R = R" = H, R' = Et) and (70, R = R' = H, R" = Et) were not interconverted at 0° in 30 min in THF-hexane, indicating a relatively high rotation barrier about the bond connecting the atoms bearing the alkyl groups.[92] This is in accord with the expected concentration of charge on the oxygen atoms with resultant increased double bond character for this bond. (70, R' = R" = H, R = Me) appeared to be in rapid equilibrium with (71) at room temperature, with the latter compound favored.[93] (72, R = Et and φ), which includes two sp hybridized carbons in the conjugated system containing the negative charge, has also been reported.[94]

Many dioxygen analogs of the type (73) have also been described: R = R' = H;[15,95] R = alkyl, R' = H;[23,15,96,31] R = alkoxy, R' = H;[15,97] and R = methoxy, R' = alkyl.[97,98].

Analogs (17)[22], (74),[25] and (75)[99] with three heteroatoms bearing charge have also been prepared.

(73)   (74)   (75)

An attempt to prepare dianion (76), which is calculated to have less delocalization energy than isomeric dianions (69) and (27), gave little if any of this dianion under conditions used successfully for the preparation of these other isomers,[10] but heteroatom analog (77) has been made.[33] (78), the fourth and last isomer in this group, calculated to have considerable delocalization energy,[10] has·been prepared by metalating 2,3-dimethyl-1,3-butadiene,[12] and its dioxygen analog (79) has been described.[100]

(76)   (77)

18

(78) (79)

None of the possible cyclic 6-carbon dianions has been reported, but a few derivatives are known: Trimethylenecyclopropane dianions (80) as the tetrabutylammonium salts with many combinations of Y = -CN and/or -CO$_2$Me;[101] trioxygen analog (81);[102,103] and the very stable dianion (82).[104] The anti-aromatic benzene dianion (6) has been calculated to have a singlet ground state.[105]

(80) (81) (82)

D. 8-Carbon Dianions

Surprisingly (in view of the considerable literature on its cyclic analog), octatetraene dianion (83) has only recently been prepared.[106] Its conjugated system, with some perturbation due to homoconjugation, is present in homocyclooctatetraene dianion (84, R = R' = H).[107-109] The NMR parameters of the dilithium salt of (84) suggest that one substituent (R) lies over the ring as depicted, with a high barrier to the rotations which would make R and R' equivalent. The coupling constants between protons on adjacent sp^2 carbons were all 7.9-9.1 Hz, suggesting that these atoms are not quite coplanar, with a similar degree of twist around each of the involved bonds.[109] Methyl derivatives (84, R = H, R' = Me) and (R = R' = Me) have also been prepared and their NMR spectra described.[110]

(83)

(84)

A few heteroatom-substituted acyclic analogs are known, mostly with branched chains: (85, R, R' = H, Me);[90] (86)[95] and (87),[111] which share the same pattern of three oxygens bearing negative charge, but probably not the same shape; and (88, R = H, p-MeOC$_6$H$_4$).[112]

(85)

(86)

(87)

(88)

Of the cyclic 8-atom dianion systems that have been described, those with the smallest rings are (89)[7] and squarate ion (90)[102,103] and its sulfur analog (91).[113] X-ray studies have been carried out on the dipotassium salts of both, solvated by one water molecule in each case.[113,16] Both dianions show the expected D_{4h} symmetry. In the former case, the closeness of dianions to one another in the cell was felt to indicate charge transfer. In the latter case, the bond lengths suggested C-C bond orders of 1.25 and C-S π bond orders of 1.5, in accordance with the negative charges being very largely on sulfur.

(89)

(90)

20

(91)   (92)

The ^{1}H NMR parameters of the disodium salt of stable dianion (92)
have been reported,[114] and indicate that the negative charge is not
exclusively on the two sulfurs, but is to a considerable extent on the
ring atoms. This salt forms yellow air-sensitive crystals[114] which contain THF when crystallized from THF.[115]

Moving to 6-membered ring examples, thiobenzaldehyde dianion (50)
dilithium salt was recently reported as an orange suspension in
hexane.[50,28] Among the dianions (93)-(95) which might be derived by
deprotonating xylenes, the dianions (94, R = H, Me) derived from m-xylenes
were most stable, followed by (93) from o-xylene, and the p-xylene dimetalation product was not (95), but the product from dimetalation on the
same carbon atom![116] Thus dianion (94, R = H), in which the two charges
are essentially delocalized over only 5 atoms instead of all 8 as in
(93) and (95), is more stable than (93) and (95). However, as was the
case with butadiene dianion (8) vs. the isomeric cross-conjugated dianion
(7), MO calculations support the observed stability order. In valence
bond terms, while all three isomeric dianions have 10 contributing resonance forms, 4 of these have charges on adjacent carbons for both (93)
and (95), vs. none for (94). The apparent extra stability of (93) over

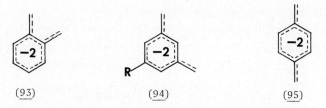

(93)   (94)   (95)

(95) may be related to the extra stabilization of Z- over E-butadiene
dianion (8; see above). That the p-form (95) is reasonable is shown by

analogy to hydroquinone dianion, whose infrared spectrum has recently been recorded and analyzed.[117] Nitrogen-substituted analogs of the m-dianion (94) are also known: (96) and (97).[118]

(96)   (97)

Methylenecycloheptatrienyl dianion (98) has been calculated and observed to be very stable for a dianion.[66]

An extraordinary amount of chemistry has been done with cyclooctatetraene (COT) dianion (4) since its first preparation in 1960[6] with K^+ and Li^+ counterions. As electron exchange between COT and COT anion radical is slow they differ in geometry; as it is fast between COT anion radical and dianion (4), these must have similar geometry. COT was known to be tub-shaped, and from the above results the dianion (4) cannot have this geometry; it was assumed to be planar. This conclusion has been supported by X-ray studies on the dipotassium salt solvated by a molecule of diglyme,[119] which show 1.40 ± 0.02 Å C-C bonds, and on 1,3,5,7-tetramethyl-COT dianion dipotassium salt with 2 diglymes.[120] Ion-pairing between (4) and various alkali metals in many solvents has been studied,[18,121,122] and its salts with alkali metals heavier than Na have been observed to fluoresce in a 2-methyl-THF glass at 77 K.[123] From the [7]Li chemical shift of its dilithium salt, it appears to be highly aromatic.[124]

(98)   (99)

COT dianion (4) is an excellent ligand for transition metals[37] and lanthanides.[19] Perhaps its most notable complex is the sandwich it forms with uranium[IV], termed uranocene (99),[125] which from an X-ray study has D_{8h} symmetry with 1.39 ± 0.01 Å C-C bonds.[126] X-ray studies have been carried out on several other COT dianion complexes,[126-129] adding the finding that with 1,3,5,7-tetramethyl-COT ligands, all of the methyls bend inward toward the uranium 4.1°, presumably to allow better overlap of the p orbitals of the ligand with 5f orbitals of the metal.[129] Both ^{1}H NMR shifts[130,131] and Mossbauer shifts[132] suggest that bonding involves charge transfer from filled ligand π MO's to vacant f orbitals of the metal.

Derivatives of COT dianion (4) which have been described include (100; Y = C, Si, Ge, and Sn),[133] (101) and (102),[134] and (103).[58] The exact geometry of (103) is not known, but there is believed to be enough distortion of the carbon atoms from coplanarity that there is not good overlap all the way around the 8-membered ring in this purple dianion (λ_{max} 545 nm (ε∿970)).

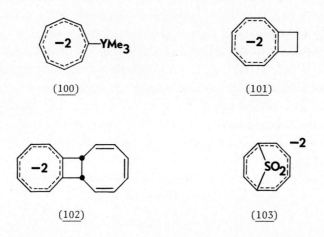

(100)   (101)

(102)   (103)

Pentalene dianion (104), which can be thought of as a bridged version of COT dianion (4), has been prepared, and unlike the antiaromatic hydrocarbon pentalene, is quite stable.[135] Bis-homocyclooctatetraene dianion (105) and tris-homocyclooctatetraene dianion (106) are probable reaction intermediates but were not spectroscopically characterized.[136]

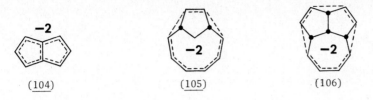

(104)   (105)   (106)

E.   10-Carbon Dianions

Monocyclics of this type with 5-membered rings are croconate dianion
(107),[102,103] which has a singlet ground state,[137] and its dithio analog
(108).[138]   An X-ray study of diammonium croconate showed coplanarity of all
atoms and 5-fold symmetry with C-C bond lengths of 1.46 ± 0.01 Å and C-O
bond lengths of 1.25 ± 0.01 Å.[139]

(107)   (108)

Among 6-membered ring monocyclics, (31)[39] and (109)[140] are possible
reaction intermediates, while (110),[141] (111),[14] (112),[61] and (113)[142,34,143]
have been prepared in high concentration, as have (114; R = R' = H;
R = H, R' = Me; R = Me, R' = H),[144] (14),[145,27,17] (115, R = H),[146,73,77,80]
(115, R = NMe$_2$ and NEt$_2$),[81] (116),[147] and (117).[148]   An X-ray study on the
dipotassium salt of the last of these showed the expected symmetry.

(109)   (110)   (111)

24

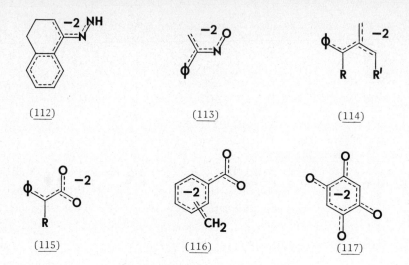

(112)   (113)   (114)

(115)   (116)   (117)

    Bicyclic dianions in this class include (118),[145] azulene dianion
(119), for whose dilithium salts ^{7}Li NMR shifts have been measured,[124]
and naphthalene dianion (120).[29,149-152] Only the dilithium salt of the
latter is appreciably soluble in ethers;[149,152] an X-ray study on this
salt with the lithium atoms each solvated by a TMEDA molecule has shown
the 10-carbon system to be not quite planar, with a lithium above one
ring and the other lithium below the other ring.[150] Using a general correlation between Li-N bond length and carbanion stability, the relatively
long (2.11 Å) bonds in this structure were used as indication of its
decreased stability as compared to certain resonance-stabilized monoanion
salts. It was noted that naphthalene dianion (120) is a stronger base than
the corresponding anion radical.[151]

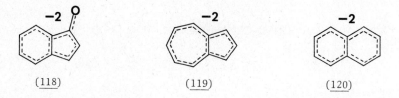

(118)   (119)   (120)

F. 12-Carbon Dianions

Monocyclics with 6-membered rings include (30);[39] (121),[153,15,154-156] in which rotation about the far right C-C bond is slow on the NMR time scale as shown by the non-equivalence of the attached protons;[153,154] and (122).[102]

(121)

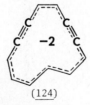

(122)

The simplest 12-membered ring case, [12]annulene dianion (123), with its 14 πe system, is as expected from the Hückel rule much more stable than [12]annulene itself.[157] Dianion (123) exhibits a diamagnetic ring current with the 3 inner protons absorbing at τ14.60. Unlike the hydrocarbon, there is not fast conformational mobility in the dianion. For steric reasons, the dianion is believed to deviate slightly form coplanarity. Dehydro[12]annulenes (124) and (125)[158] are also aromatic. The internal proton in (124) absorbs at τ16.88 and the others at τ2-4, again indicating a diatropic molecule; rotations are slow up to 30°C, fitting the generalization that charged systems have more to gain by delocalization than do neutral molecules. The ^{1}H NMR spectrum of (126) consists of a singlet at τ3.26, again showing a diamagnetic ring current. Similarly, the bridge protons in (126) absorb at τ15.52 and 16.08 (compared to 7.71 and 3.00 in the hydrocarbon), and in (127) at τ16.44 (compared to 3.96); the outer protons absorb 1-2 ppm to lower field in both these dianions than in the hydrocarbons.[159]

(123)   (124)   (125)

(126)   (127)

The various bicyclic systems in this class include biphenyl dianion
(128),[29] whose resonance Raman spectrum was measured,[160] and which forms
stable dilithium[152] and dicesium salts.[161] Besides simple naphthalenediol
dianions such as (129),[117,162] a more complex heteroatom-substituted
analog (130) is known.[118] Benzo-COT dianion (131) appears from dispropor-
tonation equilibrium studies on the corresponding anion radical to have
the negative charge largely on the 8-membered ring.[163] Heptalene dianion
(132) with its 14 πe periphery is much more stable than heptalene itself,
and exhibits a large diamagnetic ring current; it is probably planar, with
$\underline{D}_{2h}$ symmetry.[164]

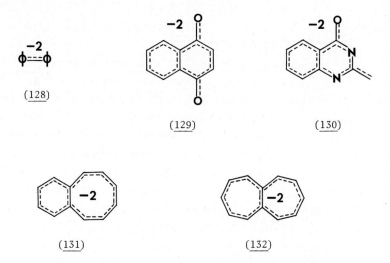

(128)   (129)   (130)

(131)   (132)

Among tricyclics in this series, biphenylene dianion (133),[29,124]
(134),[165] and (135)[166] have 14 πe peripheries and are relatively stable.
Acenaphthylene dianion (136) does not, but can still be prepared.[29,124,
167,168] The ¹H NMR spectra of (136) and related dianions exhibit
broadening due to electron exchange with the corresponding anion radical.[167]

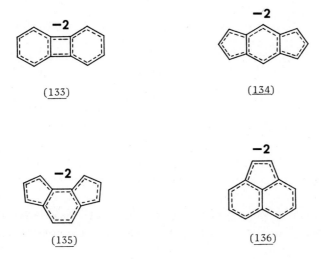

(133)

(134)

(135)

(136)

G. 14-Carbon Dianions

Monocyclics are the violet (137) with a 5-membered ring,[169] (138)[15] and (139)[170] with 6-membered rings, and (140)[171] and (141)[124,171] with 14-membered rings. The ^{1}H NMR shifts of the last two of these dianions as compared to the corresponding hydrocarbons were used to support the generalization that deviations of the perimeter from planarity reduce paramagnetic ring current more effectively than diamagnetic ones. The shift differences in going from the hydrocarbon to the dianion for (140) were +2.1 ppm for outer H's and -3.1 for bridge H's, and for (141) were +12.1 for outer H's and -25.3 for inner H's.

(137)

(138)

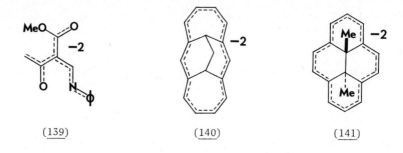

(139) (140) (141)

The most extensively studied bicyclic with a 14-carbon π system is
stilbene dianion (48),[172-174] on whose dilithium salts solvated by TMEDA
and pentamethyldiethylenetriamine X-ray studies have been carried out.[48]
The anions in these salts have all carbons essentially coplanar, with
trans configurations, and central bonds longer than in trans-stilbene by
about 0.1 Å as expected from MO calculations. From their electronic
spectra, it has been deduced that simple stilbene dianions like (48)
are trans and coplanar or nearly coplanar in solution whereas when there
are alkyl substituents on both carbons of the double bond as in (142),
the molecule is twisted about the central bond.[172] The cis-trans isomerization in stilbene catalyzed by electron transfer agents has been deduced
to proceed via the corresponding dianions, taking advantage of the much
lower barrier to rotation in the dianions than in the hydrocarbons or
anion radicals.[173,174] Dianion (143) has been prepared to serve as a
model cis-stilbene dianion and its electronic spectrum recorded.[175]
Derivatives (144)[176] and (145)[51] have also been described.

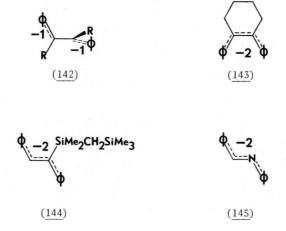

(142) (143)

(144) (145)

Bicyclics with different skeletons include benzophenone dianion (146, Ar = φ),[177,160,178] its nitrogen analogs (146, Ar = α-, β-, and γ-pyridyl),[179,180] naphthalene derivative (147),[181] and various biphenyl derivatives (148: R = Me, R' = φ; R = φCH$_2$CH$_2$, R' = φ; R = φ, R' = H).[118]

(146)   (147)   (148)

A tricyclic example with one 5-membered ring is fluorenone dianion (149).[182] The commonest tricyclic dianions of this class contain only 6-membered rings: Phenanthrene dianion (150)[29] and anthracene dianion (151, R = R' = H).[29,167,171,124,178,152,183] The infrared[184] and Raman spectra[185] of the latter have been extensively studied and indicate D$_{2h}$ symmetry. Derivatives of (151) which have been prepared include: R = H, R' = D;[185] R = R' = D;[185,184] R = H, R' = Me or Et; R = Me, R' = Et; R = R' = Me; R = R' = Et;[186] and perdeutero.[185,184]

(149)   (150)   (151)

Two isomeric tetracyclic 14-carbon dianions have been described: (152)[187] and (153).[188] The properties of each can be well approximated by a model with a central double bond and a 14 πe periphery.

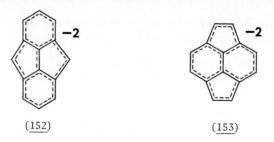

(152)   (153)

H. 16-Carbon Dianions

With a single ring are (154), in which the charges are claimed to be located mainly on the carbons α to -CN;[189] (155);[190] (156);[191] and [16]annulene dianion (157).[192,193] The latter is quite stable, as is expected from its favorable number of pi electrons. It has a strong diamagnetic ring current (inner protons absorb at τ18.2, outer at τ2.6 and 1.2) and a temperature independent ^{1}H NMR spectrum up to at least 140°C, indicating considerable barriers to rotation. This and analysis of its UV spectrum suggest that it is essentially planar.

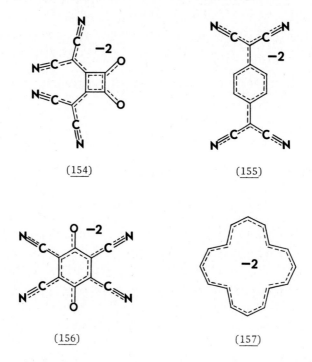

(154)   (155)

(156)   (157)

Most of the bicyclic examples have two benzene rings and four other atoms in the π systems: (158),[194] (159),[39] (160; M = Si, Sn),[195] (34)[40] (161),[142] (162),[141] (163),[142] (164, Y = H),[142,196,61] (164; Y = F, Me, Cl, MeO),[196] (165, a yellow indicator),[197,80] (166, with possible delocalization between the π systems),[198] and (167).[199] A bicyclic with 8-membered rings only is (168).[122]

(158)

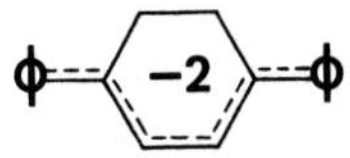

(159)

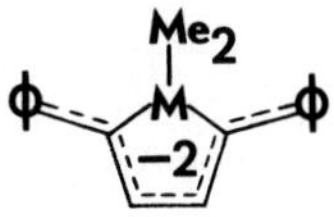

(160)

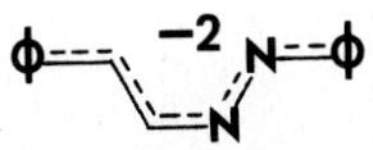

(161)

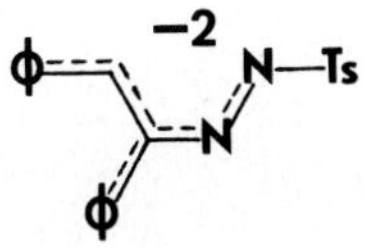

(162)

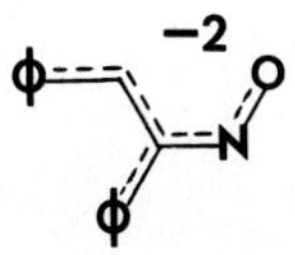

(163)

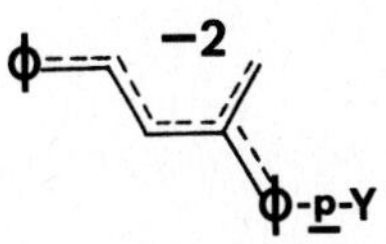

(164)

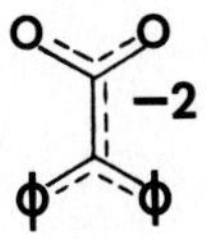

(165)

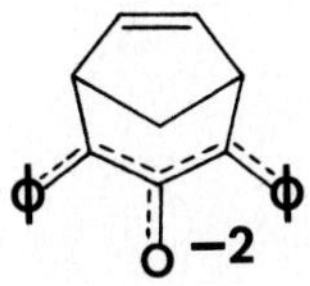

(166)

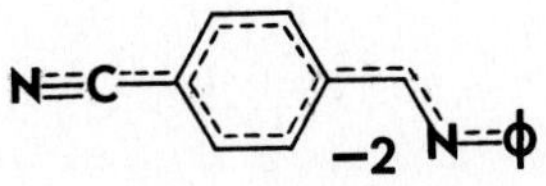

(167)

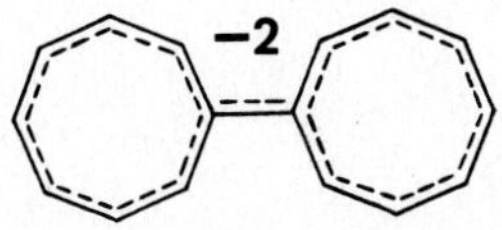

(168)

32

Tricyclics in this series are known with ring sizes in the 5-8 range: (169, which form crystalline Na salts melting above 300°C),[200] (170),[80] (171),[201] (172),[117] and (173, in which the extra electrons are believed to reside largely in the 8-membered ring).[163,122] Several tetracyclics have been described: (174, R = H, Me),[202] (175),[124,167] and pyrenide dianion (176).[29,124,203]

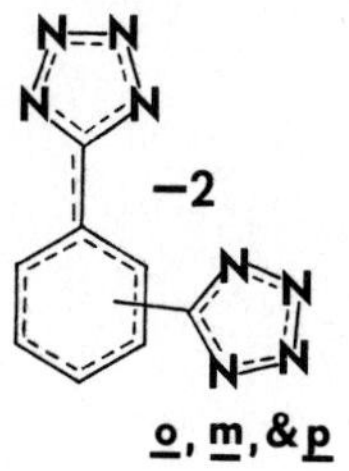

(169)

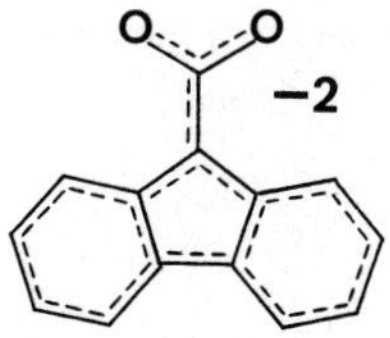

(170)

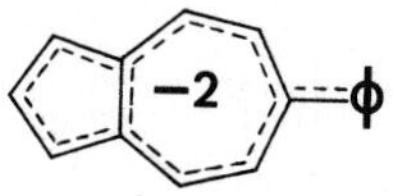

(171)

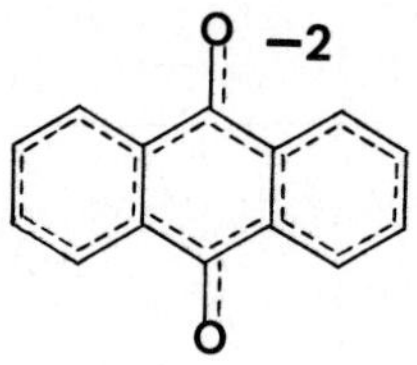

(172)

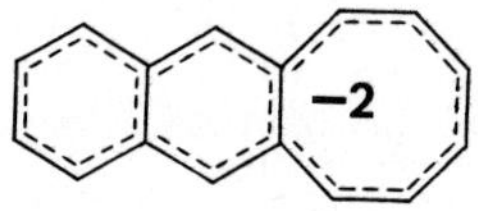

(173)

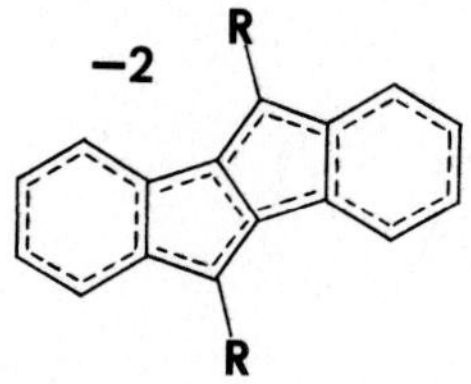

(174)

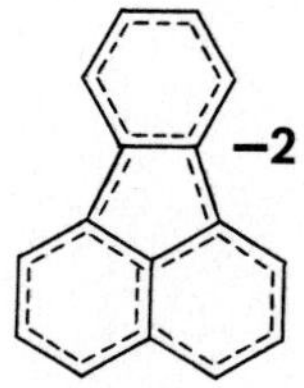

(175)

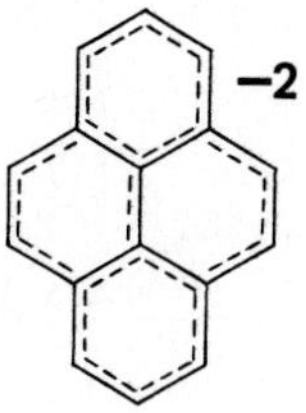

(176)

I. 18-Carbon Dianions

The violet dipotassium salt of monocyclic dianion (177) is a semiconductor; an X-ray study confirms its structure.[169]

The monocyclic [18]annulene dianion (178) or (179) has 20 πe and should be antiaromatic, with a calculated resonance energy of -8.7 to -5 kcal/mole.[204] In accordance with this, it exhibits π bond alternation; two rapidly interconverting structures were observed by NMR, but it was not clear whether they were of type (178) or (179).

(177)   (178)   (179)

Most of the bicyclics have two benzene rings: (33),[142,40] (180),[109] (181),[143] and (182).[205] A case with two 9-membered rings is (183).[206]

The only tricyclics described in this series are terphenyl dianion (184)[160] and dark green peripherally anti-aromatic dianion (185), which may be planar.[207]

(180)   (181)

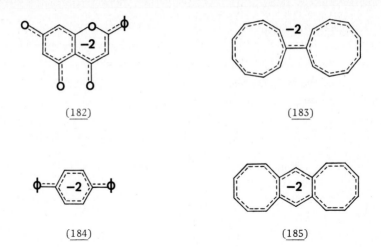

(182)   (183)

(184)   (185)

Among tetracyclics, tetracene dianion (186) has been especially well studied;[167,124,184,208-211] its isomers (187),[29,124,183] (188),[29,124,183] (189),[29,124] and (190),[212,213] have also been prepared. The last of these is of special interest as it has been shown by ESR measurements to be a ground state triplet. Actually, three distinct triplet spectra appear as a 2-methyl-THF solution is diluted with diglyme, suggesting successive solvation of the two counterions (Na$^+$ or K$^+$) by the new ether in contact ion pairs or progress to solvent-separated ion pairs.

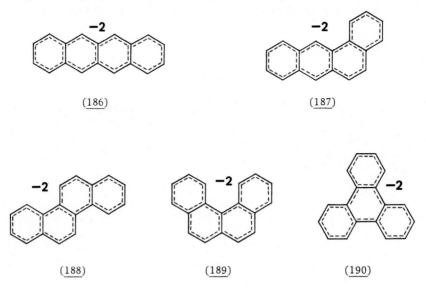

(186)   (187)

(188)   (189)   (190)

J. 20-Carbon Dianions

A bicyclic example is (191).[15] Tricyclics with three 6-membered rings include: (24);[214,125,36] (192), more stable than (193), with interconversion essentially stopped at -78°C;[216,217] and (194).[118] A further tricyclic (195) has been prepared.[122]

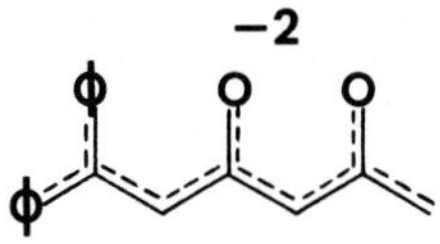

(191) 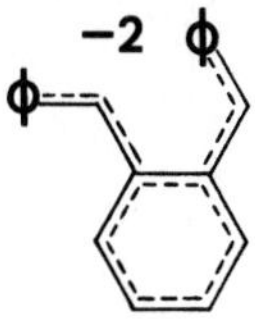   (192) 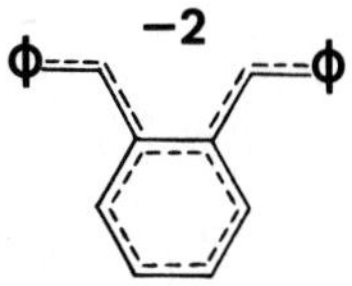   (193)

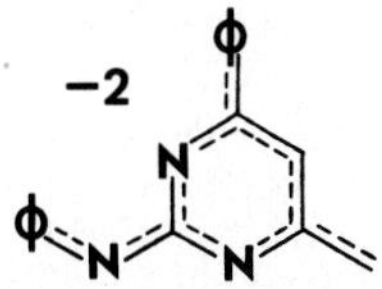

(194) 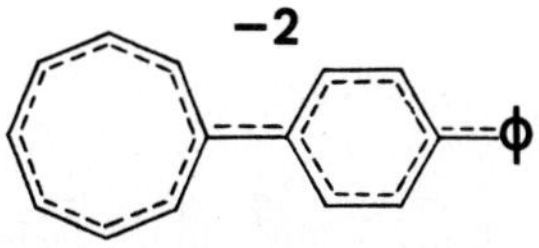   (195)

Pentacyclics include (196),[218] (197),[201] and perylene dianion (198).[29,167,183,160,124,219]

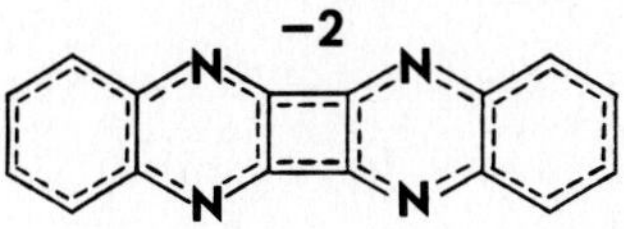

(196) 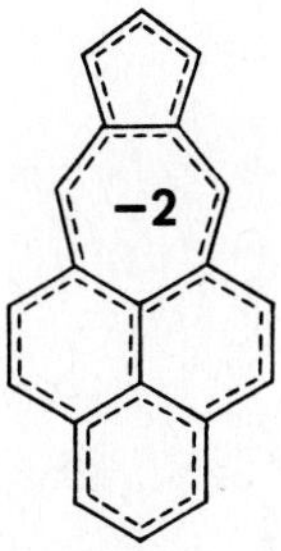   (197) 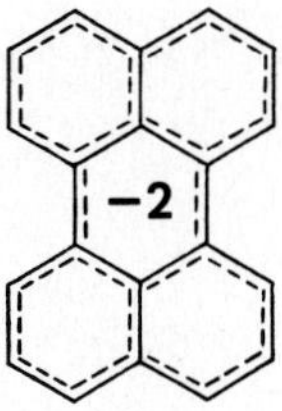   (198)

K.   22-Carbon Dianions

Tricyclics in this series are (199),[142] (200),[199] and (201).[199]

A tetracyclic (202) has been reported, with a 22 πe periphery.[220] It was assumed to be planar from inconclusive NMR evidence; models suggest great angle strain in planar structure (202). It was prepared by warming a "non-planar partially delocalized structure" which from its nmr parameters could be (203). Pentacyclics described are (204),[208,184] and (205)-(208).[29]

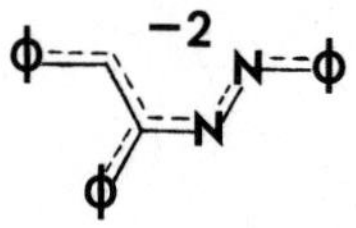

(199) 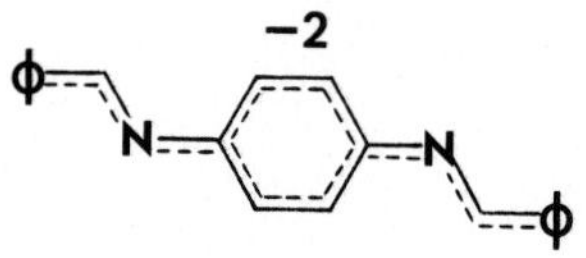   (200) 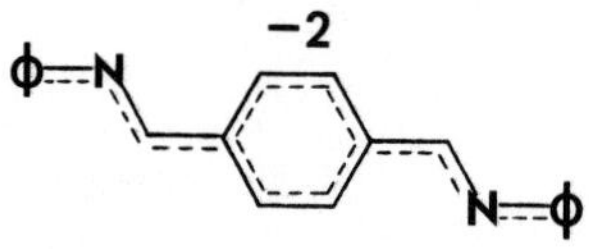   (201)

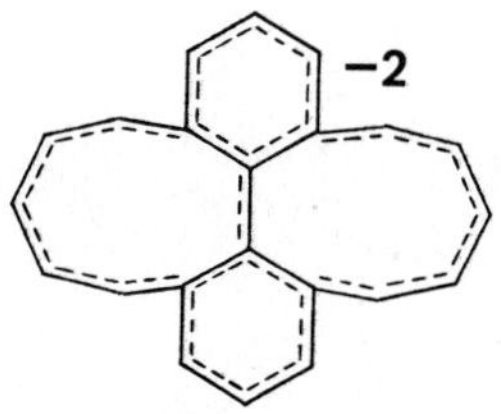

(202) 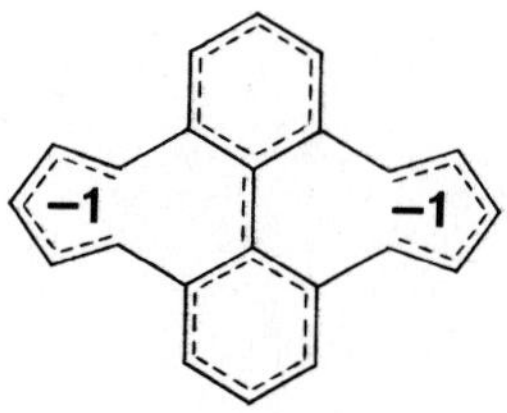   (203)

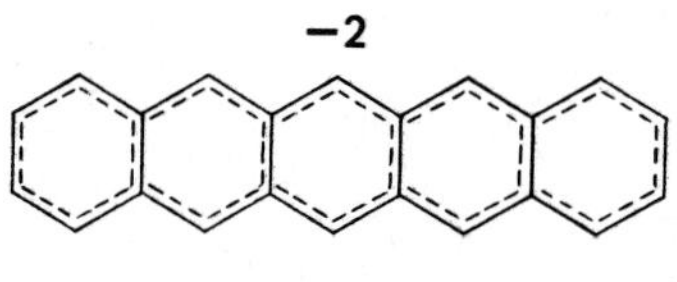

(204) 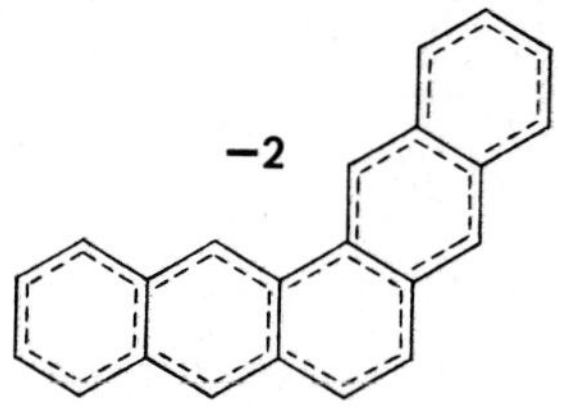   (205)

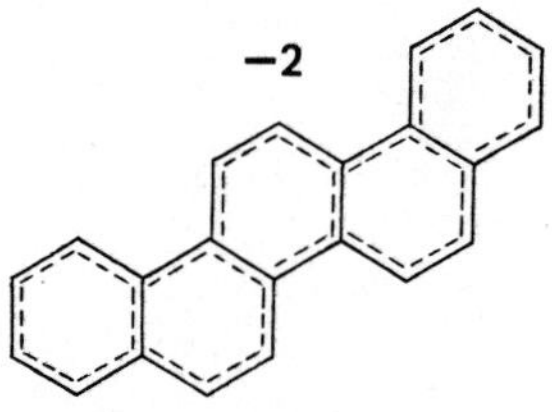

(206) 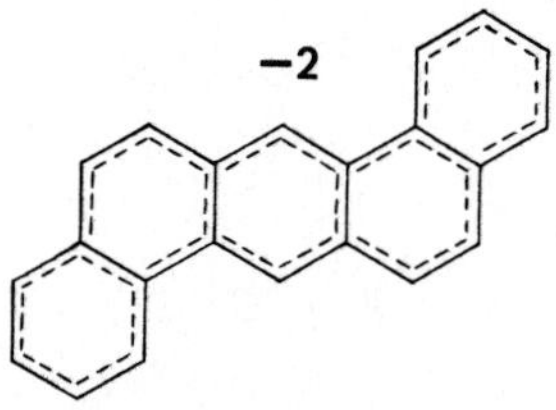   (207) 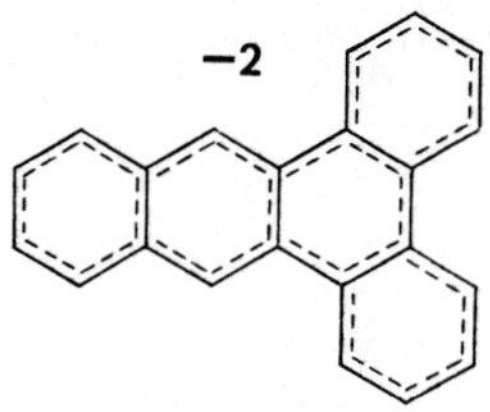   (208)

37

L. 24-Carbon Dianions

Monocyclic aromatic 26 πe dianion (209) from a dehydro[24]annulene has been prepared.[221] The tetracyclic species (210) is, like (190), a ground state triplet which exhibits three different triplet ESR spectra when a 2-methyl-THF solution is diluted with diglyme.[222,223,213] Dianion (34, Ar = β-naphthyl) is a likely reaction intermediate.[40] Various porphyrin dianions (211; R = H, Me, Et; nothing or Zn in center) have been demonstrated to have D_{4h} symmetry.[224-226] The heptacyclic coronene dianion (212) may have a triplet ground state.[227,183]

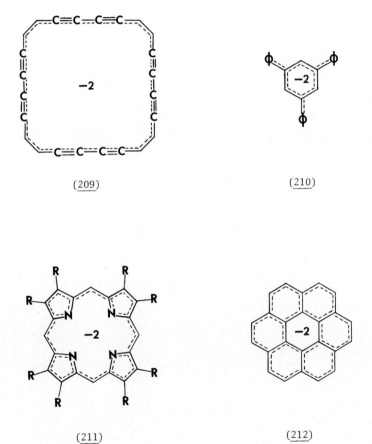

(209)

(210)

(211)

(212)

38

M. 26-Carbon Dianions

Tricyclic dianion (213) forms a yellow-orange potassium salt with mp > 360°C.[228] Tetracyclic dianion (214) has been prepared from chlorophyll a.[229] Tetracyclic dianion (33, Ar = β-naphthyl) is a probable reaction intermediate.[40] Tetracyclic dianion (46), studied extensively,[230-233,45,210,46] is twisted considerably about the central bond, as is the closely related hexacyclic dianion (47).[47] Pentacyclic dianion (215)[183] and hexacyclic dianions (216)[234] and (217)[188] are probably closer to planarity.

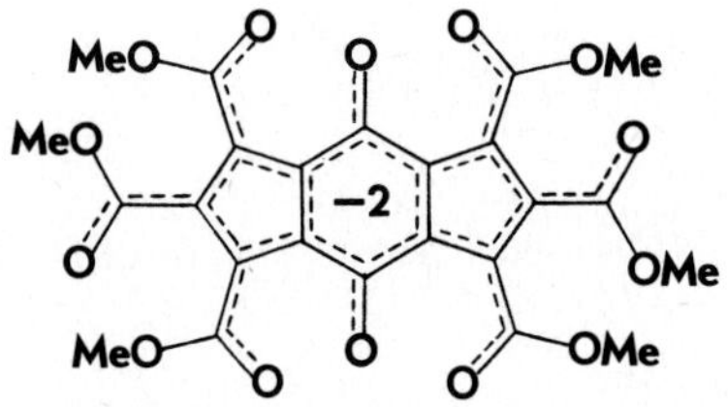

(213)

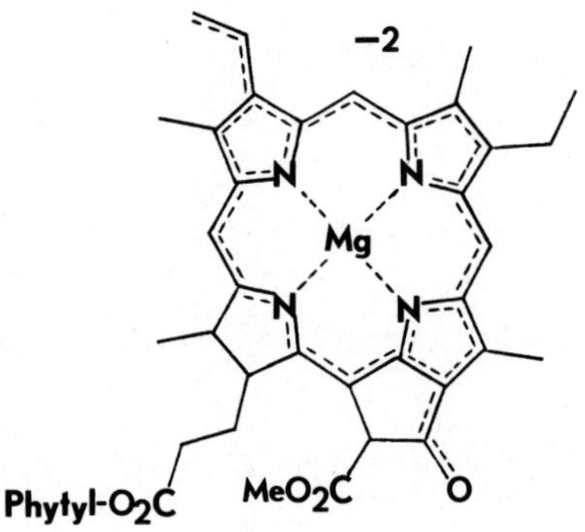

(214)

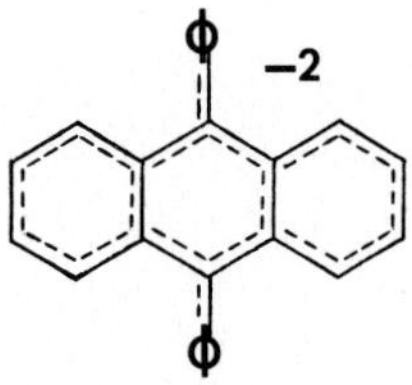

(215)

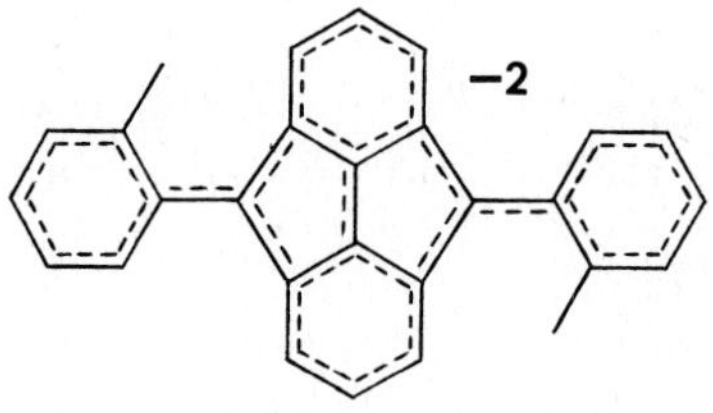

(216)

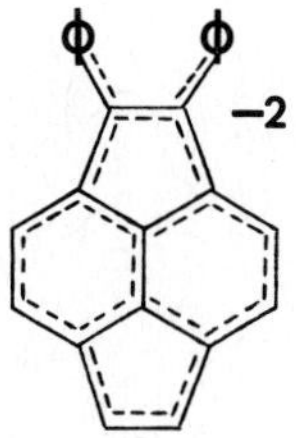

(217)

N.   28-Carbon Dianions

The shapes of the symmetrically substituted tetraphenylbutadiene dianions (218)[194,235] and (219)[236] have not been demonstrated but may well be as depicted. The same is true for nitrogen analog (220)[179] of the former.

(218)   (219)   (220)

Hexacyclic dianions (3)[5] and (221)[237] have been demonstrated by ESR and CD measurements, respectively, to possess triplet ground states with the two conjugated systems essentially perpendicular.

(221)

O.   30-Carbon Dianion

Dianion (36) is the only current member of this group.[40]

P.   36-Carbon Dianion

Like (190) and (210), decacyclic dianion (222) with its three-fold symmetry axis is predicted[222] and observed[223] to have a triplet ground state.

40

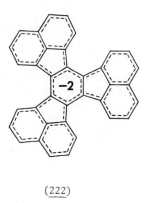

(222)

III. TRIANIONS

A. 5-Carbon Trianions

Trianions (223, R = H, Me) were suggested as reaction intermediates but not characterized.[35]

B. 7-Carbon Trianions

Acyclic linearly-conjugated heptatrienyl trianion (224; calculated $E_\pi = 10\alpha + 6.5\beta$)[238] and cross-conjugated trianion (225; $E_\pi = 10\alpha + 6.8\beta$)[10] have been prepared but no spectral data has been recorded on them. Oxygen analogs (226),[239] (19),[26] and (227),[240] of (225), and trianions of type (228),[43] have also been described. Cycloheptatrienyl trianion (229, R = H; $E_\pi = 10\alpha + 7.2\beta$) and its n-butyl derivative (R = n-Bu) are readily prepared, in keeping with their expected aromaticity.[238] The former exhibits one-line ^{1}H and ^{13}C NMR spectra as expected.

R −3 O

O

(223)

−3

(224)

−3

(225)

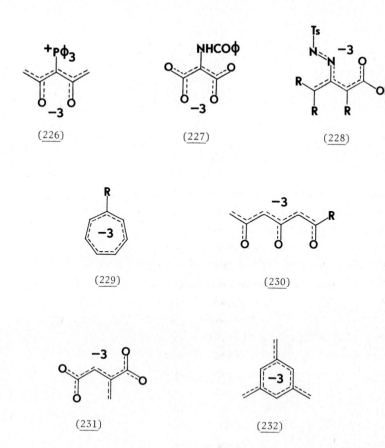

(226) (227) (228)

(229) (230)

(231) (232)

C. 9-Carbon Trianions

Branched acyclic trianions in this series are: (230, R = alkyl),[96],[241,156] (230, R = OMe),[95] and 231;[112] monocyclic (232) is also known.[116]

D. 11-Carbon Trianions

(233)[61] and (234)[35] have recently been prepared.

E. 13-Carbon Trianion

(235) appears to be the only current representative of this group.[26]

(233)   (234)   (235)

F. 15-Carbon Trianions

Representatives are monocyclic (230, R = φ, p-MeOC$_6$H$_4$)[242,96,156] and bicyclics (236)[243] and (237).[20]

(236)   (237)

G. 17-Carbon Trianion

The only example described to date is (238).[96]

H. 21-Carbon Trianion

The cesium salt of (16) was black, whereas other alkali metal salts were reddish-brown. The salts quenched normally with D$_2$O and Me$_2$SO$_4$, but via electron transfer gave products expected from quench of the corresponding monoanion with Et$_2$SO$_4$, MeI, and Me$_3$SiCl.[20]

I. 33-Carbon Trianion

Red solutions containing trianion (239) have been described.[244]

(238)   (239)

IV. TETRAANIONS

12-Atom (240, R = alkyl),[156] 16-carbon (241, with rings probably perpendicular),[245] 18-atom (242),[246] (243, stable and red but solubility too low for spectral examination),[207] and (240, R = φ),[156] 26-atom chlorophyll a (214 with two added electrons),[229] and 28-carbon tetraanion (244)[236] have been reported.

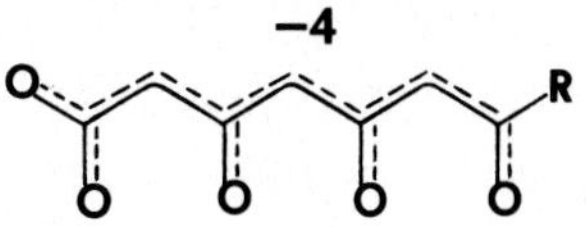

(240)

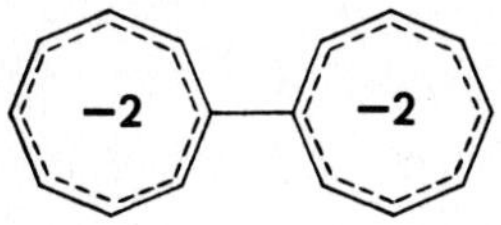

(241)

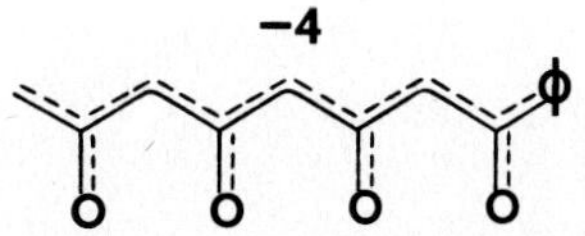

(242)

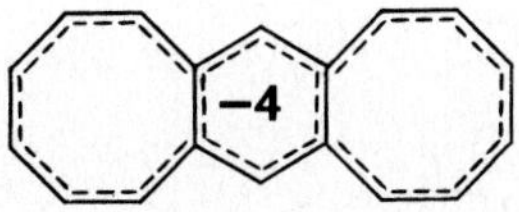

(243)

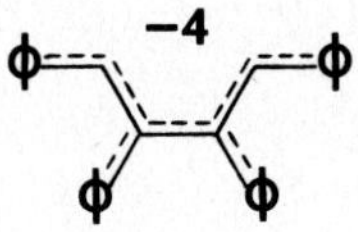

(244)

V. HIGHER ANIONS

Violet pentaanion (245, n = 5), deeper violet hexaanion (n = 6), and still more deeply colored heptaanion (n = 7) have all been reported.[246]

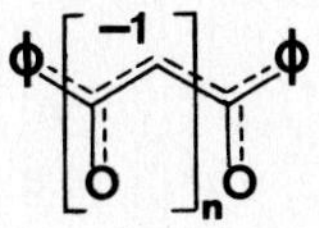

(245)

REFERENCES

1. J.G. Smith, J. Chem. Soc. P1, (1975) 1474.
2. E.M. Kaiser, L.E. Solter, R.A. Schwarz, R.D. Beard and C.R. Hauser, J. Am. Chem. Soc., 93 (1971) 4237.
3. N. Bosworth and P. Magnus, J. Chem. Soc. P1, (1973) 2319.
4. W. Priester, R. West and T.L. Chwang, J. Am. Chem. Soc., 98 (1976) 8413.
5. M. Hoshino, K. Kimura and M. Imamura, Chem. Phys. Lett., 20 (1973) 193.
6. T.J. Katz, J. Am. Chem. Soc., 82 (1960) 3784, 3785.
7. P.J. Garratt and R. Zahler, J. Am. Chem. Soc., 100 (1978) 7753.
8. J.S. McKennis, L. Brener, J.R. Schweiger and R. Pettit, J. Chem. Soc., Chem. Commun., (1972) 365.
9. G.A. Olah and G. Liang, J.Am. Chem. Soc., 99 (1977) 6045.
10. R.B. Bates, W.A. Beavers, M.G. Greene and J.H. Klein, J. Am. Chem. Soc., 96 (1974) 5640.
11. J. Klein and A. Medlik, J. Chem. Soc., Chem. Commun., (1973) 275.
12. J.J. Bahl, R.B. Bates and B. Gordon III, J. Org. Chem., 44 (1979) in press.
13. M.E. Jung, P.A. Blair and J.A. Lowe, Tetrahedron Lett., (1976) 1439.
14. L.J. Ciochetto, D.E. Bergbreiter and M. Newcomb, J. Org. Chem., 42 (1977) 2948.
15. T.M. Harris and C.M. Harris, J. Org. Chem., 31 (1966) 1032.
16. W.M. Macintyre and M.S. Werkema, J. Chem. Phys., 40 (1964) 3563.
17. J.P. Bays, J. Org. Chem., 43 (1978) 38.
18. R.H. Cox, L.W. Harrison and W.K. Austin, Jr., J. Phys. Chem., 77 (1973) 200.
19. K.O. Hodgson, F. Mares, D.F. Starks and A. Streitwieser, Jr., J. Am. Chem. Soc., 95 (1973) 8650.
20. G. Boche and K. Buckl, Angew. Chem., Int. Ed. Engl., 17 (1978) 284.
21. R.M. Carlson, Tetrahedron Lett., (1978) 111.
22. E.G. Lovett and D. Lipkin, J. Org. Chem., 42 (1977) 2574, 4281.
23. K.G. Hampton, T.M. Harris and C.R. Hauser, Org. Syn. Collective Vol. V (1973) 848.
24. P.L. Creger, Org. Syn., 50 (1970) 58.
25. J.E. McMurry and J.H. Musser, J. Org. Chem., 40 (1975) 2556.
26. A.P. Krapcho and D.S. Kashdan, Tetrahedron Lett., (1975) 707.

27. G.B. Trimitsis, J.M. Hinkley, R. TenBrink, M. Poli, G. Gustafson, J. Erdman and D. Rop, J. Am. Chem. Soc., 99 (1977) 4838.

28. D. Seebach, K.H. Geiss and M. Pohmakotr, Angew. Chem., Int. Ed. Engl., 15 (1976) 437; K.H. Geiss, D. Seebach and B. Seuring, Chem. Ber., 110 (1977) 1833.

29. A. Streitwieser, Jr., and S. Suzuki, Tetrahedron, 16 (1961) 153.

30. N.S. Mills, Ph.D. Thesis, University of Arizona, 1976.

31. K.G. Hampton, T.M. Harris and C.R. Hauser, J. Org. Chem., 30 (1965) 61.

32. J.J. Bahl, R.B. Bates, W.A. Beavers and N.S. Mills, J. Org. Chem., 41 (1976) 1620.

33. G.N. Barber and R.A. Olofson, J. Org. Chem., 43 (1978) 3015.

34. C.F. Beam, M.C.D. Dyer, R.A. Schwarz and C.R. Hauser, J. Org. Chem., 35 (1970) 1806.

35. M. Newcomb and D.E. Bergbreiter, J. Org. Chem., 43 (1978) 3963.

36. J.G. Smith and D.J. Mitchell, J. Am. Chem. Soc., 99 (1977) 5045.

37. H. Breil and G. Wilke, Angew. Chem., Int. Ed. Engl., 5 (1966) 898.

38. G.N. Shrauzer, Accounts Chem. Res., 2 (1969) 72.

39. R.M. Magid and S.E. Wilson, Tetrahedron Lett., (1971) 19.

40. Y. Tamaru, T. Harada and Z. Yoshida, J. Org. Chem., 43 (1978) 3370.

41. W.R. Moore, L.N. Bell and G.P. Daumit, J. Am. Chem. Soc., 92 (1970) 6680.

42. R.H. Shapiro, Organic Reactions, 23 (1976) 405; K.J. Kolonko and R. H. Shapiro, J. Org. Chem., 43 (1978) 1404.

43. C.A. Bunnell and P.L. Fuchs, J. Am. Chem. Soc., 99 (1977) 5184.

44. R.T. Taylor, C.R. Degenhardt, W.P. Melega and L.A. Paquette, Tetrahedron Lett., (1977) 159.

45. K. Takahashi, Y. Inoue and R. Asami, Org. Mag. Resonance, 3 (1971) 349.

46. G. Levin, B. Lundgren, M. Mohammad and M. Szwarc, J. Am. Chem. Soc., 98 (1976) 1461.

47. M. Walczak and G.D. Stucky, J. Organomet. Chem., 97 (1975) 313.

48. M. Walczak and G. Stucky, J. Am. Chem. Soc., 98 (1976) 5531.

49. D. Seebach and N. Meyer, Angew. Chem., Int. Ed. Engl., 15 (1976) 438.

50. D. Seebach and K.H. Geiss, Angew. Chem., 86 (1974) 202.

51. J.G. Smith, I. Ho and G.E.F. Simpson, J. Org. Chem., 40 (1975) 495.

52. K. Fujita, Y. Ohnuma, H. Yasuda and H. Tani, J. Organomet. Chem., 113 (1976) 201.

53. J.A. Morrison, C. Chung and R.J. Lagow, J. Am. Chem. Soc., 97 (1975) 5015.

54. S.K. Arora, R.B. Bates, W.A. Beavers and R.S. Cutler, J. Am. Chem. Soc., 97 (1975) 6271.

55. R.C. Bingham, J. Am. Chem. Soc., 98 (1976) 535.

56. M. Yang, K. Yamamoto, N. Otake, M. Ando and K. Takase, Tetrahedron Lett., (1970) 3843; M. Yang, M. Ando and K. Takase, ibid., (1971) 3529; Y. Nakano, K. Natsukawa, H. Yasuda and H. Tani, ibid., (1972) 2833.

57. S. Akutagawa and S. Otsuka, J. Am. Chem. Soc., 98 (1976) 7420.

58. L.A. Paquette, R.H. Meisinger and R. Gleiter, J. Am. Chem. Soc., 95 (1973) 5414.

59. G. Sturtz, B. Corbel and J. P. Paugam, Tetrahedron Lett., (1976) 47.

60. K.H. Geiss, B. Seuring, R. Pieter and D. Seebach, Angew. Chem., 86 (1974) 484.

61. C.F. Beam, R.M. Sandifer, R.S. Foote and C.R. Hauser, Synth. Commun., 6 (1976) 5.

62. E. Vedejs, D.A. Engler and J.E. Telschow, J. Org. Chem., 43 (1978) 188.

63. J.J. Bloomfield, D.C. Owsley and J.M. Nelke, Organic Reactions, 23 (1976) 259.

64. S.R. Wilson, M.E. Walters and B. Orbaugh, J. Org. Chem., 41 (1976) 378.

65. P. Gund, J. Chem. Ed., 49 (1972) 100.

66. T. Clark and P.V.R. Schleyer, J. Chem. Soc., Chem. Commun., (1976) 798.

67. I. Kuwajima and H. Iwasawa, Tetrahedron Lett., (1974) 107.

68. P.A. Grieco, D. Boxler and C.S. Pogonowski, J. Chem. Soc., Chem. Commun., (1974) 497.

69. P.A. Grieco and C.S. Pogonowski, J. Org. Chem., 39 (1974) 732.

70. P.A. Grieco and C.S. Pogonowski, J. Am. Chem. Soc., 95 (1973) 3071.

71. P.A. Grieco and R.S. Finkelhor, J. Org. Chem., 38 (1973) 2909.

72. J.D. Taylor and J.F. Wolf, J. Chem. Soc., Chem. Commun., (1972) 876.

73. H. Normant and B. Angelo, Bull. Soc. Chim. France, (1962) 810.

74. P.L. Creger, J. Am. Chem. Soc., 89 (1967) 2500.

75. B. Angelo, C. R. Acad. Sci. C., 270 (1970) 1471.

76. B. Angelo, C. R. Acad. Sci. C., 271 (1970) 865.

77. Y.-N. Kuo, J.A. Yahner and C. Ainsworth, J. Am. Chem. Soc., 93 (1971) 6321.

78. P.E. Pfeffer and L.S. Silbert, US Patent 3652612 (1972).

79. P.E. Pfeffer and L.S. Silbert, US Patent 3963784 (1976).

80. W. Adam and O. Cueto, J. Org. Chem., 42 (1977) 38.

81. B. Angelo, C.R. Acad. Sci. C., 278 (1974) 383.

82. B. Angelo and H. Normant, Izv. Khim., 8 (1975) 5.

83. W. Adam and H.H. Fick, J. Org. Chem., 43 (1978) 772.

84. P.A. Grieco, C.L.J. Wang and S.D. Burke, J. Chem. Soc., Chem. Commun., (1975) 537.

85. B.M. Trost and Y. Tamaru, Tetrahedron Lett., (1975) 3797.

86. P.A. Grieco and C.L.J. Wang, J. Chem. Soc., Chem. Commun., (1975) 714.

87. F.E. Ziegler and C.M. Chan, J. Org. Chem., 43 (1978) 3065.

88. R. Hoffmann and R.A. Olofson, J. Am. Chem. Soc., 88 (1966) 943.

89. G.A. Koppel, Tetrahedron Lett., (1973) 4233.

90. R.I. Bodina, E.S. Lipina and V.V. Perekalin, Zh. Org. Khim., 12 (1976) 2095.

91. P.E. Pfeffer, L.S. Silbert and E. Kinsel, Tetrahedron Lett., (1973) 1163.

92. P.E. Pfeffer and L.S. Silbert, J. Org. Chem., 36 (1971) 3290.

93. G. Cainelli, G. Cardillo, M. Contento, G. Trapani and A. Umani Ronchi, J. Chem. Soc. P1, (1973) 400.

94. D. Ivanoff, B. Jordanov and B. Blagoev, Naturwissenschaften, 51 (1964) 286.

95. D. Seebach and V. Ehrig, Angew. Chem., 86 (1974) 446.

96. T.M. Harris and R.L. Carney, J. Am. Chem. Soc., 89 (1967) 6734.

97. S.N. Huckin and L. Weiler, J. Am. Chem. Soc., 96 (1974) 1082.

98. L. Weiler, J. Am. Chem. Soc., 92 (1970) 6702.

99. J.F. Wolfe and T.G. Rogers, J. Org. Chem., 35 (1970) 3600.

100. A.S. Kende and R.G. Eilerman, Tetrahedron Lett., (1973) 697.

101. T. Fukunaga, J. Am. Chem. Soc., 98 (1976) 610.

102. R. West and J. Niu in J.P. Snyder, Nonbenzenoid Aromatics, Academic Press, New York (1969).

103. C. Leibovici, J. Mol. Struct., 13 (1972) 185.

104. R.E. Benson and R.V. Lindsey, Jr., J. Am. Chem. Soc., 79 (1957) 5471.

105. L.S. Gutyrya, Izv. Vyssh. Uched. Zaved., Fiz., 17 (1974) 157.

106. R.B. Bates and C.A. Ogle, unpublished results.

48

107. R. Rieke, M. Ogliaruso, R. McClung and S. Winstein, J. Am. Chem. Soc., 88 (1966) 4729.

108. M. Ogliaruso, R. Rieke and S. Winstein, J. Am. Chem. Soc., 88 (1966) 4731.

109. M. Barfield, R.B. Bates, W.A. Beavers, I.R. Blacksberg, S. Brenner, B.I. Mayall and C.S. McCulloch, J. Am. Chem. Soc., 97 (1975) 900.

110. S.V. Ley and L.A. Paquette, J. Am. Chem. Soc., 96 (1974) 6670.

111. R.J. Highet and T.J. Batterham, J. Org. Chem., 29 (1964) 475.

112. R.M. Carlson and A.R. Oyler, J. Org. Chem., 41 (1976) 4065.

113. R. Allmann, T. Debaerdemaeker, K. Mann, R. Matusch, R. Schmiedel and G. Seitz, Chem. Ber., 109 (1976) 2208.

114. P.C. Salvino and R.D. Bereman, Inorg. Chem., 12 (1973) 173.

115. B.J. Kalbacher and R.D. Bereman, Inorg. Chem., 12 (1973) 2997.

116. J. Klein, A. Medlik and A.Y. Meyer, Tetrahedron, 32 (1976) 51.

117. B.R. Clark and D.H. Evans, J. Electroanal. Chem. Interfacial Electro-chem., 69 (1976) 181.

118. T.P. Murray, J.V. Hay, D.E. Portlock and J.F. Wolfe, J. Org. Chem., 39 (1974) 595.

119. J.H. Noordik, T.E.M. van den Hark, J.J. Mooij and A.A.K. Klaassen, Acta Crystallogr., Sect. B., 30 (1974) 833.

120. S.Z. Goldberg, K.N. Raymond, C.A. Harmon and D.H. Templeton, J. Am. Chem. Soc., 96 (1974) 1348.

121. G.R. Stevenson and I. Ocasio, J. Phys. Chem., 79 (1975) 1387.

122. G.R. Stevenson and I. Ocasio, J. Am. Chem. Soc., 98 (1976) 890.

123. V. Dvorak and J. Michl, J. Am. Chem. Soc., 98 (1976) 1080.

124. R.H. Cox, H.W. Terry, Jr. and L.W. Harrison, Tetrahedron Lett., (1971) 4815.

125. A. Streitwieser, Jr. and U. Müller-Westerhoff, J. Am. Chem. Soc., 90 (1968) 7364.

126. A. Zalkin and K.N. Raymond, J. Am. Chem. Soc., 91 (1969) 5667; A. Avdeef, K.N. Raymond, K.O. Hodgson and A. Zalkin, Inorg. Chem., 11 (1972) 1083.

127. K.O. Hodgson, D. Dempf and K.N. Raymond, J. Chem. Soc. D., (1971) 1592.

128. K.O. Hodgson and K.N. Raymond, Inorg. Chem., 11 (1972) 171.

129. K.O. Hodgson and K.N. Raymond, Inorg. Chem., 12 (1973) 458.

130. A. Streitwieser, Jr., D. Dempf, G.N. La Mar, D.G. Karraker and N. Edelstein, J. Am. Chem. Soc., 93 (1971) 7343.

131. N. Edelstein, G.N. La Mar, F. Mares and A. Streitwieser, Jr., Chem. Phys. Lett., 8 (1971) 399.

132. D.G. Karraker, J.A. Stone, E.R.H. Jones, Jr. and N. Edelstein, J. Am. Chem. Soc., 92 (1970) 4841.

133. L. A. Paquette, C.D. Wright III, S.G. Traynor, D.L. Taggart and G.D. Ewing, Tetrahedron, 32 (1976) 1885.

134. S.W. Staley, G.M. Cramer and A.W. Orvedal, J. Am. Chem. Soc., 96 (1974) 7433.

135. T.J. Katz and M. Rosenberger, J. Am. Chem. Soc., 84 (1962) 865; T.J. Katz, M. Rosenberger and R.K. O'Hara, ibid., 86 (1964) 249.

136. L.A. Paquette, M.J. Kukla, S.V. Ley and S.G. Traynor, J. Am. Chem. Soc., 99 (1977) 4756.

137. D.H. Phillips and J.C. Schug, J. Chem. Phys., 60 (1974) 1597.

138. G. Seitz, K. Mann and R. Matusch, Arch. Pharm., 308 (1975) 792.

139. N.C. Baenziger, J.J. Hegenbarth and D.G. Williams, J. Am. Chem. Soc., 85 (1963) 1539.

140. D.R. Dimmel and S.B. Ghardure, J. Am. Chem. Soc., 93 (1971) 3991.

141. R.F. Sandifer, S.E. Davis and C.F. Beam, Synth. Commun., 6 (1976) 339.

142. F.E. Henoch, K.G. Hampton and C.R. Hauser, J. Am. Chem. Soc., 91 (1969) 676.

143. R.M. Sandifer, L.M. Shaffer, W.M. Hollinger, D.C. Reames and C.F. Beam, J. Heterocycl. Chem., 13 (1976) 607.

144. J. Klein, A. Medlik-Balan, A.Y. Meyer and M. Chorev, Tetrahedron, 32 (1976) 1839.

145. C. Mao, C.R. Hauser and M.L. Miles, J. Am. Chem. Soc., 89 (1967) 5303.

146. V. Grignard, Bull. Soc. Chim. France, (1904) 751.

147. P.L. Creger, J. Am. Chem. Soc., 92 (1970) 1396.

148. S. Kulpe and S. Dahne, Tetrahedron Lett., (1968) 2591.

149. A. Essel, B. Graveron, G. Merle and C. Pillot, C. R. Acad. Sci. C, 275 (1972) 925.

150. J.J. Brooks, W. Rhine and G.D. Stucky, J. Am. Chem. Soc., 94 (1972) 7346.

151. M.I. Terekhova, E.S. Petrov and A.I. Shatenshtein, Zh. Org. Khim., 9 (1973) 857.

152. N.L. Holy, Chem. Rev., 74 (1974) 243.

153. C.R. Hauser and T.M. Harris, J. Am. Chem. Soc., 80 (1958) 6360.

50

154. M.L. Miles, C.G. Moreland, D.M. von Schriltz and C.R. Hauser, Chem. Ind. (London), (1966) 2098.

155. T.P. Murray and T.M. Harris, J. Am. Chem. Soc., 94 (1972) 8253.

156. T.M. Harris, G.P. Murphy and A.J. Poje, J. Am. Chem. Soc., 98 (1976) 7733.

157. J.F.M. Oth and G. Schröder, J. Chem. Soc. B., (1971) 904.

158. P.J. Garratt, N.E. Rowland and F. Sondheimer, Tetrahedron, 27 (1971) 3157.

159. J.F.M. Oth, K Muellen, H. Koenigshofen, M. Mann, Y. Sakata and E. Vogel, Angew. Chem., 86 (1974) 232.

160. I.V. Aleksandrov, Ya.S. Bobovich, V.G. Maslov and A.N. Siderov, Pis'ma Zh. Eksp. Teor. Fiz., 17 (1973) 306.

161. E. Grovenstein, Jr., T.H. Longfield and D.E. Quest, J. Am. Chem. Soc., 99 (1977) 2800.

162. J.S. Jaworski and M.K. Kalinowski, Rocz. Chem., 49 (1975) 1141.

163. G.R. Stevenson, M. Colon, I. Ocasio, J.G. Concepcion and A.McB. Block, J. Phys. Chem., 79 (1975) 1685.

164. J.F.M. Oth, K. Muellen, H. Koenigshofen, J. Wassen and E. Vogel. Helv. Chim. Acta, 57 (1974) 2387.

165. K. Hafner, Angew. Chem., Int. Ed. Engl., 3 (1964) 165.

166. T.J. Katz, V. Balogh and J. Schulman, J. Am. Chem. Soc., 90 (1968) 734.

167. R.G. Lawler and C.V. Ristagno, J. Am. Chem. Soc., 91 (1969) 1534.

168. C.V. Ristagno and R.G. Lawler, Tetrahedron Lett., (1973) 159.

169. A.J. Fatiadi, J. Am. Chem. Soc. 100 (1978) 2586.

170. B. Ganem, J. Am. Chem. Soc., 98 (1976) 224.

171. F. Gerson, K. Muellen and E. Vogel, Angew. Chem., Int. Ed. Engl., 10 (1971) 920.

172. H. Suzuki, K. Koyano and T.L. Kunii, Bull. Chem. Soc. Jap., 45 (1972) 1979.

173. G. Levin, T.A. Ward and M. Szwarc, J. Am. Chem. Soc., 96 (1974) 270.

174. T.A. Ward, G. Levin and M. Szwarc, J. Am. Chem. Soc., 97 (1975) 258.

175. G. Levin and M. Szwarc, Chem. Phys. Lett., 35 (1975) 323.

176. J.J. Eisch and M. Tsai, J. Am. Chem. Soc., 95 (1973) 4065.

177. M.I. Mostova and D.V. Ioffe, Zh. Org. Khim., 8 (1972) 1547.

178. B.S. Jensen and V.D. Parker, J. Chem. Soc., Chem. Commun., (1974) 367.

179. D.V. Ioffe and T.R. Strelets, Khim. Geterotsikl. Soedin., (1972) 129.

180. T.R. Strelets and D.V. Ioffe, Khim. Geterotsikl. Soedin., (1974) 238.

181. B.M. Trost and Y. Tamaru, J. Am. Chem. Soc., 99 (1977) 3101.

182. J.A. Campbell and J.F. Wolfe, Org. Prep. Proced. Int., 3 (1971) 303.

183. B.S. Jensen and V.D. Parker, J. Am. Chem. Soc., 97 (1975) 5211.

184. I.Ya. Kachkurova, Zh. Prikl. Spektrosk., 22 (1975) 689.

185. I.V. Aleksandrov, Ya.S. Bobovich, V.G. Maslov and A.I. Sidorov, Dokl. Akad. Nauk SSSR, 221 (1975) 567.

186. R.G. Harvey and H. Cho, J. Am. Chem. Soc., 96 (1974) 2434.

187. B.M. Trost and P.L. Kinson, J. Am. Chem. Soc., 92 (1970) 2591; 97 (1975) 2438.

188. B.M. Trost, D. Buhner and G.M. Bright, Tetrahedron Lett., (1973) 2787.

189. B. Lunelli, C. Corvaja and G. Farnia, Trans. Faraday Soc., 67 (1971) 1951.

190. A.S. Kanev and V.I. Baranovskii, Zh. Org. Khim., 12 (1976) 1639.

191. M.R. Suchanski and R.P. Van Duyne, J. Am. Chem. Soc., 98 (1976) 250.

192. J.F.M. Oth, G. Anthoine and J.-M. Gilles, Tetrahedron Lett. (1968) 6265.

193. J.F.M. Oth, H. Baumann, J.-M. Gilles and G. Schroeder, J. Am. Chem. Soc., 94 (1972) 3498.

194. W. Schlenk and E. Bergmann, Ann., 463 (1928) 98.

195. E.G. Janzen, W.B. Harrison and C.M. Dubose, Jr., J. Organometal. Chem., 40 (1972) 281.

196. C.F. Beam, D.C. Reames, C.E. Harris, L.W. Dasher, W.M. Hollinger, N.L. Shealy, R.M. Sandifer, M. Perkins, and C.R. Hauser, J. Org. Chem., 40 (1975) 514.

197. W.G. Kofron and L.M. Baclawski, J. Org. Chem., 41 (1976) 1879.

198. G.B. Trimitsis, E.W. Crowe, G. Slomp and T.L. Helle, J. Am. Chem. Soc., 95 (1973) 4333.

199. J.G. Smith and I. Ho, J. Org. Chem., 38 (1973) 2776.

200. P. Scheiner, E. Stockel, D. Cruset and R. Noto, J. Org. Chem., 37 (1972) 4207.

201. F. Gerson, J. Jachimowicz and C. Jutz, Helv. Chim. Acta, 57 (1974) 1408.

202. I. Willner and M. Rabinovitz, J. Am. Chem. Soc., 100 (1978) 337.

203. K. A. Engdahl and G. Ramme, Chem. Phys. Lett., 41 (1976) 100.

204. J.F.M. Oth, E.P. Woo and F. Sondheimer, J. Am. Chem. Soc., 95 (1973) 7337.

205. J.J. Beirne, N.M. Carroll, W.I. O'Sullivan and J. Woods, Tetrahedron, 31, (1975) 265.

206. K. Hafner, S. Braun, T. Nakazawa and H. Tappe, Tetrahedron Lett., (1975) 3507.

207. L.A. Paquette, G.D. Ewing, S. Traynor and J.M. Gardlik, J. Am. Chem. Soc., 99 (1977) 6115.

208. I.Ya. Kachkurova, Dolk. Akad. Nauk SSSR, 206 (1972) 568.

209. T.L. Netzel and P.M. Rentzepis, Chem. Phys. Lett., 29 (1974) 337.

210. W.S. Struve, T.L. Netzel, P.M. Rentzepis, G. Levin and M. Szwarc, J. Am. Chem. Soc., 97 (1975) 3310.

211. T. Ikeshoji, T. Mizuno and T. Sikine, Chem. Lett., (1976) 1275.

212. H. van Willigen, J.A.M. van Broekhoven and E. de Boer, Molec. Phys., 12 (1967) 533.

213. H. van Willigen, Chem. Phys. Lett., 11 (1971) 294.

214. J.G. Smith and G.E.F. Simpson, Tetrahedron Lett., (1971) 3295.

215. J.G. Smith and R.A. Turle, J. Org. Chem., 37 (1972) 126.

216. N.L. Bauld, J. Cessac, C.-S. Chang, F.R. Farr and R. Holloway, J. Am. Chem. Soc., 98 (1976) 4561.

217. N.L. Bauld, C.-S. Chang and F.R. Farr, J. Am. Chem. Soc., 94 (1972) 7164.

218. S. Hünig and H. Pütter, Angew. Chem., 85 (1973) 143.

219. H.C. Wang, G. Levin and M. Szwarc, J. Am. Chem. Soc., 99 (1977) 5056.

220. I. Willner and M. Rabinovitz, J. Am. Chem. Soc., 99 (1977) 4507.

221. R.M. McQuilkin, P.J. Garratt and F. Sondheimer, J. Am. Chem. Soc., 92 (1970) 6682.

222. R.E. Jesse, P. Biloen, R. Prins, J.D.W. van Voorst and G.J. Hoijtink, Mol. Phys., 6 (1963) 633.

223. J.A.M. van Broekhoven, H. van Willigen and E. de Boer, Mol. Phys., 15 (1968) 101.

224. G.M. Maggiora and L.J. Weimann, Chem. Phys. Lett., 22 (1973) 297.

225. G.N. Sinyakov, V.P. Suboch, A.M. Shul'ga and G.P. Gurinovich, Dokl. Akad. Nauk Beloruss. SSR, 17 (1973) 660.

226. G. Barth, R.E. Linder, E. Bunnenberg and C. Djerassi, J. Chem. Soc. P2, (1974) 696.

227. G.J. Hoijtink, Mol. Phys., 2 (1959) 85.

228. E. LeGoff and R.B. LaCount, Tetrahedron Lett., (1964) 1161.

229. B.A. Kiselev, Yu.N. Kozlov and V.B. Evstigneev, Biofizika, 19 (1974) 645.

230. R.C. Roberts and M. Szwarc, J. Am. Chem. Soc., 87 (1965) 5542.

231. T.E. Hogen-Esch and J. Smid, J. Am. Chem. Soc., 88, (1966) 307.

232. J.F. Garst, J. Am. Chem. Soc., 93 (1971) 6312.

233. D.H. Eargle, Jr., J. Am. Chem. Soc., 93 (1971) 3859.

234. A. Dagan and M. Rabinovitz, J. Am. Chem. Soc., 98 (1976) 8268.

235. M. Ushio, M. Takaki, K. Takahashi and R. Asami, Bull. Chem. Soc. Jap., 44 (1971) 2559.

236. V.R. Sandel, B. Belinky, J. Stefaniak and D. Kreil, J. Org. Chem., 40 (1975) 2116.

237. O. Ito and M. Hatano, J. Am. Chem. Soc., 96 (1974) 4375.

238. J.J. Bahl, R.B. Bates, W.A. Beavers and C.R. Launer, J. Am. Chem. Soc., 99 (1977) 6126.

239. M.P. Cooke, Jr. and R. Goswami, J. Am. Chem. Soc., 95 (1973) 7891.

240. A.P. Krapcho and E.A. Dundulis, Tetrahedron Lett., (1976) 2205.

241. T.T. Howarth, G.P. Murphy and T.M. Harris, J. Am. Chem. Soc., 91 (1969) 517.

242. K.G. Hampton, T.M. Harris, C.M. Harris and C.R. Hauser, J. Org. Chem., 30 (1965) 4263.

243. S.G. Kukes, N.N. Bubnov, A.I. Prokof'ev, S.P. Solodovnikova, G.A. Nikiforov and V.V. Ershov, Izv. Akad. Nauk SSSR, Ser. Khim., (1973) 2375.

244. C.F. Koelsch, J. Am. Chem. Soc., 79 (1957) 4439; E.G. Janzen and J.G. Pacifici, ibid., 87 (1965) 5504.

245. L.A. Paquette, G.D. Ewing and S.G. Traynor, J. Am. Chem. Soc., 98 (1976) 279.

246. P.J. Wittek and T.M. Harris, J. Am. Chem. Soc., 95 (1973) 6865.

CHAPTER 2

GAS-PHASE ACIDITIES OF CARBON ACIDS

Mark J. Pellerite and John I. Brauman
Department of Chemistry, Stanford University, Stanford, California

Table of Contents

I. INTRODUCTION

Brønsted acidity--the tendency to lose a proton--must be included among the fundamental properties of any organic molecule. Loss of a proton is the primary step in many organic reactions and frequently is the key to understanding and controlling the chemistry. Qualitative and quantitative studies of acidity have played a critical role in understanding structure-reactivity relationships such as the Hammett σ-ρ constants, the Branch and Calvin treatment, and Brønsted catalysis. However, solution-phase acidities reflect solvent effects as well as the intrinsic proton-donating power of the solute. Acidities measured under solvent-free conditions must therefore be available before the interplay between solute properties and solvent effects can be understood. Efforts in that direction have been hampered until recently due to lack of methods for measurement of gas-phase acidities.

The treatment of solute-solvent interactions[1] is an extremely complex problem. As will be seen, these interactions often mask purely molecular properties to such an extent that discussion of condensed-phase acidity measurements in terms of characteristics of isolated solute molecules is rendered impossible. For instance, it has been observed that acetophenone is 10^6 times more acidic than fluorene in benzene,[2] but in dimethyl sulfoxide (DMSO) fluorene is 10^2 times stronger. Also, malononitrile[3] (pK = 11) is a much stronger acid than phenol[4] (pK = 16) in DMSO, but in water the order is reversed[5,6] (pK_a's 11.1 and 10, respectively). Solvation energies, which are of the order of 50-90 kcal/mole,[7] are often sufficient to dominate any effects due to intrinsic acidity differences, and it is data of this sort which exemplify the need for experimental gas-phase acidities free of factors introduced in condensed-phase determinations.

Carbon acids[8-10] are a particularly interesting class of acids, partly because the wide structural variations which are possible within these compounds result in solution-phase acidities spanning the entire spectrum of experimentally determined pK_a's. Trinitromethane[1] (pK_a = 0) is competitive with some mineral acids in acid strength, while saturated hydrocarbons[11] (pK_a's $\sim$ 40-50) are among the weakest acids known. The low acidity of many hydrocarbons often requires kinetic acidity studies[11] involving hydrogen isotope exchange, and the use of kinetic acidity data in the development of pK_a tables for weak hydrocarbon acids is an important ongoing area of research. Among the other significant results

of this work are several classic correlations of carbanion structure and reactivity such as electron donation by alkyl groups and the linear relationship
between pK_a and percentage s-character at the charge-bearing carbon for the
series acetylene, ethylene, cyclopropane, ethane. In many instances, gas-phase
data allow one to discern whether correlations deduced from solution-phase data
can legitimately be interpreted in terms of properties of isolated molecules or
should be attributed to solvation phenomena.

The current availability of gas-phase acidities for many organic compounds is
due primarily to the development within the past 15 years of three experimental
techniques. These are high-pressure mass spectrometry,[12,13] flowing afterglow[14-16] and ion cyclotron resonance (ICR) spectrometry.[17-19] Section II presents brief descriptions of each method.

A table of all the gas-phase carbon acid acidities reported to date, along
with some qualitative acidity orderings, is presented in Section III. Also
included are comments concerning discrepancies in and reliability of the experimental acidities gathered from the three methods.

Whereas quantitative discussions of solution-phase acidities are usually
couched in terms of pK's, it is most convenient to express the gas-phase acidity
of the neutral AH in terms of the proton affinity (PA) of the anion A^-, defined
as the standard enthalpy change ΔH^o for the deprotonation reaction

$$AH \rightarrow A^- + H^+ \tag{1}$$

From consideration of the following thermochemical cycle, the proton affinity is
given by

$$PA(A^-) = D(A-H) - EA(A) + IP(H)$$

in which D(A-H) is the homolytic dissociation energy of the A-H bond, EA(A) is
the electron affinity of the radical A, and IP(H) is the ionization potential of
atomic hydrogen, 313.6 kcal/mole.

$A-H \rightarrow A + H$		$D(A-H)$
$A + e^- \rightarrow A^-$		$-EA(A)$
$H \rightarrow H^+ + e^-$		$IP(H)$
$A-H \rightarrow A^- + H^+$	$\Delta H^o = D(A-H) - EA(A) + IP(H)$	

Since IP(H) is a constant for every reaction, it is usually omitted for simpli-
city; in Section III, the acidities are thus expressed as D - EA. Note that
acid strength increases as D - EA decreases.

58

We can also consider a fourth method for determination of gas-phase acidities, the thermochemical cycle method. That is, one can calculate the acidity of a molecule provided the corresponding bond dissociation energy and electron affinity are known. Results from the thermochemical method are included where appropriate.

Since reaction 1 as written is strongly endothermic (320-400 kcal/mole for most species) the thermochemical method is the only one of the four amenable to direct determination of gas-phase acidity. Experimentally, the acidity of a neutral molecule A_1H is determined through measurement of the equilibrium constant K_{eq} for the proton-transfer reaction 2,

$$A_1^- + A_2H \underset{k_{-1}}{\overset{k_1}{\rightleftharpoons}} A_2^- + A_1H \tag{2}$$

where A_2H is a reference compound for which D-EA is known absolutely. K_{eq} can be measured either by determining the concentrations of the species involved once equilibrium has been attained (high pressure mass spectrometry and ICR spectrometry) or by measuring the rate constants for the forward and reverse reactions (flowing afterglow and ICR spectrometry). Once K_{eq} is known, ΔG^o for reaction 2 is calculated from $\Delta G^o = -RT \ln K_{eq}$, and ΔH^o can then be determined if ΔS^o is known. It is common practice to compute ΔS^o using standard statistical mechanical methods. Furthermore, since the reaction involves only proton transfer, for large molecules the entropy change is governed primarily by changes in the rotational symmetry numbers, σ.[20] This has been verified experimentally through the use of van't Hoff plots for proton-transfer reactions involving protonated benzenes.[21] Thus, in these cases the entropy calculation can often be simplified by computing ΔS^o based only on the rotational symmetry changes. A simple extension of the thermochemical cycle presented above shows that the acidities of A_1H and A_2H are related to ΔH^o for reaction 2 by

$$\Delta H^o = [D(A_2-H) - EA(A_2)] - [D(A_1-H) - EA(A_1)].$$

So, finally, use of ΔH^o and $D(A_2-H) - EA(A_2)$ enables the acidity of A_1H, $D(A_1-H) - EA(A_1)$, to be computed.

The data of Section III reveal some gas-phase acidity relationships which are strikingly different from those in solution. Section IV is a discussion of a few of the observed trends within the framework of polarization, resonance, inductive, and hybridization effects. Brief discussions of kinetic versus thermodynamic acidity and theoretical studies of carbon acid acidities are also included.

II. Experimental Methods

Each method is discussed within the context of measuring K_{eq} for reaction 2,

$$A_1^- + A_2H \underset{k_{-1}}{\overset{k_1}{\rightleftharpoons}} A_2^- + A_1H \tag{2}$$

$$K_{eq} = \frac{[A_2^-][A_1H]}{[A_1^-][A_2H]}$$

A. High-Pressure Mass Spectrometry[12,13] (HPMS)

All gas-phase carbon acidities measured thus far by HPMS are the results of work performed by Kebarle and co-workers. A diagram of the high-pressure mass spectrometer currently in use in Kebarle's laboratory is shown[13] in Fig. 1. Ions are formed by introducing an appropriate sample mixture into the thermostated ion source [(2), Fig. 1] where the sample is bombarded by 10-20 μs pulses of 2000-eV electrons. Pressure in the ion source is typically 0.5-10 Torr: the neutral compounds A_1H and A_2H contributing a few mTorr, with the balance a bath gas such as methane. Small amounts of SO_2F_2 or NF_3, which produce F^- by dissociative electron capture, are also added to enhance ion formation. Fluoride ion, a strong base (Section III, Table 1), quickly abstracts protons from the neutral molecules to produce the ions of interest, A_1^- and A_2^-. These ions begin reacting and diffusing toward the walls of the apparatus. Prior to any ion losses through collisions with walls, however, thermal and chemical equilibrium is attained through many collisions with bath gas and reactant molecules. Some of the equilibrated ions diffuse through an exit slit into a high-vacuum region where they are magnetically mass analyzed and detected [(3)-(5), Fig. 1]. A multichannel scaler triggered by the electron pulse allows observation of ion signal intensities (proportional to ion concentrations) as a function of time, and hence one can determine that the system has reached equilibrium, i.e. the ratio $[A_2^-]/[A_1^-]$ has become constant. The time for this to occur is typically less than 3 ms. Measurement of the equilibrium ion signal intensity ratio and the reactant gas pressures allows K_{eq} for the proton transfer to be calculated. Determination of acidity then proceeds as outlined earlier.

HPMS yields accurate values for gas-phase acidities because ion concentration ratios rather than absolute concentrations are measured. Also, the system's progress toward equilibrium can be monitored, and thermal distribution is ensured due to numerous collisions. A typical problem in these experiments is formation of ion-neutral molecule clusters;[12] this is avoided by using high ion source temperatures ($\sim 600^\circ K$).

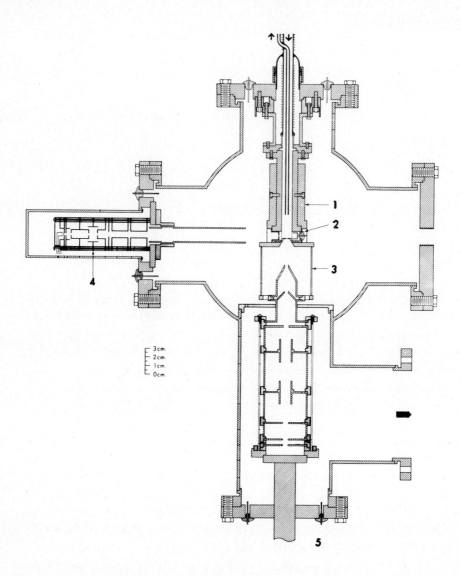

Fig. 1. Schematic diagram of high-pressure mass spectrometer. (1) Ion source block with heating or cooling mantle; (2) Ion source with ion exit slit; (3) Ion acceleration region; (4) Pulsed electron gun; (5) To magnetic mass analysis. Diagram furnished courtesy of Professor P. Kebarle, reprinted with permission from A. J. Cunningham, J. D. Payzant, and P. Kebarle, J. Amer. Chem. Soc. 94 (1972) 7627. Copyright by the American Chemical Society.

B. Flowing Afterglow[14-16,22]

Much of the work in applying the flowing afterglow technique to the study of
gas-phase acidities has been performed by Bohme and co-workers. A schematic
diagram of a flowing afterglow apparatus appears in Fig. 2. The apparatus

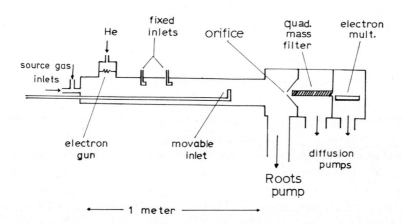

Fig. 2. Schematic diagram of flowing afterglow apparatus. Diagram furnished
courtesy of Professor C. H. DePuy, reproduced with permission from V. M.
Bierbaum, C. H. DePuy, R. H. Shapiro, and J. H. Stewart, J. Amer. Chem. Soc. 98
(1976)4229.

incorporates a drift tube with sample inlets at one end and extensive vacuum
pumps and a quadrupole mass spectrometer at the other. Reactant gases are present
at pressures of ~10^{-3} Torr (0.2% of the total pressure) in a buffer gas of
hydrogen or helium. The vacuum pumps and Roots blowers provide a high flow
velocity on the order of 10^4 cm/sec. Primary ions are formed by electron impact
on a source gas. Commonly used primary ions are H^- and NH_2^- (from NH_3) and H^-
and OH^- (from H_2O). The anion of interest, say A_1^- in reaction 2, is generated
by addition of A_1H through one of the fixed inlets allowing reaction to occur
with the primary ions; finally, A_2H addition through the movable gas inlet
initiates the desired proton-transfer reaction. This sequence is shown in Scheme
I. As in HPMS, the high buffer gas pressure results in a thermal energy distribution for all species. At the end of the reactant region, most of the gas mixture is exhausted through the pump; some of it passes through the sampling
orifice into a quadrupole mass filter and ion detector. K_{eq} is measured by
determining the forward and reverse rate constants; thus, two separate experiments
are needed to measure one equilibrium constant. Observation of reactant and

(A) Source gas $\xrightarrow{e^-}$ Primary ions

(B) Primary ions + A_1H $\longrightarrow$ A_1^- SCHEME I

(C) $A_1^- + A_2H$ $\rightleftharpoons$ $A_2^- + A_1H$

product ion signal intensities as a function of neutral substrate addition leads
to the rate constants. Alternatively, the rate constants can be obtained by
varying the drift tube length (and hence the reaction time) at constant reactant
flow[16] through adjustment of the movable inlet.

Knowledge of the neutral substrate concentration is essential in the determination of rate constants; this concentration measurement is the major source of
uncertainty in rate constants determined by flowing afterglow. In the case of a
neutral compound which is a stable gas at $300°K$, standard flow measurement techniques are available for determination of concentrations.[14] For liquids, the
concentration of the vapor must be measured by monitoring the pressure increase
with a capacitance manometer as the vapor is bled into the drift tube. This
introduces an estimated uncertainty of a factor of 2 in the rate constants, compared with ± 30% for rate constants in which the concentration of neutral species
is measured by monitoring the vapor flow.[22]

One important feature of the flowing afterglow method which distinguishes it
from both HPMS and ICR is the spatial separation of ion production and reaction
regions. Because of the high collision rate with the buffer gas, the reactant
ions are assured of being in their ground electronic and vibrational states upon
entering the reaction region. Also, all ions formed from reactions of the primary
ions with the neutral molecules A_1H (Step B, Scheme I) can be monitored before
any A_2H is added. This provides information on the primary ion-reactant ion
conversion (which must be virtually complete if reliable rate constants are to
be obtained) and allows any side reactions which could interfere with the rate
constant determinations to be followed.

C. Pulsed Ion Cyclotron Resonance (ICR) Spectrometry[17-19]

Measurement of equilibrium constants for acidities of neutral molecules by
ICR spectrometry has been accomplished largely by McIver and collaborators. In
this method ions are trapped in a magnetic field and undergo circular motion in
a plane normal to the field direction. The frequency of this cyclotron motion
depends on the ion's charge-to-mass ratio. Use of a trapped-ion cell[18,19] (a
rectangular box consisting of plates to which dc voltages are applied) and total
pressure of 10^{-6}-10^{-5} Torr allows ions to be trapped for several seconds, during
which time they undergo hundreds of collisions. A marginal oscillator[23] serves
as the ion detection system and produces a signal which can be related to the
concentration of ions of a given m/e present in the cell. This is accomplished

by applying an oscillating electric field to one of the cell plates. When the frequency of this applied field matches the cyclotron frequency of an ion in the cell, the ion absorbs power from the field and its orbital radius increases. This absorption causes a voltage drop in the marginal oscillator, which is detected as a signal. Other detection methods can also be used.[19] In pulsed ICR, a 2-10 ms pulse of electrons produces the ions, A_1^- and A_2^-, either by dissociative electron capture or by proton transfer from a neutral substrate to a primary ion such as F^-. At some later time, the ions are detected. They are then quenched and the process is repeated, varying the time to detection; this allows the concentration of each ion in the cell to be observed as a function of time. Equilibrium is assumed to have been reached when the ratio $[A_1^-]/[A_2^-]$ becomes constant. The pulsed ICR analysis scheme is completely analogous to a classical kinetics study in which a reaction is followed by examining at different times the contents of a series of identical reaction vessels.

A powerful feature of ICR is the double-resonance capability. This allows observation of the time-dependent concentration of an ion while ejecting another from the cell. Ion ejection is accomplished by the application of a second oscillating electric field having a frequency equal to the cyclotron frequency of the ion to be ejected. Power absorption by an ion results in an increase in orbital radius. If this increase continues until the radius is so large that the ion comes in contact with a cell plate, the ion is neutralized and hence ejected. Double resonance finds use in the measurement of forward and reverse rate constants in an equilibrium. In reaction 2, for instance, k_1 can be measured by continuously ejecting A_2^- and observing the decay of A_1^-; likewise, k_{-1} is measured by observing the decay of A_2^- while ejecting A_1^-. Equilibrium constants can also be measured, as in HPMS, by conversion of equilibrium signal intensity ratios to ion concentration ratios and using the known pressure ratio of the neutral species. As is the case for both HPMS and FA as well, in ICR experiments the ratio of the number of ions to the number of neutral molecules is usually 10^{-5} or less and so the neutral concentrations remain essentially constant.

The question has been raised whether ICR actually measures thermal equilibrium constants, since total pressure in the ICR cell is so much lower than that employed in HPMS and FA studies. This question was recently investigated by subjecting some ICR equilibrium constants to several classical tests of equilibrium,[24] with the conclusion that equilibrium constants from ICR are indeed thermal. It is worth noting that if ΔH^o is fairly small, which is usually the case for measured equilibrium constants and since $\Delta S^o \approx 0$, K_{eq} is rather insensitive to temperature or internal energy. Perhaps the strongest evidence that ICR equilibrium constants are thermal is that they are generally in excellent agreement with those measured by HPMS and FA.

There is one potential problem inherent in all three of these methods.
Because the experimental conditions are adjusted to study reactions which occur
on essentially every collision, slow reactions may not reach equilibrium. Recent
studies of carbon acids with delocalized anions[25] have shown their reactions to
be slow, therefore limiting the study of some of these molecules.

III. Results

Table 1 presents all gas-phase carbon acid acidities currently available.
Also included are gas-phase acidities of several other compounds such as water,
methanol, and HCl to aid the reader's orientation. Acidities calculated from
the thermochemical cycle (TC) method appear for those compounds for which the
appropriate bond energy and electron affinity are available.

Estimated uncertainty in the reported values is ± 1 kcal/mole for the ICR and
HPMS measurements, and ± 3 kcal/mole for those from FA. Note that in the cases
where a compound's acidity has been measured by more than one method, the agreement is generally within experimental error. There are exceptions: acetylene
(3.3 kcal/mole discrepancy), dimethyl sulfoxide (2.3 kcal/mole discrepancy), and
acetone (2.0 kcal/mole discrepancy).

Comparison of the calculated (TC) and experimental acidities reveals good
agreement for almost all cases. Minor discrepancies appear for H_2S and HCN.
Since the experimental acidities are referenced to absolutely known (by TC)
standards (HF in the ICR measurements, HCl in HPMS) one generally expects fairly
good agreement. Once a set of compounds has been ordered relative to the standard,
it is customary to cross-check the ordering by comparing the compounds among
themselves. All of the ICR and HPMS data have been subjected to numerous internal
checks of this sort, with the result that all acidities are internally consistent
to within ～1 kcal/mole. Even though the standards used to anchor each data set
lie 37.7 kcal/mole apart in acidity, in only the three compounds mentioned above
do ICR and HPMS fail to agree within experimental error. However, there are
some small systematic differences between experimental and TC results, the
origins of which remain unknown. As reliable electron affinities become increasingly available,[26] these gas-phase acidities can be used to determine bond dissociation energies--an important alternative to the conventional thermokinetic
methods.

In addition to the quantitative acidities presented below, several qualitative
acidity orderings have been reported involving several compounds not included in
the table. The compounds are listed in order of decreasing acidity (increasing
D-EA).

TABLE 1

D - EA for carbon acids

Compound	D-EA(kcal/mole)[a]	Method	Ref.
CH_4	103.0	TC	b
NH_3	90.4	FA	29
	86.0	TC	c
H_2O	77.2	TC	d
$CH_2=CHCH_3$	77.8	FA	32
	77.2	ICR	33
	76.3	TC	e
CH_3OH	67.4	FA	32
	65.6	ICR	33
	67.3	TC	f
CH_3-⬡-CH_3 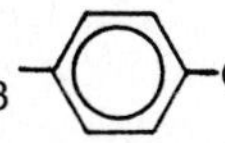	67.2	ICR	33
$CH_3C\equiv CH$	66.0	ICR	33
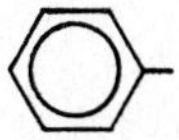 ⬡-CH_3	65.4	ICR	33
	64.7	TC	g
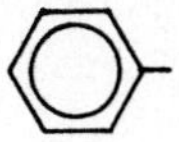 ⬡-CH_2CH_3	64.7	ICR	33
n-$PrC\equiv CH$	64.7	ICR	33
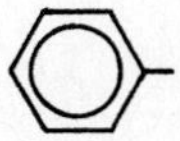 ⬡-$CH(CH_3)_2$	63.9	ICR	33
t-$BuC\equiv CH$	63.0	ICR	33
$HC\equiv CH$	64.4	FA	39
	61.8	ICR	33
CF_3H	62.0	ICR	33
	~64.0	TC	h
CH_3SOCH_3	61.0	HPMS	41
	59.1	ICR	33
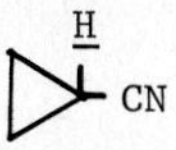 ▷-CN (H)	60.5	ICR	33
CH_3CH_2CN	60.1	ICR	33

Compound	D-EA(kcal/mole)[a]	Method	Ref.
$(CH_3)_2C\underline{H}CN$	60.2	ICR	33
CH_3CN	59.9	HPMS	41
	61.4	FA	42
	58.6	ICR	33
	58.2	TC	i
(cycloheptatriene, H $\underline{H}$)	60.3	ICR	33
$(CH_3)_2NCOC\underline{H}_3$	59.9	ICR	33
$CH_3OC\underline{H}_2CN$	57.8	ICR	33
HF	57.7	TC	j
$CH_3OCOC\underline{H}_3$	57.4	ICR	33
$CH_3COC\underline{H}_3$	56.4	HPMS	41
	55.2	ICR	33
	56.7	TC	
$PhC{\equiv}C{-}\underline{H}$	56.7	ICR	33
$CH_3COC\underline{H}_2CH_3$	54.6	HPMS	41
	53.8	TC	l
$CH_3CH_2COC\underline{H}_2CH_3$	54.6	HPMS	41
$CH_3COC\underline{H}(CH_3)_2$	54.0	HPMS	41
$C\underline{H}_3CHO$	52.8	HPMS	41
	52.3	ICR	33
$CH_3C\underline{H}_2CHO$	52.3	HPMS	41
	51.7	ICR	33
$CH_3SO_2C\underline{H}_3$	52.8	HPMS	41
	53.0	ICR	33
$PhSO_2C\underline{H}_2CH_3$	50.9	HPMS	41
$PhSO_2C\underline{H}_2CH_2CH_3$	50.0	HPMS	41
$(Ph)_2C\underline{H}_2$	49.1	HPMS	41
	50.9	ICR	33
$PhCOC\underline{H}_3$	49.6	HPMS	41
	48.9	ICR	33
$PhSO_2C\underline{H}_3$	49.1	HPMS	41
$PhSO_2C\underline{H}_2CH(CH_3)_2$	49.0	HPMS	41

Compound	D-EA(kcal/mole)[a]	Method	Ref.

CH$_3$O–⟨benzene⟩–COCH$_3$ 49.2   ICR   33

PhSO$_2$–⟨cyclopropane, H⟩   47.7   HPMS   41

PhCOCH$_2$CH$_3$ 47.6 / 48.8   HPMS / ICR   41 / 33

Compound	D-EA(kcal/mole)[a]	Method	Ref.
CH$_3$O–C$_6$H$_4$–COCH$_3$	49.2	ICR	33
PhSO$_2$–C$_3$H$_4$(H) (cyclopropane)	47.7	HPMS	41
PhCOCH$_2$CH$_3$	47.6	HPMS	41
	48.8	ICR	33
Cl–C$_6$H$_4$–COCH$_3$	45.7	ICR	33
CH$_3$NO$_2$	44.0	FA	39
	44.0	HPMS	41
	45.1	ICR	33
CH$_3$CH$_2$NO$_2$	43.7	HPMS	41
	44.5	ICR	33
(CH$_3$)$_2$CHNO$_2$	43.0	HPMS	49
	44.6	ICR	33
t-BuCH$_2$NO$_2$	42.7	HPMS	41
	43.4	ICR	33
cyclopentadiene (H H)	41.9	HPMS	41
	42.5	ICR	33
	38.8	TC	m
O$_2$N–C$_6$H$_4$–CH$_3$	39.5	HPMS	41
H$_2$S	38.4	HPMS	41
	39.8	ICR	33
	38.1	TC	n
CH$_3$COCH$_2$Ph	38.2	HPMS	41
	38.9	ICR	33

Compound	D-EA(kcal/mole)[a]	Method	Ref.
(fluorene, H H)	39.7	HPMS	41
$PhC\underline{H}_2CN$	39.7	HPMS	41
	38.5	ICR	33
$CH_3COC\underline{H}_2OCOCH_3$	36.7	HPMS	41
$CF_3COC\underline{H}_3$	36.7	HPMS	41
HCN	36.4	FA	50
	39.5	ICR	33
	35.7	TC	o
$CH_3CO_2\underline{H}$	34.9	HPMS	41
$(CH_3CH_2O_2C)_2C\underline{H}_2$	34.7	HPMS	41
$PhO\underline{H}$	36.2	HPMS	41
	37.8	ICR	33
$CH_3COC\underline{H}_2COCH_3$	30.1	HPMS	41
$PhCOC\underline{H}_2COCH_3$	26.3	HPMS	41
(dimedone structure, H H, O O, H_3C CH_3)	25.3	HPMS	41
HCl	19.7	TC	p
$(CN)_2C\underline{H}_2$	22.4	HPMS	41
$CF_3COC\underline{H}_2COCH_3$	14.9	HPMS	41
HBr	10.0	TC	q
HI	0.7	TC	r

Footnotes to Table I.

a) All acidities, bond energies, and electron affinities expressed in kcal/mole.

b) D = 104.8 (ref. 27), EA = 1.8 (ref. 28).

c) D = 103.2 (ref. 27), EA = 17.2 (ref. 30).

d) D = 119.3 (ref. 27), EA = 42.1 (ref. 31).

e) D = 89 (ref. 34), EA = 12.7 (ref. 35).

f) D = 104 (ref. 36), EA = 36.7 (ref. 37).

g) D = 85 (ref. 34), EA = 20.3 (ref. 38).

h) D = 106 (ref. 34), EA $\approx$ 42 (ref. 40).

i) D = 92.9 (ref. 43), EA = 34.8 (ref. 35).

j) D = 136.1 (ref. 27), EA = 78.4 (ref. 31).

k) D = 98.0 (ref. 44), EA = 41.3 (ref. 45).

ℓ) D = 92.3 (ref. 46), EA = 38.5 (ref. 45).

m) D = 81.2 (ref. 47), EA = 42.4 (ref. 48).

n) D = 91.6 (ref. 27), EA = 53.4 (ref. 49).

o) D = 123.8 (ref. 27), EA = 88.1 (ref. 51).

p) D = 103.1 (ref. 27), EA = 83.4 (ref. 31).

q) D = 87.6 (ref. 27), EA = 77.6 (ref. 31).

r) D = 71.3 (ref. 27), EA = 70.6 (ref. 31).

Qualitative Orderings

> CHCl$_3$ > CH$_3$COCH$_3$ > CH$_3$CN > CH$_2$Cl$_2$, CH$_3$SOCH$_3$ $\geq$ HC≡CH

> H$_2$C=C=CH$_2$, PhCH(CH$_3$)$_2$ > PhCH$_3$ > CH$_3$CH=CH$_2$ > H$_2$O   (Ref. 22)

> > H$_2$ > NH$_3$ > C$_2$H$_4$, , , CH$_4$

CH$_3$COCH$_2$COCH$_3$ > CH$_3$COCN > HCN   (Ref. 52)

HI > > HBr   (Ref. 53)

IV. Discussion

A. General

Even a cursory glance at Table I reveals acidity orders dramatically different from those observed in solution. Toluene is more acidic than water in the gas phase but 20 orders of magnitude less acidic in solution.[11] In the gas phase malononitrile is a stronger acid than acetic acid, while trifluoroacetylacetone is stronger than HCl. Both of these acidity orders are reversed in aqueous solution.

Although many such reversals can be found in Table I, some features of the pK$_a$ scale are retained in the gas-phase data. The acidity of the halogen acids decreases in the order HI > HBr > HCl > HF, both in solution and in the gas phase. This is due to increases in the bond energies upon going from HI to HF, since the electron affinities of the halogens are relatively constant. Methane is an extremely weak acid in both the gas phase and in solution.

Some of the most drastic acidity reversals between solution-phase and gas-phase data involve carbon acids; this section contains a discussion of some of the effects currently believed to be important in the acidities of these compounds. These effects can be roughly divided into four groups: polarization, resonance, inductive, and hybridization. Each is treated separately. The section concludes with discussions of kinetic acidity and theoretical studies of gas-phase carbon acidity.

It may seem surprising that fluorene, while almost 10^5 times less acidic than cyclopentadiene in solution, suddenly becomes the stronger of the pair in the

gas phase. This reversal is an example of the correlation between charge
delocalization and solvation and can be understood qualitatively using the Born
treatment of solvation energies.[54] In this treatment, the free energy change
accompanying the transfer of one mole of ions from vacuum into a medium of dielectric constant D is given[55] by eq. (3),

$$\Delta G^{o}_{solv} = - \frac{N(Ze)^2}{8\pi\epsilon_0 r}(1 - 1/D) \tag{3}$$

where N is Avogadro's number, Ze is the ion's charge and r its radius assuming
it to be a hard sphere. In comparing the solvation energies of a delocalized ion
and an ion in which the charge resides primarily on one atom, we can approximate
the delocalized ion as n identical centers each bearing charge Ze/n. Assuming
equal radii, the solvation energy ratio for these two ions is thus

$$\frac{\Delta G_{solv,deloc}}{\Delta G_{solv,loc}} = \frac{n(Ze/n)^2}{(Ze)^2} = \frac{1}{n} \tag{4}$$

with the result that solvation energy decreases with increasing delocalization.
Thus, fluorenyl anion should be less solvated than cyclopentadienide since the
charge is distributed over more centers. Alternatively, to the extent that
fluorenyl anion is delocalized, its effective radius r is larger than that of
cyclopentadienide so that, again, ΔG^{o}_{solv} should be smaller for the more delocalized
anion. Since solvation energies[55] of 50-90 kcal/mole are much larger than intrinsic acidity differences for most pairs of compounds (2.0 kcal/mole for the
fluorene-cyclopentadiene example given above) the relative acidities in solution
are often dictated by the differential solvation energies. Thus, in solution the
acidity order may favor the smaller, more highly solvated anion even though the
compound producing the larger, more delocalized anion is more acidic in the gas
phase. However, this is not meant to imply that for two compounds with similar
intrinsic acidities the relative solution- and gas-phase acidities will always be
reversed. A recent study[7] of some carbon acids in DMSO showed the acidity order
to parallel quite closely the order in the gas phase. Plots of gas-phase versus
solution acidities were linear for each family of compounds. This was thought
to be due to the conjugate bases all being delocalized, hence solvation should
exert a fairly constant effect on each anion, leaving the intrinsic acidities to
determine the acidity ordering. In protic solvents such as water the order is
different, probably because of specific solute-solvent interactions such as
hydrogen bonding. It must be remembered that differential solvation of the
neutrals as well as the ions and factors such as ion pairing will all play a

role in determining solution-phase acidities. Also, the above argument deals
only with nonspecific solvation and says nothing about specific interactions.
The entire picture is of course much more complex than that presented by the
Born treatment of solvation energies.

B. Polarization Effects

Polarization is believed to be the dominant effect responsible for the general
increase in acidity with increasing molecular size. This trend is seen in many
classes of compounds, including carbon acids. For instance, phenyl isobutyl
sulfone > phenyl propyl sulfone > phenyl ethyl sulfone; t-butylacetylene > n-
propylacetylene > methylacetylene; and 3-pentanone > 2-butanone, all in order of
decreasing acidity. A spectacular reversal of solution acidities appears[56] in
the gas-phase data for simple alcohols: t-BuOH > i-PrOH > EtOH > MeOH. Prior
to the availability of gas-phase data, the opposite order of acidities in solution was taken as evidence of anion destabilization through electron donation by
methyl groups. It is now clear that the solution-phase ordering is due entirely
to differential solvation. In fact, the above gas-phase data and the observation
that gas-phase basicity of simple amines increases with alkyl substitution[57]
shows that alkyl groups can stabilize a charge of either sign, withdrawing or
donating electrons as needed.

Polarization of alkyl groups is not a new idea, having been suggested
previously in interpretations of alkyl group effects on electronic and infrared
spectra of substituted benzenes,[58,59] dipole moments of alkylbenzenes,[60] and
kinetics of gas-phase eliminations from alkyl halides.[61] The physical basis of
polarization effects in an ion can be understood qualitatively through a classical electrostatic argument[56] in which the alkyl group is approximated by a sphere
of polarizability α and the charge-bearing center replaced by a point charge q;
the sphere and the point charge are separated by a distance r. The presence of
the point charge results in an induced dipole in the polarizable sphere. According to classical electrostatics, the potential energy U(r) of this system is[56]

$$U(r) = -\frac{1}{2}\frac{\alpha q^2}{r^4} .$$
(5)

An increase in α lowers the ion's total energy. Since polarizability generally
increases with molecular volume, this model therefore accounts qualitatively for
the observed acidity increase with increased alkyl substitution. Equation 5
predicts acidity differences of the correct order of magnitude for pairs of compounds within a series such as MeOH, EtOH, i-PrOH, t-BuOH using alkyl group
polarizabilities estimated by bond additivity[62] and reasonable values for r.[63]

However, the quantitative treatment of acidities based on the ion-induced dipole model is rendered essentially impossible by the existence of anisotropic polarizabilities of alkyl groups[64] and extremely large electric fields ($\sim 10^5$ V/cm) within molecular ions. Because of this latter factor, hyperpolarizability effects[65] (dependence of polarizability on the field at very high field values) may also play a role in charge-alkyl group interactions.

A complementary interpretation of alkyl group effects can be couched in terms of perturbation molecular orbital theory,[66] and was first described by Hudson et al.[67] in their ab initio calculations of the acidities of water and methanol. The model is best illustrated in its application to the acidities of the simple aliphatic alcohols.[26] For these compounds, the O-H bond energy remains constant[36] and hence acidity differences will be determined by electron affinity differences in the radicals. Within the Koopmans' theorem approximation,[68] the electron affinity of a radical is given by

$$EA = -E_{HOMO} \qquad\qquad (6)$$

where E_{HOMO} is the energy of the highest occupied molecular orbital in the radical (or anion). Anion stability (relative to the neutral radical) increases as EA increases.

Consider methoxide ion to consist of a methyl radical and O^-. If we now bring the fragments together to form the ion, examination of the orbitals on an energy level diagram (Figs. 3,4) shows that the HOMO and LUMO of the methyl radical, the π and π^* C-H orbitals, are of proper symmetry to overlap with the occupied $2p_x$ and $2p_y$ orbitals of O^-. Interaction between $\pi(CH_3)$ and $2p(O^-)$ is closed-shell (four electrons) and hence destabilizing (Fig. 3), but the $\pi^*(CH_3)$-$2p(O^-)$ interaction is stabilizing (Fig. 4). Increasing the size of the alkyl group introduces more π^* orbitals of the appropriate symmetry to interact with $2p(O^-)$. These additional interactions produce a lowering of E_{HOMO} and hence an increase in electron affinity. Since the O-H bond strength remains fixed, the net effect of increasing alkyl group size is to increase the acidity (decrease D-EA). This overlap between alkyl group π^* and oxygen 2p orbitals corresponds qualitatively to a hyperconjugative withdrawal of electrons by the alkyl group. Note that the polarizability of an alkyl group is related to the number and energies of vacant π^* orbitals available for stabilizing interaction with the orbitals of the charged center.[37] Calculations on methoxide anion and methoxyl radical[26,37] show an increase in electron density at the hydrogens and a decrease in C-H bond order in the anion relative to the radical, this latter result being indicative of $\pi^*(CH_3)$ mixing in the ion. This mixing is absent in the radical since the 2p orbitals lie at lower energy in $O\cdot$ than in O^-. One interpretation of this

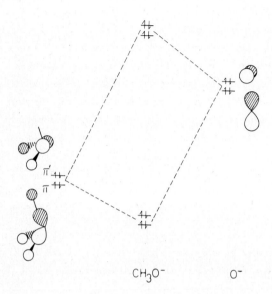

$\overset{*}{\pi}'$ ___

$\overset{*}{\pi}$ ___

CH_3O^- O^-

Fig. 3.   Interaction of $\pi(O^-)$ and $\pi(CH_3)$ orbitals. Diagram furnished courtesy
of B. K. Janousek, reprinted with permission from B. K. Janousek, A. H. Zimmerman,
K. J. Reed, and J. I. Brauman, J. Amer. Chem. Soc. 100 (1978) 6142. Copyright
by the American Chemical Society.

decreased bond order and increased electron density in the anion is that the
effects arise due to contribution by hyperconjugative resonance structures:

$$
\begin{array}{ccc}
\text{H} & & \text{H}^- \\
| & & | \\
\text{H-C-O}^- & \longleftrightarrow & \text{H-C=O} \\
| & & | \\
\text{H} & & \text{H}
\end{array}
$$

The above argument can be applied to delocalized systems in much the same way.
The HOMO obtained from a CNDO/2 calculation[69] on propionaldehyde enolate anion[70]
consists of a bonding $\pi(CH_3)$ orbital overlapping with a π-type orbital of acetaldehyde enolate (minus a hydrogen), entirely analogous to the $\pi(CH_3)$-$2p(O^-)$
overlap in methoxide. The influence of the $\overset{*}{\pi}$ methyl orbital is again seen in
decreased C-H bond order in the methyl group upon going from propionaldehyde
enolate radical to the anion. Calculations on butyraldehyde enolate[70] reveal
similar features. In addition, the HOMO for this ion lies lower in energy than
that of propionaldehyde, consistent with the effects of increasing alkyl group

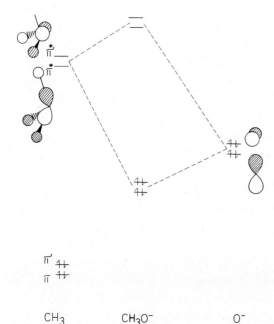

π' ⤉
π ⤉

CH₃   CH₃O⁻   O⁻

Fig. 4.   Interaction of $\pi(O^-)$ and $\pi^*(CH_3)$ orbitals. Diagram furnished courtesy
B. K. Janousek, reprinted with permission from B. K. Janousek, A. H. Zimmerman,
K. J. Reed, and J. I. Brauman, J. Amer. Chem. Soc. 100 (1978) 6142. Copyright
by the American Chemical Society.

size noted earlier.

Polarization effects are not limited to alkyl groups; they also appear in the
gas-phase acidities of unsaturated hydrocarbons. Table I shows toluene to be
more acidic than propene, and fluorene more acidic than cyclopentadiene. Both
of these results are opposite to those predicted by simple HMO theory,[71] and
show that in addition to simple resonance effects one must also consider molecular
size. Incidentally, it is precisely this size effect which, as discussed earlier,
is primarily responsible for the solution acidity orders for these pairs of compounds being opposite those in the gas phase.[11] The more delocalized ion is
more stable in the gas phase, but less well solvated in solution. One is safe
in these cases in discussing relative acidity in terms of anion stability only,
since the difference in the C-H bond energies of fluorene and cyclopentadiene is
probably fairly small, and that for toluene and propene (~ 4 kcal)[72] is much
smaller than the observed acidity difference for the two compounds.

Thus far our discussion of polarization effects has utilized only examples in which one alkyl group is replaced by another, rather than cases in which a hydrogen has been replaced by a methyl, as in acetylene and methylacetylene. If pairs such as acetylene-methylacetylene are included the polarization argument appears to break down. Note, for instance, that EtCN is less acidic than MeCN, acetone is less acidic than acetaldehyde, and methylacetylene is less acidic than acetylene. These results appear contradictory to the alkyl group size-acidity correlation. One reason for some of these deviations has been hinted at previously; that is, within some of these pairs of compounds the C-H bond energies do not remain constant, and thus one is not justified in discussing acidity changes solely in terms of effects on anion stability (electron affinity). Relative stabilities of the radicals must also be considered. A detailed discussion of the overall effects on acidity of substituting methyl for hydrogen at the deprotonation site is deferred until a later section.

C. Resonance Effects

As is also commonly observed in solution, introducing an unsaturated linkage adjacent to the deprotonation site tends to increase a compound's gas-phase acidity relative to that of its saturated analog. This is particularly well illustrated by the carbon acids. Thus, propene is a much stronger acid than propane, toluene is much stronger than methylcyclohexane, and cyclopentadiene much stronger than cyclopentane, both in solution and in the gas phase. As yet no one has succeeded in observing the anion of any saturated hydrocarbon by ion equilibrium methods. Methane does not undergo gas-phase proton transfer to any known base, including NH_2^- and O^-.[22] Recent results of Ellison et al.[28] indicate that the electron affinity of methyl radical is 0.08 eV, yielding D-EA = ~102 kcal/mole for the acidity of methane. Isobutane, with a much lower bond energy[72] (92 kcal/mole) than methane, also does not transfer a proton to NH_2^-.[73] A simple thermochemical calculation using this observation and eq. 3, Section I, shows that the electron affinity of isobutyl radical, if positive, must also be near zero. Based on this evidence, we have assumed that all alkanes will show D-EA $\geq$ 90 kcal/mole even though no equilibrium acidities have been measured for these compounds.

Carbonyl, cyano, nitro and other functions act to increase dramatically acidity relative to the alkanes. Resonance effects on trends of solution and gas-phase acidities are quite similar, in marked contrast to some of the data discussed in the previous section in which several acidity reversals between the gas phase and solution were noted. Resonance effects on solution acidities have been carefully discussed.[74]

As mentioned earlier, one must use caution when discussing the acidities of two compounds within the framework of resonance effects. For instance, the unsaturated substituents (vinyl, phenyl) are inductively electron withdrawing and would increase acidity even without conjugation. Or, if the molecules are of disparate size, polarization can often be the dominant effect, as was seen in the case of toluene being more acidic than propene contrary to the HMO prediction. There are a few pairs of hydrocarbons listed in Table I, however, which because of their comparable molecular sizes are quite amenable to a resonance treatment. Perhaps the most outstanding example is cycloheptatriene vs. cyclopentadiene. Based on polarization arguments alone we would expect cycloheptatriene to be slightly more acidic, since it is slightly larger. However, cyclopentadiene is more acidic by 18 kcal/mole. This ordering is duplicated in solution, where the pK_a of cyclopentadiene is at least 15 less than that of cycloheptatriene. The origin of this result is the famous 4n + 2 "aromaticity" of the 6π-electron system. Here we have an excellent example of resonance effects dominating polarization.

One pair of hydrocarbons for which the polarizability difference should be in-significant is fluorene and diphenylmethane. Here HMO theory predicts fluorene to be slightly more acidic. This ordering is indeed observed in solution and in the gas phase, but the difference (~10 orders of magnitude in water[75] and DMSO[7] and 11 kcal/mole in the gas phase) is larger than expected, possibly because the phenyl rings in diphenylmethane anion are probably not coplanar.[76] This results in decreased anion resonance stabilization and decreased acidity for diphenyl-methane; fluorene, on the other hand, does not encounter this problem since its molecular framework is constrained to planarity. Two other compounds which would appear to be ideally suited for this type of comparison are cyclopentadiene and an open-chain pentadiene. An attempt to measure the acidity of 1,4-pentadiene has been made,[54] but due to isomerization in the reprotonation,[77] the results are not easily interpretable. Qualitatively, however, all indications are that cyclopentadiene is more acidic than 1,4-pentadiene, in accord with expectations based on resonance arguments.

In the case of two isomers such as 1,3- and 1,4-pentadiene which upon proton abstraction yield a common anion, knowledge of the acidity of one of the isomers allows the acidity of the other to be calculated provided the stability differ-ence between the two neutral molecules is known. This is shown pictorially in Fig. 5.

A plot of pK_a vs. the HMO resonance parameter ΔM for unsaturated hydrocarbons shows a fairly good linear correlation for those molecules which can be safely assumed to yield planar anions.[78] Even if one restricts the data to molecules appearing in Table I, a good straight line can still be drawn through the points for toluene, propylene, fluorene, and cyclopentadiene. An analogous plot of the gas phase acidities vs. ΔM for the same molecules has been shown by Bartmess and McIver[33] to give a much poorer correlation. The main reason for this is probably the

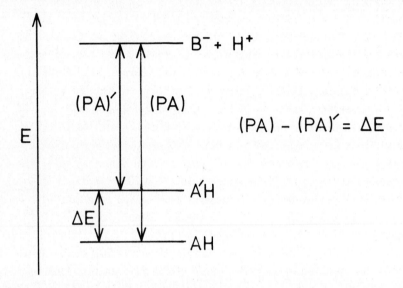

Fig. 5. Relationship between acidities of two isomers, AH and A'H, which upon deprotonation produce the same anion, B⁻.

large variation in size among the molecules in the plot, ranging from propene to fluorene. This results in the gas-phase data points reflecting various mixtures of polarization and resonance effects, making a good correlation between gas-phase acidity and ΔM impossible. HMO theory is of course incapable of taking polarization effects into consideration. In solution, polarization effects are at least partly cancelled by differential solvation, since the larger, more polarizable anion is also less solvated, and the relationship between pK_a and ΔM is fairly linear.

One might hope that more sophisticated semi-empirical molecular orbital calculations could be used to predict correct orderings of gas-phase acidities. This is indeed the case: For instance, CNDO/2 calculations of the acidities of toluene[79] and propene[80] predict toluene to be more acidic, as observed experimentally. The CNDO/2 calculated acidity difference for these compounds is 12 kcal/mole, in good agreement with the experimental value. This result should probably be considered fortuitous in view of the large structural differences between the molecules. The CNDO/2 method is generally regarded as a poor source of numerical results--for example, the calculated absolute acidities of toluene[79] and propene[80] are several hundred kcal/mole higher than the actual values. We shall see later that *ab initio* methods[81] such as 4-31G are capable of predicting absolute acidities (D-EA + IP(H)) to within 10% of the observed values, and relative acidities to within a few kcal/mole.

Non-additivity of substituent effects, or resonance saturation,[82] is a familiar phenomenon in organic chemistry. Examples abound:[8] Substitution of an acetyl group for a hydrogen in methane decreases the pK_a some 28 units, but substitution of a second acetyl group produces a further drop of only 11. Also, the pK_a of nitromethane is 37 below that of methane, but another nitro group lowers the pK_a only 7 more. This attenuation may arise from charge delocalization in the anion upon substitution of the first acidifying group.[82] As a result there is only a partial negative charge at the acidic site when the second group is substituted, so the effect of the second substituent must be smaller than that of the first. An alternative explanation is the normal attenuation of substituent effects as molecular size increases. As more substituents are added, each successive one becomes a smaller perturbation on the molecular orbitals. If the groups are sufficiently bulky, steric inhibition of resonance can also be a factor. Gas-phase acidities show resonance saturation effects, although available data are less extensive. For instance, acetone is ~ 48 kcal/mole more acidic than methane in the gas phase, while acetylacetone is only 26 kcal/mole more acidic than acetone. Likewise, acetonitrile is ~ 44 kcal/mole more acidic than methane, but malononitrile is 37 kcal/mole more acidic than acetonitrile. The attenuation in the acetyl group effects is much more pronounced than in the nitrile series. The effect on acidity of the second acetyl group is only about half that of the first, while the cyano group effects are almost equal. This difference is presumably due to steric inhibition of resonance acting in addition to resonance saturation in the acetylacetone anion. The linear cyano linkage causes no steric problems, so the much smaller attenuation observed in the nitrile series can probably be ascribed solely to resonance saturation.[33] Solution-phase data also display this trend. Relative to the respective monosubstituted methanes, the second cyano group decreases the pK_a to a greater extent than either a second acetyl or a second nitro group. The effect is not as dramatic as in the gas-phase data, probably due to differential solvation effects.

D. Inductive (Polar) Effects

1. General. Although separation of resonance and inductive effects in solution has been accomplished through the use of Taft parameters,[83] this analysis involved an enormous amount of data of which the gas-phase counterpart is simply unavailable. A similar treatment of gas-phase substitution effects is thus currently impossible. For this reason the substituted methanes CH_3X, where $X = NO_2$, CN, etc., are perhaps not the ideal compounds on which to base a discussion of inductive effects in carbon acids since resonance must also play a role in the acidities of these compounds. In cases where the charged center can interact electronically with a substituent, the distinction between resonance and inductive

effects is often poorly defined. p-Nitrotoluene is substantially more acidic than toluene, but clearly both resonance and inductive effects are important.

Mixing of resonance and inductive effects in acidities is less serious in the series of ketones X-COCH$_3$, in which a node near the carbonyl carbon in the highest-occupied π orbital of the anion substantially reduces resonance inter-action between the enolate π-system and the substituent X. Unfortunately, gas-phase acidity data on those compounds are rather limited, but if an approximate acidity for acetyl cyanide[33] is included, a reasonably good linear correlation between the gas phase acidities and Taft σ^* substituent parameters is observed (Fig. 6). The slope of the line is ~11, much larger than those typically observed in σ^*-ρ^* plots of solution-phase data. Linear free energy relationships

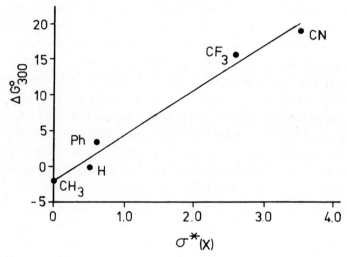

Fig. 6. Plot of ΔG^o_{300} (XCOCH$_2^-$ + HCOCH$_3$ $\rightleftarrows$ XCOCH$_3$ + HCOCH$_2^-$)(kcal/mole) versus σ^*(X). $\rho^* \approx 11$.

are also observed for the gas-phase acidities of substituted benzoic acids and phenols,[84] and for gas-phase basicities of substituted pyridines.[85] The values of ρ for these cases are 10.6, 6.8, and 3.6 times larger, respectively, than those observed in solution. Thus, it is clear that polar substituent effects in solution can be greatly attenuated relative to solvent-free conditions. This compression appears to have its origin in anion stabilization through solute-solvent interaction. Any additional stabilization of an anion in solution by a substituent effect will then appear as only a small fraction of the total stabilization energy since solvation energies are generally much larger than substituent effects. Therefore, $\Delta G^o / \Delta G^o_0$ (and hence log (K/K$_0$)) in solution is attenuated compared to $\Delta G^o / \Delta G^o_0$ in the gas phase where the substituent accounts for all of the stabilization relative to the unsubstituted anion. Another contributing factor is the decrease in strength of specific anion-solvent interactions such as hydrogen bonding with increased acidity,[86] which results in partial cancellation of substituent effects.

It was noted earlier that the effect on acidity of replacing hydrogen by a methyl group varies with the location of the substitution. Replacement of hydrogen by methyl away from the acidic site (i.e. ethanol vs. methanol) generally increases acidity through polarization effects, although there are exceptions such as p-xylene vs. toluene in which the resulting anion is delocalized. The effect of a methyl group at the acidic site, however, depends on the type of compound being considered. Discussion of methyl group effects is facilitated by considering separately the influence of methyl substitution on bond dissociation energies and electron affinities.

2. **Methyl Group Effects on Bond Energies.** Substituting a methyl group for hydrogen at the acidic site transforms the acidic hydrogen from primary to secondary or secondary to tertiary. Accompanying this change is a 3-6 kcal/mole decrease in the C-H bond strength,[72] in compounds which upon hydrogen abstraction yield localized alkyl radicals and those in which the radical center is adjacent to a vinyl or carbonyl group. Restated, this means simply that methyl substitution stabilizes the radical more than the parent molecule. ESR experiments[87] indicate that some of this differential stabilization may arise from hyperconjugative delocalization of the odd electron onto the methyl group hydrogens. Another contributing factor is the intrinsic stabilizing nature of a methyl group when attached to an sp^2-hybridized carbon as illustrated by the greater thermodynamic stability of cis- and trans-2-butene relative to 1-butene.

Generally, substitution of methyl for hydrogen away from the acidic site is assumed to have little or no effect on the bond strength to the acidic hydrogen. However, there is at least one exception to this generalization, for it will be seen shortly that the α C-H bond strength in acetone is larger than that in acetaldehyde.

3. **Methyl Group Effects on Electron Affinities.** Electron affinities can be raised or lowered by methyl group substitution. If the substitution occurs on an sp^3-hybridized carbon away from the acidic site, the result is generally an increase in the electron affinity of the radical relative to the unsubstituted analog. Thiomethoxyl (EA = 42.9 kcal/mole) and thioethoxyl (EA = 45.1 kcal/mole) form one example.[88] In these cases, substitution stabilizes the anion more than the radical. Polarization and MO arguments given earlier can account for the extra stabilization in the anion. Qualitatively, these effects correspond to hyperconjugative electron withdrawal by the methyl (alkyl) group. On the other

hand, an interaction which lowers the electron affinity is present when the methyl substitution occurs at the charged center or at an sp^2- or sp-hybridized carbon which may or may not form part of a delocalized anionic system such as acetaldehyde-propionaldehyde or acetylene-methylacetylene. Here, methyl substitution stabilizes the radical more than the anion. This effect can be interpreted either by a preferential stabilization of the radical which is not present in the anion, or a preferential destabilization of the anion not present in the radical.

The former approach has been taken[26] in a rationalization of the electron affinity drop upon going from hydroxyl to methoxyl radical. Consider once again Fig. 4 for methoxide anion. It was noted earlier that interaction between the 2p orbitals of O^- and the π orbitals of methyl is closed-shell and destabilizing. However, the 2p orbitals of neutral oxygen will lie below those of O^-, and thus will interact more strongly with the methyl π orbitals. In the radical this interaction is open-shell (3 electrons) and stabilizing. Since the effect is not present in the anion or in the hydroxyl-hydroxide system it accounts for methoxyl's electron affinity being lower than that of hydroxyl. This argument can easily be extended to carbon acids such as the pair acetaldehyde-propionaldehyde. In a rough qualitative sense it corresponds to hyperconjugative withdrawal by methyl being more important in the radical than in the anion. This is intuitively pleasing because it is consistent with the accepted view of enolate radicals as having most of the unpaired spin density on the α-carbon and the enolate anions in which the charge resides predominantly on the oxygen.

Destabilization of anions by methyl (inductive effect) has been a much-debated topic. Although the exact mechanism of this destabilization is unknown, for enolates,[45] acetylides,[89] and methylcyclopentadienide[48] it has been discussed in terms of a dipolar destabilization in which the methyl group donates electron density to a more electronegative unsaturated carbon. This electron donation results in the local dipole being oriented unfavorably with respect to the anionic charge. A quantum mechanical description of the dipole effect in methylacetylide is possible by considering the effect of methyl substitution on the electron distribution in the neutral molecule, freezing the orbitals, removing the acidic proton, and allowing the orbitals to relax. In the case of acetylene, CNDO/2 calculations show that substitution of methyl for hydrogen results in a transfer of π-electron density from the α- to the β-carbon--a "polarization" of the triple bond in the direction away from the methyl group.[90] Little net electron withdrawal from methyl occurs. If we now imagine keeping the orbitals fixed and removing the acetylenic proton, what results is an anion with its π-electron density polarized unfavorably toward the negative charge. Allowing the orbitals to relax results in delocalization of charge onto the methyl group hydrogens and away from the β-carbon. Thus, the mechanism of methyl group stabilization in the neutral is less available in the anion due to electron repulsion effects. This simple line of reasoning is strictly applicable only to methylacetylide, since the π-system of the triple bond is orthogonal to the orbital in which most of the charge resides and one can safely ignore any effects due to orbital mixing and rehybridization. However, electron repulsion may also be responsible for the methyl group effects observed in p-xylene and methylcyclopentadiene.

These arguments have recently been restated in somewhat more formal terms by Pross and Radom[91] using ab initio molecular orbital calculations. They described the effect of methyl substitution on the acidity of acetylene by considering interactions of the unoccupied $\pi^*(C{\equiv}C^-)$ and $\pi^*(C{\equiv}C\text{-}H)$ orbitals with the $\pi(CH_3)$ orbital (analogous to Fig. 3, except that the interaction is open-shell). In both cases (neutral and anion) the interaction is open-shell and stabilizing, but less so for the anion since the $\pi^*(C{\equiv}C^-)$ orbital lies higher in energy than $\pi^*(C{\equiv}C\text{-}H)$. Thus methyl substitution stabilizes the neutral more than the anion, resulting in decreased acidity and hence decreased electron affinity if the bond energy is assumed unchanged. The effects of methyl substitution on acidities of water and acetaldehyde were also rationalized within this framework which is dealt with in more depth in the next section. It should be noted however, that application of this model to electron affinities is more complex than application to acidities because more interactions must be considered. Interactions which are closed-shell and destabilizing in the parent anion become open-shell and potentially stabilizing in the radical, so the analysis becomes considerably more involved.

4. Methyl and Alkyl Group Effects on Gas-Phase Acidities. The influence of methyl substitution on a molecule's gas-phase acidity reflects a combination of effects on the radical and anion. It is important to bear in mind that decreases in bond energy and electron affinity act on the gas-phase acidity D-EA in opposite ways, and so the net effect of methyl substitution at the acidic site in a carbon acid will depend on which effect is larger.

Gas-phase acidities of aldehydes and ketones are well-suited to analysis in terms of bond energy and electron affinity effects, since bond energies for primary and secondary C-H bonds α to a carbonyl group[44,46] and electron affinities for several alkyl-substituted enolates[45] are known. Figure 7 displays the pertinent data. Thus, we see that methyl substitution at the carbonyl carbon in acetaldehyde produces an increase in D-EA and a decrease in EA. The electron affinity change is consistent with the effects discussed above, but the bond energy also increases. This is rather unexpected since the substitution occurs away from the acidic site; further, it means that the parent neutral molecule is stabilized more by methyl substitution than is the radical. The origin of this effect is unknown.

CH$_3$CHO

D - EA = 53.4
D = 95.1
EA = 41.7

CH$_3$COCH$_3$

D - EA = 56.4
D = 97.0
EA = 40.6

CH$_3$COCH$_2$CH$_3$

D - EA = 54.6
D = 93.2
EA = 38.6

CH$_3$CH$_2$CHO

D - EA = 52.8
D = 91.7
EA = 38.9

Fig. 7. Alkyl group effects on acidities, bond strengths, and electron affinities of aldehydes and ketones (all quantities in kcal/mole).

Although methyl substitution at the carbonyl carbon makes acetone less acidic than acetaldehyde, methyl substitution at the acidic site (α-carbon) increases acidity--propionaldehyde is more acidic than acetaldehyde. The electron affinity is again seen to decrease upon methyl substitution; now, however, this acid-weakening effect is outweighed by the larger decrease in bond energy. This result is also seen for acetone and 2-butanone. Figure 7 shows that the effect of methyl substitution on electron affinity is much larger at the α-carbon than at the carbonyl group. This difference is not at all surprising, and is consistent with a larger charge density at the acidic site than at the carbonyl carbon.

Although acidity data for various other alkyl-substituted carbon acids are available, discussion of methyl group effects in these compounds must be less quantitative than for the carbonyls since in most cases the necessary bond energies and/or electron affinities are lacking. However, it seems reasonable to predict that the 3-6 kcal/mole difference in primary and secondary C-H bond strengths and the decrease in electron affinity upon methyl substitution at an sp^2 or sp carbon will be characteristic of all carbon acids.

The methyl-substituted compounds are more acidic in the pairs toluene-ethylbenzene, acetophenone-propiophenone, and nitromethane-nitroethane. This is probably due to the same combination of factors noted earlier for acetone--2-butanone. For these compounds differential stabilization of the methyl-substituted radical is primarily responsible for the increase in acidity. An exception to these cases, both in location of the substitution and its effect, is the pair toluene--p-xylene in which the latter is the weaker acid. Here, the bond energies are probably very similar,[72] so that the change in acidity must be due to a decrease in electron affinity of the methyl-substituted radical, which is entirely

analogous to the trend observed for cyclopentadienyl and methylcyclopentadienyl
radicals.

In the pairs acetonitrile-propionitrile and phenyl methyl sulfone-phenyl
ethyl sulfone, substitution of methyl for hydrogen is acid-weakening. In these
cases, the decreases in bond energies must be smaller than the electron affinity
decreases. This observation for the sulfones has been the basis for the conclusion that conjugation is more important in enolate anions than in sulfone anions.[92]
However, arguments such as this are rather risky in view of the lack of appropriate bond energy and electron affinity data since the effects involved are
quite small. It is well known that the difference between primary and secondary
C-H bond energies can vary, depending on the particular compounds involved, over
a range at least as large as the acidity differences on which the aforementioned
sulfone-ketone argument is based.

An acidity decrease in going from acetylene to methylacetylene is also observed
but here, as in the toluene--p-xylene case, no change in C-H bond type occurs, so
the change in bond energies is probably small and the acidity decrease should
arise from a decrease in electron affinity. Unfortunately, no bond energy or
electron affinity data for methylacetylene are available, so at present this
point cannot be substantiated or refuted.

Bordwell and co-workers have done a recent survey[93] of acidities in DMSO and
water of many of the carbon acids treated here, and noted that trends in gas
phase acidities of these compounds are often mirrored in solution. Our analysis
of methyl group effects has proceeded along much the same lines as theirs in
terms of hyperconjugation and polar electron release.

At this point it should be clear that substitution of methyl for hydrogen can
have very different effects on gas-phase acidity depending upon the substitution
site and the type of compound. This is in dramatic contrast to solution acidities, in which methyl has for many years been treated as primarily electron-
donating (although Bordwell et al.[93] have observed exceptions). The origins of
this varying behavior have only recently begun to be explained.

The most complete description of methyl group effects presented to date is
the model of Pross and Radom[91] mentioned earlier. (Note also Hudson et al.[67])
Pross and Radom rationalized the effects of methyl substitution on acidities of
water, acetylene, acetaldehyde and a number of other compounds by breaking the
methyl group effect down into interactions between the π and π^* orbitals of
methyl (shown in Figs. 3 and 4) and the π-type orbitals of the acidic function.
For instance, based on this model, stabilization of CH_3O^- through interaction of
$\pi^*_{CH_3}$ and $2p(O^-)$ is responsible for methanol being more acidic than water. This
is the same interaction which was seen earlier to be important in the polarizability effects of alkyl groups. Likewise, interaction between $\pi(CH_3)$ and the

empty $\pi^*(C\equiv C-H)$ and $\pi^*(C\equiv C^-)$ orbitals causes preferential stabilization of neutral methylacetylene relative to the deprotonated anion with the result that methylacetylene is less acidic than acetylene. Thus in methanol the primary interaction occurs with the $\pi^*(CH_3)$ orbital while in methylacetylene it is with the $\pi(CH_3)$ orbital. Methyl substitution increases acidity in the former case and decreases it in the latter. The authors make the generalization that when the acidic function has high-lying occupied orbitals of the proper symmetry, anion stabilization by $\pi^*(CH_3)$ will occur and methyl substitution will increase acidity. Conversely, anion destabilization by $\pi(CH_3)$ and decreased acidity results upon methyl substitution if the acidic function has low-lying occupied orbitals of proper symmetry. In general, however, it will not be possible to predict the effect of methyl substitution on acidity without the aid of calculations, since it is often difficult to estimate without calculation the relative orbital energies and overlap terms. Thus, Pross and Radom's model is basically a perturbation theory interpretation of ab initio calculations.

Nevertheless, this framework is quite useful in providing a rationalization of general alkyl group effects on gas-phase acidities. Although substitution of methyl for hydrogen can produce varying results, substitution of ethyl and larger alkyl groups for methyl is acid-strengthening in every known case. This indicates that for these cases the polarizability effect is dominant; in the Pross and Radom model, this can be interpreted as the interactions between the empty π^* alkyl orbitals and occupied π orbitals of the acidic function becoming important. The net result of this polarizability interaction is anion stabilization, which can be viewed as electron withdrawal by the alkyl group. The classical inductive effect in which methyl appears as electron-releasing is seen in the examples above in which alkyl substitution decreases acidity relative to hydrogen. This net anion destabilization can be attributed to interaction of the acidic function π orbitals with the occupied π alkyl orbitals, e.g., as described above for methylacetylene. Thus electron withdrawal by the polarizability effect arises from interactions with π^* alkyl orbitals, while inductive "electron release"[90] stems from interaction with filled π alkyl orbitals. The connection between polarizability and unoccupied orbitals has been previously pointed out.[26,37] A priori, both mechanisms can operate in a given molecule; the dominant one in a particular example will be determined by the energies and overlap properties of the orbitals involved.

Evidence of mechanisms for both electron withdrawal and release by alkyl groups was recently provided by Taft et al.[94] in a treatment designed to separate alkyl polarizability and inductive effects. This work involved measurements of ΔG^o for the proton transfer reactions 7 and 8,

$$ROH + CH_3OH_2^+ \rightleftharpoons ROH_2^+ + CH_3OH \tag{7}$$

$$ROH + CH_3O^- \rightleftharpoons RO^- + CH_3OH \tag{8}$$

The polarizability effect (P) of R relative to CH_3 will stabilize both ROH_2^+ and RO^-, whereas the inductive effect (I) of R will stabilize ROH_2^+ but destabilize RO^-. Thus, if the assumption is made that the magnitudes of each effect are equal for the two reactions, one obtains

$$-\Delta G_7^{\,o} \approx I + P \tag{9}$$

$$-\Delta G_8^{\,o} \approx -I + P \tag{10}$$

Subtracting (8) from (7) yields a hypothetical double proton transfer reaction in which polarizability effects have been eliminated (within the approximations inherent in eqs. (9)-(10)). This treatment yielded results consistent with the classical inductive order for alkyl groups, values of I ranging up to 2.3 kcal/mole for t-Bu (relative to I = 0.0 kcal/mole for CH_3) with Et and i-Pr displaying intermediate values. For electron-withdrawing groups, I < 0. Values of P were also seen to increase with alkyl group size, but turned out to be three to seven times larger than the corresponding I values--as expected from the observation that polarizability effects dominate in determining gas-phase acidity order. It should be noted, however, from the previous quantum mechanical descriptions of inductive and polarizability effects that their relative and absolute magnitudes may depend on whether one is dealing with a cation or anion.

The above work demonstrates that mechanisms exist by which alkyl groups can both stabilize and destabilize anions. That the magnitude of each effect should increase with alkyl group size is consistent with the molecular orbital picture discussed earlier in this section. Increasing the alkyl group size introduces more π and π^* alkyl group orbitals and hence more interactions with the acid function orbitals. Domination of the polarizability effect for alkyl groups relative to methyl appears in both experiment and calculation even though, in the absence of such data, it could not have been conclusively predicted. The effect on acidity of substituting methyl and alkyl for hydrogen (as in acetylene and alkylacetylenes, for instance) cannot be easily predicted and will depend on the particular system.

To summarize, substitution of a methyl group for hydrogen can be either acid-strengthening or acid-weakening depending on whether interaction of the acid function orbitals with the π^* or π methyl orbitals is more important. The effect depends on the particular system and is difficult to predict without the aid of calculation. However, substitution of a larger alkyl group for methyl appears always to be acid-strengthening (relative to methyl--the alkyl-substituted compound may still be weaker than the hydrogen-substituted parent) due to the interaction with the alkyl π^* orbitals (polarizability) becoming more important.

Based on this model one would expect that, if the acid function orbitals were sufficiently low in energy so as to substantially reduce the interactions with the methyl or alkyl π^* orbitals, acidity of alkyl-substituted derivatives would be governed solely by the interactions with the alkyl π orbitals and hence the classical inductive order. The observed reversal of the acidities of the simple aliphatic alcohols between the gas phase and solution can be rationalized on this basis.[67] Solvation effects will drastically lower the energies of the 2p orbitals on oxygen in RO^-, diminishing the importance of the $\pi^*(R)-2p(O^-)$ interactions. Relative acidities will then be governed by the inductive effect. Interactions with the filled alkyl π orbitals result in net anion destabilization relative to the neutral; since these interactions become more important as the alkyl group size increases, this model accounts for t-butyl alcohol being a weaker acid than methanol in solution.

E. Hybridization and Geometry Effects

The linear correlation between pK_a and percentage s-character of the ionizing carbon in the series ethane, cyclopropane, ethylene, acetylene[95] is well known from classical organic chemistry. Although lack of data for the first three compounds prevents an analogous treatment of gas-phase acidities, qualitatively the trend is observed to the extent that acetylene is by far the most acidic of the four in the gas phase as well.

Effects of molecular geometry on gas-phase acidity constitute an interesting research area which has been little explored. Although no studies of geometry effects on carbon acidities have yet been reported, some conclusions regarding acidities of cyclic ketones can be drawn from a study of electron affinities of cyclic enolate radicals which has recently appeared.[96] One would of course need the appropriate bond energies in order to extend rigorously the results of this study to the parent compound acidities. However, it is doubtful that the bond energies vary by more than 2 kcal/mole over the entire series of compounds studied. This is much smaller than the variation in electron affinities of the radicals, and hence the acidity order should parallel the electron affinity order. This prediction awaits experimental verification, but as will be seen the EA order duplicates the solution-phase kinetic acidity order[96] cyclobutanone > cyclopentanone > cyclohexanone. A plot[96] of EA vs. ring size for cyclic enolates is shown in Fig. 8. From cycloheptanone enolate upward, EA increases with ring size, consistent with expectations based on polarizability. However, below this point the

electron affinities also increase. This remarkable observation was rationalized
with an argument involving angle strain. In an unconstrained enolate anion, the
O-C-C angle tends to be larger than in the radical (interaction between the
termini is antibonding and destabilizing). As it turns out, this bond angle in
cyclobutanone is optimal for the anion--the radical is destabilized, whereas in
cycloheptanone the angle favors the radical relative to the anion. More quantitatively, CNDO/2 calculations for acetaldehyde enolate[45] predict an optimum
O-C-C bond angle of 132° in the anion and 123° in the radical. Any factor which
produces a decrease in this angle in the anion will destabilize the anion relative
to the radical and lower the EA. In cyclobutanone enolate the O-C-C angle is
constrained to ~ 135°; this angle decreases to ~ 126°, 120°, and 116° in cyclopentanone, cyclohexanone, and cycloheptanone enolates, respectively. Thus, as
the ring size increases the anion is differentially destabilized relative to the
radical, leading to decreases in electron affinity. The data suggest that for
rings larger than C_7 the O-C-C angle is not especially sensitive to ring geometry,
since above this point the EA merely increases with increasing molecular size.

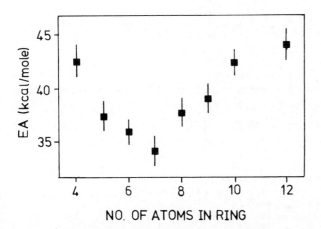

Fig. 8. Plot of electron affinity versus ring size for cyclic enolate radicals.
Reprinted with permission from A. H. Zimmerman, R. L. Jackson, B. K. Janousek,
and J. I. Brauman, J. Amer. Chem. Soc. 100 (1978) 4674. Copyright by the American
Chemical Society.

An interesting effect of molecular geometry on acidity is manifested in the
~ 5 kcal/mole difference in gas-phase acidity of acetylacetone and dimedone
(5,5-dimethyl-1,3-cyclohexanedione), with the latter being more acidic. There
are several factors in addition to molecular size which are believed to contribute
to this difference.[54] Geometric constraints require that in dimedone the carbonyl group dipoles be oriented unfavorably with respect to one another, while

this repulsion can be at least partially relieved in acetylacetone. However, the π-system in dimedone enolate can easily assume a planar conformation whereas this is not the case for acetylacetone enolate due to unfavorable steric interactions. Thus, neutral dimedone is slightly destabilized relative to acetylacetone, while acetylacetone enolate is slightly destabilized relative to dimedone enolate. These effects add to make dimedone a stronger acid than acetylacetone.

F. Kinetic Acidity

Kinetic acidity measurements have proven useful in solution particularly when the position of equilibrium is difficult to establish--for instance, when the solvent is more acidic than the substrate being studied. Provided a linear free energy relationship exists, acidities (or at least relative acidities) can be inferred from isotope exchange rate measurements. In general one does not use such methods in the gas phase, since highly endothermic reactions are too slow to measure and one can monitor directly only the concentration of ions. (Occurrence or nonoccurrence of gas-phase proton transfers is the basis of the "bracketing" method[56] used for the establishment of qualitative acidity orders.) Nonetheless, there are several gas-phase kinetic acidity experiments discussed below which have direct relevance to solution acidities.

Part of the early dogma of gas-phase ion-molecule reactions was that proton-transfer reactions proceeded with unit efficiency, that is, reaction occurred on every collision between the reacting partners. Subsequent work[25] has shown that this is not always the case--reactions involving delocalized carbanions are relatively slow when compared with, say, alkoxides. In fact, it is possible to catalyze the proton exchange reaction between allyl anion and toluene by addition of methanol.[97] This behavior, as in solution, indicates that energy barriers to proton transfers involving delocalized anions are intrinsic and not merely a solvation effect. These energy barriers are believed to arise from structural and electronic reorganization occurring upon protonation.[98] For instance, protonation of allyl or benzyl anion requires charge localization and subsequent loss of resonance energy in the transition state, leading to a barrier to protonation. For oxygen- and nitrogen-containing anions, protonation can occur orthogonal to the π-system, hence avoiding the barrier and resulting in a fast rate. Enolate anions are a particularly interesting case since protonation on oxygen can occur; however, this leads to thermodynamically unfavorable products, and so protonation is forced to follow the high-barrier pathway.

DePuy and co-workers have made the important observation that certain carbanions can exchange protons with substrates not sufficiently acidic to protonate them at equilibrium.[99] Thus, although reaction 11 is endothermic and gives essentially no OH$^-$ at equilibrium, benzyl anion can still exchange protons with water in a short-lived encounter complex, reaction 12. This type of exchange mechanism has also been proposed for solution-phase processes.[11]

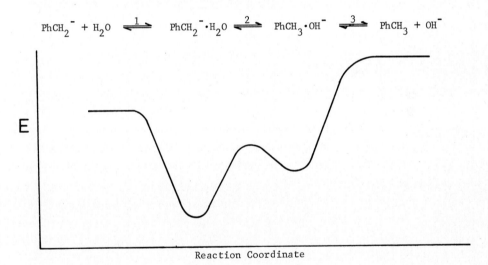

$$\text{PhCH}_2^- + \text{H}_2\text{O} \xrightleftharpoons{\quad 1 \quad} \text{PhCH}_2^- \cdot \text{H}_2\text{O} \xrightleftharpoons{\quad 2 \quad} \text{PhCH}_3 \cdot \text{OH}^- \xrightleftharpoons{\quad 3 \quad} \text{PhCH}_3 + \text{OH}^-$$

(The figure: energy diagram with two wells along the Reaction Coordinate; E on vertical axis.)

The reason the exchange reaction can occur in the gas phase is that sufficient energy is released in complex formation to allow proton transfer in the complex, but this energy is not sufficient to produce separated product ions. That is, after collision, step 2 is fast but 3 is slow.

Reaction Coordinate

G. Theoretical Studies

Literature reports of calculated gas phase carbon acidities are fairly few in number. Ab initio calculations at the STO-3G and 4-31G levels[81] duplicate the experimental acidity orders for substituted acetylenes[91,100] and the pair toluene--p-xylene,[101] with the calculated relative acidities lying within a few kcal/mole of the observed values. This work also demonstrated that these methods are capable of calculating absolute acidities, D - EA + IP(H), in fair agreement

(within 10-30%) with experimental values, although this is somewhat misleading
since IP(H) is by far the largest of the three terms; calculated values of D - EA
are generally poor. However, in some cases agreement can be excellent, as
evidenced by recent _ab initio_ calculations of the absolute acidity of nitromethane.[102] Here the calculated D - EA + IP(H) values were within 7 kcal/mole of
the experimental value.

Although CNDO/2 calculations reproduce the correct orders for acidities of
alcohols[103,104] and basicities of alkylamines,[105] the method fails for the pairs
acetylene--methylacetylene and toluene--p-xylene.[89] Further, absolute acidities
calculated from CNDO/2 are generally ~200 kcal/mole too high.[79,80,103] However,
CNDO/2 wave functions have been used with reasonable success in an interesting
method of calculating relative acidities.[106] This method, known as the proton
potential model (PPM), calculates electrostatic potentials at the acidic site
with and without the proton present, and uses these quantities to break down an
anion's proton affinity into contributions from electrostatic and polarization
energies. Relative acidities of aliphatic acids and alcohols determined in this
fashion agree very well with experiment as long as the molecules being compared
are of similar structures. Discrepancies appear when delocalized anions (phenols,
carbon acids) are considered, but the method should be less applicable in these
cases since a dramatic change in orbital structure occurs upon going from neutral
to anion.

Acknowledgment. We are grateful to the National Science Foundation for support
of this research and for Fellowship support to M. J. P. Part of this chapter
was written during the tenure of a Guggenheim Fellowship to J. I. B. for which
he expresses his thanks.

References

1. J. F. Coetzee and C. D. Ritchie, eds., Solute-Solvent Interactions, Marcel Dekker, New York, 1969.

2. W. K. McEwen, J. Amer. Chem. Soc., 58 (1936) 1124.

3. C. D. Ritchie and R. E. Uschold, J. Amer. Chem. Soc., 89 (1967) 2752.

4. F. G. Bordwell and W. S. Matthews, J. Amer. Chem. Soc., 96 (1974) 1216.

5. K. Bowden and R. Stewart, Tetrahedron, 21 (1965) 261.

6. H. C. Brown, D. H. McDaniel and O. Häfliger, Chap. 14 in Determination of Organic Structures by Physical Methods, E. A. Braude and F. C. Nachod, eds., Academic Press, New York, 1955.

7. F. G. Bordwell, J. E. Bartmess, G. E. Drucker, Z. Margolin, and W. S. Matthews, J. Amer. Chem. Soc., 97 (1975) 3226.

8. D. J. Cram, Fundamentals of Carbanion Chemistry, Academic Press, New York, 1965.

9. J. R. Jones, The Ionization of Carbon Acids, Academic Press, New York, 1973.

10. E. Buncel, Carbanions: Mechanistic and Isotopic Aspects, Elsevier, New York, 1975.

11. Ref. 8. Chapter 1.

12. P. Kebarle, Ann. Rev. Phys. Chem., 28 (1977) 445.

13. A. J. Cunningham, J. D. Payzant, and P. Kebarle, J. Amer. Chem. Soc., 94 (1972) 7627.

14. E. E. Ferguson, F. C. Fehsenfeld, and A. L. Schmeltekopf, Advan. At. Mol. Phys., 5 (1969) 1.

15. A. L. Schmeltekopf and F. C. Fehsenfeld, J. Chem. Phys., 53 (1970) 3173.

16. F. C. Fehsenfeld, Int. J. Mass Spec. Ion Phys., 16 (1975) 151.

17. J. D. Baldeschwieler and S. S. Woodgate, Acc. Chem. Res., 4 (1971) 114.

18. R. T. McIver, Jr., Rev. Sci. Instr., 41 (1970) 555.

19. R. T. McIver, Jr., Rev. Sci. Instr., 49 (1978) 111.

20. K. S. Pitzer, J. Amer. Chem. Soc., 59 (1937) 2365.

21. Y. K. Lau and P. Kebarle, J. Amer. Chem. Soc., 98 (1976) 7452.

22. D. K. Bohme, E. Lee-Ruff, and L. B. Young, J. Amer. Chem. Soc., 94 (1972) 5153.

23. R. T. McIver, Jr., Rev. Sci. Instr., 44 (1973) 1071.

24. J. F. Wolf, R. H. Staley, I. Koppel, M. Taagepera, R. T. McIver, Jr., J. L. Beauchamp, and R. W. Taft, J. Amer. Chem. Soc., 99 (1977) 5417.

25. W. E. Farneth and J. I. Brauman, J. Amer. Chem. Soc., 98 (1976) 7891.

26. B. K. Janousek and J. I. Brauman in Gas-Phase Ion Chemistry, M. T. Bowers, ed., Academic Press, New York, 1979.

27. D. R. Stull and H. Prophet, eds., JANAF Thermochemical Tables, NSRDS-NBS 37, U. S. Government Printing Office, Washington, D. C., 1971.

28. G. B. Ellison, P. C. Engleking and W. C. Lineberger, J. Amer. Chem. Soc., 100 (1978) 2556.

29. G. I. Mackay, R. S. Hemsworth, and D. K. Bohme, Can. J. Chem., 54 (1976) 1624.

30. K. C. Smyth and J. I. Brauman, J. Chem. Phys., 56 (1972) 4620.

31. H. M. Rosenstock, K. Draxl, B. W. Steiner, and J. T. Herron, J. Phys. Chem. Ref. Data, 6, Supp. 1 (1977) 736.

32. G. I. Mackay, M. H. Lien, A. C. Hopkinson, and D. K. Bohme, Can. J. Chem., 56 (1978) 131.

33. J. E. Bartmess and R. T. McIver, Jr. in Gas-Phase Ion Chemistry, M. T. Bowers, ed., Academic Press, New York, 1978.

34. D. M. Golden and S. W. Benson, Chem. Rev., 69 (1969) 125.

35. A. H. Zimmerman and J. I. Brauman, J. Amer. Chem. Soc., 99 (1977) 3565.

36. S. W. Benson, Thermochemical Kinetics, 2nd Ed., Wiley-Interscience, New York, 1976.

37. B. K. Janousek, A. H. Zimmerman, K. J. Reed, and J. I. Brauman, J. Amer. Chem. Soc., 100 (1978) 6142.

38. J. H. Richardson, L. M. Stephenson, and J. I. Brauman, J. Chem. Phys., 63 (1975) 74.

39. G. I. Mackay and D. K. Bohme, Int. J. Mass Spec. Ion Phys., 26 (1978) 327.

40. F. M. Page and G. C. Goode, Negative Ions and the Magnetron, Wiley-Interscience, New York, 1969, p. 139.

41. J. B. Cumming and P. Kebarle, Can. J. Chem., 56 (1978) 1.

42. G. I. Mackay, L. D. Betowski, J. D. Payzant, H. I. Schiff, and D. K. Bohme, J. Phys. Chem., 80 (1976) 2919.

43. K. D. King and R. G. Goddard, Int. J. Chem. Kin., 7 (1975) 837.

44. R. K. Solly, D. M. Golden, and S. W. Benson, Int. J. Chem. Kin., 2 (1970) 11.

45. A. H. Zimmerman, K. J. Reed, and J. I. Brauman, J. Amer. Chem. Soc., 99 (1977) 7203.

46. R. K. Solly, D. M. Golden, and S. W. Benson, Int. J. Chem. Kin., 2 (1970) 381.

47. S. Furuyama, D. M. Golden, and S. W. Benson, Int. J. Chem. Kin., 3 (1971) 237.

48. J. H. Richardson, L. M. Stephenson, and J. I. Brauman, J. Chem. Phys., 59 (1973) 5068.

49. J. I. Brauman and K. C. Smyth, J. Amer. Chem. Soc., 91(1969) 7778.

50. D. Betowski, G. Mackay, J. Payzant, and D. K. Bohme, Can. J. Chem., 53 (1975) 2365.

51. J. Berkowitz, W. A. Chupka, and T. A. Walter, J. Chem. Phys., 50 (1969) 1497.

52. J. I. Brauman and L. K. Blair, J. Amer. Chem. Soc., 90 (1968) 5636.

53. I. Dzidic, D. I. Carroll, R. N. Stillwell, and E. C. Horning, J. Amer. Chem. Soc., 96 (1974) 5258.

54. T. B. McMahon and P. Kebarle, J. Amer. Chem. Soc., 98 (1976) 3399.

55. V. Fried, H. F. Hameka, and U. Blukis, Physical Chemistry, Macmillan, New York, 1977, p. 834.

56. J. I. Brauman and L. K. Blair, J. Amer. Chem. Soc., 92 (1970) 5986.

57. J. I. Brauman, J. M. Riveros, and L. K. Blair, J. Amer. Chem. Soc., 93 (1971) 3914.

58. W. M. Schubert, R. B. Murphy, and J. Robins, Tetrahedron, 17 (1962) 199.

59. T. J. Broxton, L. W. Deady, A. R. Katritzky, A. Liu, and R. D. Topsom, J. Amer. Chem. Soc., 92 (1970) 6845.

60. T. L. Brown, J. Amer. Chem. Soc., 81 (1959) 3232.

61. S. W. Benson and A. N. Bose, J. Chem. Phys., 39 (1963) 3463.

62. K. G. Denbigh, Trans. Faraday Soc., 36 (1940) 936.

63. D. H. Aue, H. M. Webb, and M. T. Bowers, J. Amer. Chem. Soc., 98 (1976) 311.

64. R. J. W. LeFèvre, B. J. Orr, and G. L. D. Ritchie, J. Chem. Soc. (B) (1966) 273.

65. C. A. Coulson, A. Maccoll, and L. E. Sutton, Trans. Faraday Soc., 48 (1952) 106.

66. M. J. S. Dewar, The Molecular Orbital Theory of Organic Chemistry, McGraw-Hill, New York, 1969.

67. R. F. Hudson, O. Eisenstein, and N. G. Anh, Tetrahedron, 31 (1975) 751.

68. T. Koopmans, Physica, 1 (1934) 104.

69. J. A. Pople and D. L. Beveridge, Approximate Molecular Orbital Theory, McGraw-Hill, New York, 1970, Chaps. 3-4.

70. M. J. Pellerite, unpublished results.

71. A. Streitwieser, Jr., Molecular Orbital Theory For Organic Chemists, John Wiley & Sons, Inc., New York, 1961.

72. K. W. Egger and A. T. Cocks, Helv. Chim. Acta, 56 (1973) 1516.

73. J. I. Brauman and L. K. Blair, J. Amer. Chem. Soc., 93 (1971) 3911; L. K. Blair, Ph.D. Thesis, Stanford University, 1970.

74. See, for instance, G. W. Wheland, Resonance in Organic Chemistry, John Wiley & Sons, Inc., New York, 1955; also G. E. K. Branch and M. Calvin, The Theory of Organic Chemistry, Prentice-Hall, New York, 1944.

75. T. H. Lowry and K. S. Richardson, Mechanism and Theory in Organic Chemistry, Harper & Row, New York, 1976, p. 146.

76. T. Schaefer and W. G. Schneider, Can. J. Chem., 41 (1963) 968.

77. J. B. Cumming and P. Kebarle, J. Amer. Chem. Soc., 99 (1977) 5818. Isomerization upon reprotonation (ref. 99) also renders unreliable the results of a recent attempt (J. E. Bartmess, W. J. Hehre, R. T. McIver, and L. E. Overman, J. Amer. Chem. Soc., 99 (1977) 1976) to measure the acidities of cis- and trans-2-butene.

78. Ref. 71, p. 416.

79. P. Birner, H.-J. Köhler, and C. Weiss, Int. J. Quantum Chem., 9 (1975) 917.

80. A. Atkinson, A. C. Hopkinson, and E. Lee-Ruff, Tetrahedron, 30 (1974) 2023.

81. W. J. Hehre, Acc. Chem. Res., 9 (1976) 399.

82. F. G. Bordwell and G. J. McCollum, J. Org. Chem., 41 (1976) 2391.

83. R. W. Taft, Jr., Chap. 13 in Steric Effects in Organic Chemistry, M. S. Newman, ed., John Wiley & Sons, New York, 1956.

84. T. B. McMahon and P. Kebarle, J. Amer. Chem. Soc., 99 (1972) 2222.

85. M. Taagepera, W. G. Henderson, R. T. C. Brownlee, J. L. Beauchamp, D. Holtz, and R. W. Taft, J. Amer. Chem. Soc., 94 (1972) 1369.

86. R. Yamdagni and P. Kebarle, J. Amer. Chem. Soc., 93 (1971) 7139.

87. R. O. C. Norman and B. C. Gilbert, Adv. Phys. Org. Chem., 5 (1967) 53.

88. B. K. Janousek and J. I. Brauman, in press; B. K. Janousek, K. J. Reed, and J. I. Brauman, in press.

89. J. I. Brauman and L. K. Blair, J. Amer. Chem. Soc., 93 (1971) 4315.

90. Ref. 69, p. 118; also L. Libit and R. Hoffmann, J. Amer. Chem. Soc., 96 (1974) 1370.

91. A. Pross and L. Radom, J. Amer. Chem. Soc., 100 (1978) 6572.

92. J. B. Cumming and P. Kebarle, J. Amer. Chem. Soc., 100 (1978) 1835.

93. F. G. Bordwell, J. E. Bartmess, and J. A. Hautala, J. Org. Chem., 43 (1978) 3095.

94. R. W. Taft, M. Taagepera, J. Abboud, J. F. Wolf, D. J. DeFrees, W. J. Hehre, J. E. Bartmess, and R. T. McIver, J. Amer. Chem. Soc., 100 (1978) 7767.

95. Ref. 8, p. 49.

96. A. H. Zimmerman, R. L. Jackson, B. K. Janousek, and J. I. Brauman, J. Amer. Chem. Soc., 100 (1978) 4674.

97. J. I. Brauman, C. A. Lieder, and M. J. White, J. Amer. Chem. Soc., 95 (1973) 927.

98. R. P. Bell, The Proton in Chemistry, 2nd ed., Cornell University Press, Ithaca, N. Y., 1973, Chap. 10.

99. J. H. Stewart, R. H. Shapiro, C. H. DePuy, and V. M. Bierbaum, J. Amer. Chem. Soc., 99 (1977) 7650.

100. L. Radom, Aust. J. Chem., 28 (1975) 1.

101. L. Radom, J. Chem. Soc. Chem. Commun., (1974) 403.

102. P. G. Mezey, A. J. Kresge, and I. G. Csizmadia, Can. J. Chem., 54 (1976) 2526; J. R. Murdoch, A. Streitwieser, Jr., and S. Gabriel, J. Amer. Chem. Soc., 100 (1978) 6338.

103. T. P. Lewis, Tetrahedron, 25 (1969) 4117.

104. M. Graffeuil, J.-F. Labarre, and C. Leibovici, J. Mol. Struct., 23 (1974) 65.

105. M. Graffeuil, J.-F. Labarre, and C. Leibovici, J. Mol. Struct., 22 (1974) 97.

106. D. W. Davis and D. A. Shirley, J. Amer. Chem. Soc., 98 (1976) 7898.

CHAPTER 3

SPECTROPHOTOMETRIC INVESTIGATIONS OF ARYLMETHYL CARBANIONS

ERWIN BUNCEL AND BALACHANDRAN MENON

DEPARTMENT OF CHEMISTRY, QUEEN'S UNIVERSITY, KINGSTON, ONTARIO, CANADA K7L 3N6

I   INTRODUCTION

Arylmethyl carbanions such as the triphenylmethyl carbanion, along with
the corresponding carbonium ion and free radical species, have played a central
role in the development of the concepts of delocalization and the effect of
structure on the stability of metastable species and reactive intermediates.

However, spectroscopic characterization of these species dates back to only relatively recently, which is particularly applicable to the anionic species.

Of the various spectroscopic methods currently available, nuclear magnetic resonance and electronic absorption spectroscopy have yielded the most extensive information concerning structure and dynamics of delocalized carbanions. The chapters in this volume by Bates and by O'Brien have considered in detail the use of the former method in the investigation of a variety of such carbanions.

In this chapter, we present the results of a systematic investigation of the electronic absorption spectra of arylmethyl carbanions. The study was carried out in conjunction with various structure-reactivity studies involving these species, and these wider studies will be outlined in context. Finally, the experimental techniques which were developed in the course of this work will also be described as they may have applicability to work in related areas.

Our results on the electronic absorption spectra of the arylmethyl carbanions are found to complement those derived from nmr studies. It will be seen that the uv-vis spectra of the carbanion alkali metal salts show a striking dependence on the nature of the solvent, cation, temperature, and the presence of complexing agents.

Theoretical arguments have been advanced[1-4] to explain these spectral shifts, in terms of the perturbation of the molecular orbital energy levels of the organic anion by the field of the cation, which will be dependent on the size of the cation as well as its interaction with solvent molecules. Thus, the various spectral absorptions are assigned to different types of ion pairs, viz. contact, solvent-separated, or complexed, as discrete species.

The important role which ion pairing can have on the reactivities of carbanionic species was highlighted about 1960, on the one hand in electrophilic substitution reactions at saturated carbon, where carbanions were implicated as transient intermediates,[5] and on the other hand in anionic polymerisation of styrene derivatives.[6,7] The concept of ion pairing and its application in organic reactions has been extensively discussed by Szwarc and others.[8]

Thus, our account pertaining to the nature of ion pairing in carbanions, and the experimental criteria thereof, given in Section II, has direct bearing on the structure-reactivity studies described in Section III. Moreover, it will be shown that there is a causal relationship between the residual uncertainty concerning the nature of ion pairing in a given system and the quality of the interpretation which results from a particular set of experimental measurements.

Prior to embarking on the descriptive aspects of our studies, it is pertinent to draw attention to the nature of the media used in the spectral observation of the arylmethyl carbanions and the factors which lie at the origin. The main consideration here relates to the magnitudes of the pK_a's of the solvent and of the conjugate acids of the carbanions. Since the acid dissociation constant of Ph_3CH is ~31, it follows that for observation of the conjugate base, Ph_3C^-, a solvent medium is required with $pK_a \geqslant 33$. This rules out the use of hydroxylic solvents such as alcohols, while retaining solvents such as dimethylsulfoxide, ammonia or aliphatic amines, ethers and hydrocarbons. The weakest acid in the series of arylmethanes is $PhCH_3$ (pK_a ~41) and for observation of $PhCH_2^-$ only the ethers and hydrocarbons remain as suitable solvents.

II SPECTROPHOTOMETRIC CHARACTERIZATION OF CARBANIONS. CONTACT AND SOLVENT

  SEPARATED ION PAIRS.

1. Triphenylmethyl alkali metal salts (TPM^-M^+)

Triphenylmethyllithium (TPM^-Li^+) and triphenylmethylpotassium (TPM^-K^+) exhibit spectral properties in solutions of ethereal solvents which show a number of interesting features. We present here the observations and the arguments concerning the interpretations for the TPM^-Li^+ case in some detail; with that background, the other carbanion systems can be discussed much more briefly.

The spectra of TPM^-Li^+ in Et_2O, THF and DME at room temperature are shown in Figure 1.[9] In Et_2O the absorption maximum occurs at 446 nm with a shoulder at 390 nm, while in THF and DME the spectra exhibit λ_{max} 500, sh 435

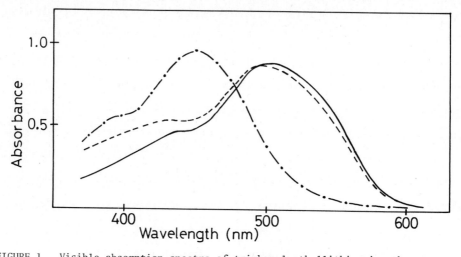

FIGURE 1. Visible absorption spectra of triphenylmethyllithium in ether
(–·–·–·–), tetrahydrofuran (———) and dimethoxyethane (– – – – –)
at room temperature.[9]

TABLE 1

Contact (R^-,M^+), solvent separated $(R^-||M^+)$ and 18-crown-6 ether complexed
(R^-,X,M^+) ion pairs of triphenylmethyl carbanions in ethereal solvents
at room temperature: effect of solvent and counterion.[9]

R^-M^+	Solvent	$\lambda_{max}(\varepsilon)$ [a] R^-,M^+	$R^-||M^+$	Fraction of $R^-||M^+$ at 25°	λ_{max} R^-,X,M^+
TPM^-Li^+	Et_2O	446,390 sh(21,900)		0.15	494,430 sh
	THF		500,435 sh(28,300)	0.95	500,435 sh
	DME		496,432 sh(30,000)	1.00	496,432 sh
TPM^-K^+	Et_2O	476,414 sh(24,800)		0.00	492,430 sh
	THF		486,420 sh(21,300)	0.65	495,430 sh
	DME		494,430 sh(30,000)	0.85	494,430 sh

[a] Extinction coefficient at absorption maximum (ℓ mole^{-1} cm^{-1}); ε(sh) is
approximately half the absorption maximum value.

and λ_{max} 496, sh 432 nm, respectively (Table 1). The striking change in λ_{max}
on going from Et_2O to THF or DME is indicative of a change in the type of

species present. Assuming that the degree of dissociation into free ions in these systems is relatively small,[10] the spectral absorptions would be assignable to contact (TPM^-, Li^+) and/or solvent separated ion pairs ($TPM^-||Li^+$), on the basis of the following considerations.[11-14] (a) Results in the literature for fluorenyl alkali metal salts (Fl^-M^+) show that the absorption maxima for the solvent separated ion pairs occur at longer wavelengths than for the contact ion pairs. (b) For a given type of ion pair, contact or solvent separated, the absorption maximum is only slightly dependent on the solvent medium over wide ranges of solvent type and polarity. (c) Structurally related carbanion alkali metal salts are known to exist in Et_2O predominantly as the contact ion pairs and in DME as the solvent separated ion pairs in accord with the solvating powers of the ethereal solvents under consideration increasing in the order Et_2O < THF < DME. Application of these criteria leads consistently to the conclusion that TPM^-Li^+ exists in Et_2O predominantly as the contact ion pair, TPM^-, Li^+, and in THF and DME predominantly as the solvent separated ion pair, $TPM^-||Li^+$.

The macrocyclic polyethers are known to be effective complexing agents for metal cations[15] and can be expected to interact with the carbanide ion pairs accordingly. It had been found in fact that addition of 18-crown-6 polyether to Fl^-, Na^+ in THF, existing as the contact ion pair, caused a spectral change corresponding to the solvent separated ion pair, i.e. the crown ether complexed ion pair and the solvent separated ion pair had almost identical spectral absorptions.[16] In the present system it was found that addition of 18-crown-6 had no effect on the absorption of TPM^-Li^+ in THF or DME but a large effect in the case of Et_2O as solvent. In the latter case a shift in absorption occurred from λ_{max} 446, sh 390 to λ_{max} 494, sh 430, corresponding almost exactly to the spectrum of $TPM^-||Li^+$ in THF or DME in the absence of crown ether.

Further evidence on contact $\rightleftarrows$ solvent separated ion pair equilibria may be obtained from their temperature dependence. Such equilibria have been found to be exothermic, due to the gain in solvation energy in formation of the solvent separated ion pair. Concomitantly, the immobilization of solvent

molecules round the cation leads to a negative entropy for the process. In the

present work it was found that solutions of TPM^-Li^+ in THF or DME were unaf-

fected when the temperature was lowered from 25° to -50°, but the Et_2O solution

on cooling showed a bathochromic shift from λ_{max} 446, sh 390 to λ_{max} 494,

sh 430 nm (Figure 2); these changes were found to be reversible. The lack of a

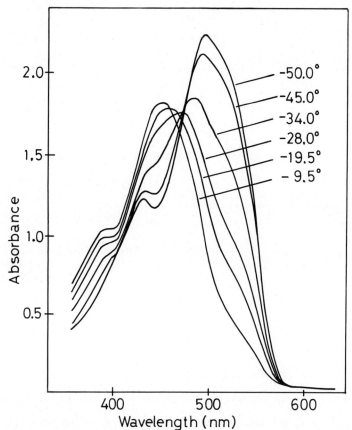

FIGURE 2.   Temperature dependence of absorption spectra of triphenylmethyllithium (7.51×10^{-5} M) in ether.[9]

noticeable effect for DME or THF is consistent with our previous conclusion

that at ambient temperature TPM^-Li^+ exists in these media predominantly as the

solvent separated ion pair. Conversely, the low temperature spectra of TPM^-Li^+

in Et_2O correspond to a shift in the equilibrium, from TPM^-,Li^+ to $\text{TPM}^-||\text{Li}^+$.

Raising the temperature of the TPM⁻Li⁺/DME system from 0 to 50° showed no change in the absorption spectrum, while the TPM⁻Li⁺/THF system showed a small hypsochromic shift, corresponding to formation of ~10% contact ion pair species over this temperature range. The moderate tendency for contact ion pair formation with increasing temperature in THF, as compared with DME, is in the expected order of the cationic solvating powers of these media.

Proceeding to TPM⁻K⁺, the pertinent spectra are displayed in Figure 3 and the spectral data included in Table 1. The assignments of contact/solvent

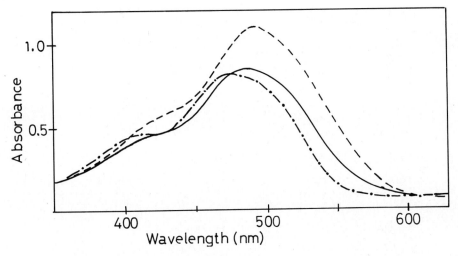

FIGURE 3. Visible absorption spectra of triphenylmethylpotassium in ether (—·—·—·—), tetrahydrofuran (————) and dimethoxyethane (------) at room temperature.[9]

separated ion pair species are in accord with the above discussion for TPM⁻Li⁺, including the effectsof crown ether and temperature. Comparing the TPM⁻Li⁺ and TPM⁻K⁺ systems, the following relationships are noteworthy. (a) The tendency for solvent separated ion pair formation is greater for TPM⁻Li⁺ than for TPM⁻K⁺. (b) For the contact ion pairs the absorption maxima show a bathochromic shift on changing the cation from Li⁺ to K⁺. (c) For the solvent separated ion pairs the absorption spectra vary only slightly with the nature of the counterion and the solvent.

The results relating to the effect of temperature on the absorption

spectra of the carbanion alkali metal salts allow the evaluation of the equilibrium constant (K) for the processes

$$TPM^-Li^+ + nS \; \overset{\rightarrow}{\leftarrow} \; TPM^-||Li^+ \tag{1}$$

$$TPM^-K^+ + mS \; \overset{\rightarrow}{\leftarrow} \; TPM^-||K^+ \tag{2}$$

as well as the thermodynamic parameters, ΔH and ΔS. The pertinent data are
given in Table 2.

TABLE 2

Thermodynamic parameters for contact $\overset{\rightarrow}{\leftarrow}$ solvated ion pair equilibria
of triphenylmethyllithium and potassium in ethereal solvents.[9]

R^-M^+	Solvent	Temp. range °C	K^a	ΔH^b kcal/mole	ΔS^b e.u.
TPM^-Li^+	Et_2O	-54° to +10°	0.1	-11.9	-46
TPM^-Li^+	THF	+ 2° to +45°	39	- 9.2	-24
TPM^-K^+	THF	-53° to +23°	2.0	- 6.7	-21
TPM^-K^+	DME	+ 1° to +34°	5.7	-11.8	-36

a $K = [R^-||M^+]/[R^-,M^+]$ at 25°C.
b Uncertainty in ΔH, ΔS is ±10% to ±20%.

  The conclusions drawn on the basis of the uv-vis absorption studies
regarding ion pairing of TPM^-Li^+ and TPM^-K^+ in these solvent systems are in
qualitative agreement with those reported by Jackman and co-workers on the
basis of ^{1}H nmr studies.[17]

  It is also interesting to compare the present results with those
obtained by Streitwieser et al.[18] when studying the triphenylmethane/lithium
cyclohexylamide/cyclohexylamine system. The reaction solution which was red at
room temperature became colorless on heating to 100° and this thermochromic
effect was interpreted on the basis of the equilibrium in eqn. 3:

$$Ph_3CH + LiCHA \; \overset{K'}{\rightleftharpoons} \; Ph_3CLi + CHA \tag{3}$$
$$\downarrow\uparrow$$
$$(LiCHA)_n$$

From measurement of the absorbance at 492 nm (λ_{max}), values of K' could be derived at various temperatures, which yielded a linear log K' vs. 1/T plot. The constant ΔH value and the absence of any shift in λ_{max} throughout the temperature range indicated that triphenylmethyllithium in CHA exists as only one type of ion pair throughout this temperature range and this was concluded to be the solvent separated ion pair species. Comparison with the present system would suggest that CHA is comparable to THF or DME in ability to form the solvent separated ion pair species.

2. Diphenylmethyl alkali metal salts (DPM⁻M⁺)

The spectra of DPM⁻Li⁺ in Et₂O, THF and DME at ambient temperature are shown in Figure 4.[19] Using arguments as in the TPM⁻Li⁺ systems, one can readily

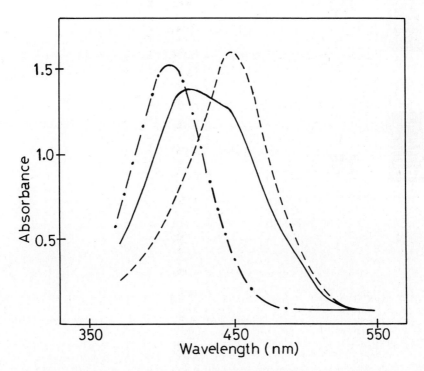

FIGURE 4. Visible absorption spectra of diphenylmethyllithium in ether (—·—·—·—), tetrahydrofuran (————) and dimethoxyethane (— — — —) at room temperature.[19]

assign the 407 nm absorption observed in Et₂O to the contact ion pair and the 448 nm absorption in DME to the solvent separated ion pair. The two absorption

maxima observed in THF point to the presence of two types of ion pairs in equilibrium in comparable concentrations. For the THF system, the 448 nm absorption
corresponds to the solvent separated ion pair species, as in the case of DME
above, but the 418 nm absorption occurs at longer wavelength than found in Et_2O
and which has been assigned to the contact ion pair.

In looking to the literature to aid with this dilemma, one recalls that
the Fl^-,Li^+ contact ion pair was found to exhibit negligible shift (2 nm) in
λ_{max} with change in solvent.[11] However, in the case of the 1,3-diphenylbutenyl-
lithium (DPB^-Li^+), a significant shift in λ_{max} was seen in ethers of increasing
solvating capability.[20] This was interpreted as due to formation of externally
solvated contact ion pairs, DPB^-,Li^+,S_n, in ethers of moderate solvating
ability, in addition to the conventional contact ion pair, DPB^-,Li^+, formed in
Et_2O, and the solvent separated ion pair, $DPB^-||Li^+$, formed in DME.

We therefore propose that in the DPM^-Li^+ system the 407 nm absorption
is associated with the conventional contact ion pair, DPM^-,Li^+ (C_1), the 418 nm
absorption with the externally solvated contact ion pair, DPM^-,Li^+,S_p (C_2), and
the 448 nm absorption with the solvent separated ion pair, $DPM^-||Li^+$ (SS). The
equilibria present in these systems can be summarised by eqns. 4,5:

$$DPM^-,Li^+ + pS \rightleftarrows DPM^-,Li^+,S_p \qquad\qquad (4)$$
$$(C_1) \qquad\qquad\qquad (C_2)$$

$$DPM^-,Li^+,S_p + qS \rightleftarrows DPM^-||Li^+ \qquad\qquad (5)$$
$$(C_2) \qquad\qquad\qquad (SS)$$

In Et_2O we have equilibrium (4) predominantly on the left hand side, while in
THF these two species are present in comparable amounts. In DME the equilibrium
(5) lies predominantly on the right hand side. The results are summarised in
Table 3.

The ambient spectra of DPM^-K^+ in these solvents are shown in Figure 5.
Analogy with the above argument indicates that in Et_2O we have predominantly
the contact ion pairs (C_1) present, while in THF and DME the predominant species
is the externally solvated contact ion pair (C_2), see Table 3.

TABLE 3

Contact (R^-,M^+), externally solvated contact (R^-,M^+,S_p), solvent separated $(R^-||M^+)$, and crown-ether complexed (R^-,X,M^+) ion pairs of[b] diphenylmethyl carbanions.[19]

R^-M^+	Solvent	λ_{max} $(\varepsilon)^{a,b}$			Fraction[c] of $R^-||M^+$ at 25°	λ_{max} R^-,X,M^+
		R^-,M^+	$R^-,M^+;S_p$	$R^-||M^+$		
DPM⁻Li⁺	Et₂O	407 (30,800)			0.0	445
	THF		418	448	0.4[d]	452
	DME			448 (37,000)	0.8[d]	448
DPM⁻K⁺	Et₂O	432 (40,000)			0.0	444
	THF		440 (43,000)		0.0	448
	DME	441 (43,800)			0.0	445

a   Extinction coefficient $(\ell\ \text{mole}^{-1}\ \text{cm}^{-1})$ at absorption maximum.

b   The λ_{max} value refers to the predominant species in the given solvent.

c   Reckoned as $[R^-||M^+]/([R^-,M^+] + [R^-,M^+,S_n] + [R^-||M^+])$.

d   This fraction is estimated from $K = [SS]/[C_2]$ at 25°, as calculated from absorbance changes at a single wavelength, i.e. λ_{max} for the solvent separated species.

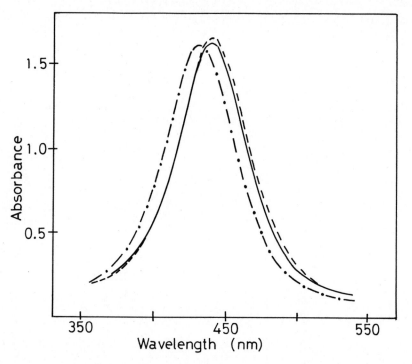

FIGURE 5. Visible absorption spectra of diphenylmethylpotassium in ether
(—·—·—·), tetrahydrofuran (————) and dimethoxyethane (- - - - -)
at room temperature.[19]

The absorption spectra of DPM⁻K⁺ solutions in Et_2O, THF and DME remained
unchanged over the temperature range 25° to -50°C, indicating in each case the
presence of only one type of ion pair over this range. The DPM⁻Li⁺ spectra
in Et_2O or DME also remained unchanged on cooling, but in THF large changes were
observed (Figure 6). The increasing absorption at 448 nm at the expense of the
418 nm absorption indicates a shift in the equilibrium (5) towards the right
hand side, i.e. increased formation of solvent separated ion pairs at low
temperatures.

Ion pairing in diphenylmethyl alkali metal salts has also been investigated by ^{13}C nmr.[21] The results are in qualitative agreement with the present
work (see Chapter 6).

An earlier spectrophotometric study had been concerned with 1,1-diphenyl-
hexyllithium, in THF or di-n-propyl ether and benzene or hexane mixtures.[22]

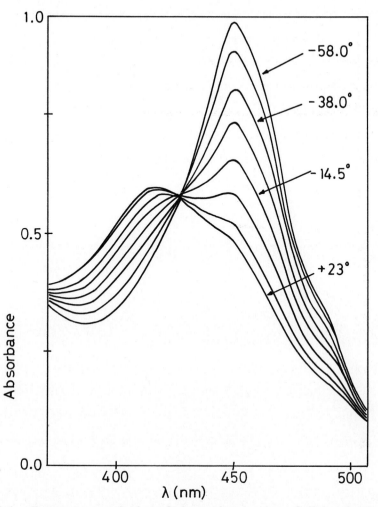

FIGURE 6. Temperature variation of absorption spectra of diphenylmethyllithium in THF.[19]

The spectral results in this work were interpreted in terms of formation of specific complexed species such as RLi.2THF and RLi.4THF. Study of the 1,1,4,4-tetraphenylbutane dianion, $Ph_2\bar{C}CH_2CH_2\bar{C}Ph_2$, in THF at various temperatures gave evidence of formation of more than one type of ion pair, though overlap of the absorption bands did not permit the separate observation of each ion pair.[23]

3. Benzylic carbanions

Extensive spectrophotometric studies of benzylic carbanions have not

been reported, excepting the "living polymer" type carbanions in the polymerisation of styrene derivatives which have been discussed thoroughly elsewhere.[24]
The limited results reported so far on benzylic anions are as follows.

Benzyllithium and benzylsodium in THF are reported to have λ_{max} at 330
and 355 nm respectively.[25,26] The bathochromic shift on going to the larger
cation is indicative of predominant contact ion pair formation in these systems.
The free benzyl carbanion has been generated via pulse radiolysis of dibenzyl-
mercury (eqn. 6) in THF and found to have λ_{max} 362 nm.[27]

$$e_s^- + (PhCH_2)_2Hg \rightarrow PhCH_2^- + PhCH_2Hg \qquad (6)$$

p-Phenylbenzyllithium in THF has λ_{max} 430 nm[28] while the potassium
derivative has λ_{max} at 470 nm,[29] which is again indicative of predominant
contact ion pair formation.

III   STRUCTURE-REACTIVITY RELATIONSHIPS

The ability of a molecule to give up a proton represents a fundamental
property, one that has wide implications in structure-reactivity relationships.[30-32] The intrinsic, or absolute, acidity corresponding to the ionization of RH (eqn. 7) in the gas phase has been determined in recent years

$$RH \rightleftarrows R^- + H^+ \qquad (7)$$

using the newly developed techniques of ion cyclotron resonance and flowing
afterglow or high pressure mass spectrometry[33-36] (see Chapter 2).
However, evaluation of the more traditional solution acidities entails the
measurement of species concentrations by conventional methods. The delocalized
anions formed from ionization of the arylmethanes are readily amenable to
accurate spectrophotometric measurement through their characteristic uv-visible
absorptions. Moreover, since the arylmethanes provide a series of substrates
of varying acidities, they have played a central role in the construction of a
pK_a scale for weak carbon acids.

1. pK$_a$ scale for arylmethanes

The relative acidities of weak carbon acids can conveniently be eval-
uated by means of eqn. 8, through spectrophotometric measurement of the position

$$R_1H + R_2^-M^+ \rightleftarrows R_1^-M^+ + R_2H \qquad (8)$$

of the equilibrium. By choosing one acid as the standard, one can then build
up, through successive comparisons, an acidity scale for any given solvent
system. Streitwieser and co-workers[37] have thus constructed an acidity scale
for cyclohexylamine as solvent, while Bordwell and co-workers[38] have done so
for dimethylsulfoxide as the medium,* the method is described in detail in
Chapter 7. The pK$_a$'s of a series of arylmethanes have thus become available
for cyclohexylamine as solvent, based on 9-phenylfluorene (pK$_a$ = 18.5) as
standard.[37] A partial list of these arylmethanes, covering the pK$_a$ range
~30-40 is given below, with their abbreviated notation and pK$_a$ values, since
these will be used in the work described in the following section.

Ph—⬡—CHPh$_2$ Ph—⬡—CH$_2$—⬡—Ph   Ph$_3$CH

p-Biphenylyl-   di-Biphenylyl-   Triphenyl-
diphenylmethane   diphenylmethane   methane
BDPM (30.2)   DBM (30.8)   TPM (31.4)

(CH$_3$—⬡)$_3$CH   Ph$_2$CH$_2$ (⬡-CH$_3$)$_2$CH$_2$

Tri-p-tolylmethane   Diphenylmethane   Di-o-tolylmethane
TPTM (33.0)   DPM (33.4)   DOTM (34.8)

(CH$_3$—⬡)$_2$CH$_2$ (CH$_3$—⬡-CH$_3$)$_2$CH$_2$

Di-p-tolylmethane   Di-2,4-xylylmethane
DPTM (35.1)   DXM (36.3)

Ph—⬡—CH$_3$ ⬡—CH$_3$

p-Phenyltoluene   Toluene
PPT (38.7)   TOL (40.9)

* The symbolism pK$_{CsCHA}$ and pK$_{DMSO}$ has been recommended by Streitwieser to distingui
between the two acidity scales.

2. Acidity of hydrogen

Though the acidities of binary hydrides, XH, and of the more complex hydrides, RH where R is composite, had been the subject of extensive investigation,[28-30] the acidity of the primary hydride H_2 had not been experimentally determined. Estimates of the pK_a of H_2 ranging between 29 and 38 had been given, however[39,40] (see also ref. 41). It appeared to us that metalation of weak hydrocarbon acids by metal hydrides, as shown in eqn. (9), could in principle

$$RH + H^-M^+ \rightleftharpoons R^-M^+ + H_2 \tag{9}$$

lead to evaluation of the pK_a of H_2, in analogous fashion to development of the equilibrium in eqn. (8) above.

Using the spectrophotometric technique to monitor the carbanion concentration, it was found that potassium hydride in the presence of 18-crown-6 ether, in THF solvent, metalates TPM to completion, indicating that H_2 is a weaker acid than TPM in this system.[28,42] Similarly, it was found that DPM and DPTM were metalated to completion, but with DXM the reaction proceeded to partial completion, while PPT was unreactive. The acidity of H_2 is therefore comparable to that of DXM in this medium. The equilibrium constant (K_{rel}) for the reaction with DXM could be calculated from the equilibrium concentration of DXM^- and the measured solubility H_2 and of KH under the experimental conditions.

The experimentally determined equilibrium constant K_{rel} is actually applicable to the equilibrium in eqn. 10 involving the crown ether (X) complexed

$$RH + (H^-,X,K^+) \underset{\phantom{K_{rel}}}{\overset{K_{rel}}{\rightleftharpoons}} (R^-,X,K^+) + H_2 \tag{10}$$

$$X = 18\text{-crown-6}$$

species. However, the ion pair acidity constant $pK_a^{H_2}$ refers to the equilibrium in eqn. 11, for which eqn. 12 can be written:

$$RH + (H^-,K^+) \overset{K_{ip}}{\rightleftharpoons} (R^-,K^+) + H_2 \tag{11}$$

$$pK_a^{H_2} = pK_a^{RH} - pK_{ip} \tag{12}$$

Since in the reaction system containing X the equilibria in eqns. 13 and 14 are established (i.e. contact ion pairs are converted into complexed ion pairs),

$$(H^-,K^+) + X \overset{K_1}{\rightleftharpoons} (H^-,X,K^+) \tag{13}$$

$$(R^-,K^+) + X \xrightleftharpoons{K_2} (R^-,X,K^+) \tag{14}$$

it follows that K_{ip} and K_{rel} are related by eqn. (15)

$$K_{rel} = K_{ip}\left(\frac{K_2}{K_1}\right) \tag{15}$$

Direct information on the magnitude of the K_2/K_1 ratio is not available but from literature data on related systems one would expect this to range from 1-10^{-2} (ref. 28). For these two limiting cases the ion pair acitity of H_2, as in eqn. 12, reduces to $pK_a^{H_2} = pK_a^{RH} - pK_{rel}$ or $pK_a^{H_2} = pK_a^{RH} - pK_{rel} + 2$. Using the experimentally determined pK_{rel} values one thus obtains $pK_a^{H_2} = 35.3$ or 37.3, respectively. Since THF and CHA are believed to be comparable in their effects on ion pair equilibria, this enables one to use the pK_a scale for the RH series constructed by Streitwieser[37] for CsCHA/CHA also in the present system.

In a complementary study,[43] the pK_a of H_2 was estimated from study of the reaction of organocesiums with H_2 in CHA solvent (eqn. 16), which is

$$R^-Cs^+ + H_2 \xrightleftharpoons{} RH + H^-Cs^+ \tag{16}$$

essentially the reverse of reaction 9. It was observed spectrophotometrically that the hydrogenolysis reaction occurs with PPT^-Cs^+ but not with DXM^-Cs^+ or with DPM^-Cs^+, indicating that the pK_a of H_2 lies between those of PPT and DXM in this system. This result is in qualitative agreement with the conclusion drawn from the metalation of RH by KH described above. However, the probable differing, unknown, degrees of aggregation of cesium hydride and the aralkyl-cesiums in the reaction medium pose a problem in the quantitative interpretation of the results regarding a pK_a value for H_2.

3. Acidities of ammonia and methylamine

A spectrophotometric study of the metalation of a series of arylmethanes by potassium amide in THF solvent (eqn. 17)[29] was carried out with the purpose

$$RH + NH_2^-K^+ \xrightleftharpoons{} R^-K^+ + NH_3 \tag{17}$$

of evaluating the pK_a of NH_3, parallel to the study described above relating to the pK_a of H_2. It was found that KNH_2 in THF metalated TPM, DPM and DXM to completion, DPTM to partial completion, while TOL was unreactive. From the

114

measured equilibrium concentrations in the DPTM system, and the solubilities of NH_3 and KNH_2 in THF, the pK_a of NH_3 was estimated as 37.8. This value, also, is subject to uncertainty due to the effect of the ion pairing equilibria involved and change in solvent.

Finally, it was found that potassium methylamide in THF metalates to completion DXM and PPT, but is unreactive towards TOL.[29] The acidity of CH_3NH_2 is hence intermediate between those of PPT and TOL. The finding that CH_3NH_2 is a weaker acid than NH_3 in this system is in accord with expectations.

4. Rates of proton transfer

The rates of protonation of benzyl carbanions, both in the absence and in the presence of counterions has been determined through the pulse radiolysis method referred to earlier (eqn. 6).[27] Thus the decay of the carbanion is monitored at the wavelength of the maximum absorption in the presence of various proton donors, yielding the data in Table 4. The enhanced reactivity of ion pairs, relative to the free benzyl anion, is clearly apparent and points to a specific role for the cation in the proton transfer processes. (See also ref. 44 for proton transfer to nitrobenzyl carbanions.)

TABLE 4

Rate constants for the protonation of free and of ion-paired benzyl carbanion in tetrahydrofuran at 24°C (units, $M^{-1} s^{-1}$)[27]

Carbanion	CH_3OH	C_2H_5OH	$(CH_3)_3COH$	H_2O
$PhCH_2^-$	2.3×10^8	1.4×10^8	1.6×10^7	5.3×10^7
$PhCH_2^-, Na^+$	5.8×10^9	3.7×10^9	1.3×10^9	5.5×10^9
$PhCH_2^-, Li^+$	3.4×10^8		9.7×10^7	
$PhCH_2^-, N(C_4H_9)_4^+$	6.0×10^8		4.6×10^8	

Ion pairing effects in the other proton transfer processes involving carbanions have been discussed extensively in two review articles.[45,46] It will

be readily apparent from the perusal of these articles that our present understanding of most of these systems is largely limited by the dearth of experimental data concerning the nature of ion pairing which obtains under given
conditions. The potential benefits to be reaped through such measurements is
illustrated by the polymerisation of styrene derivatives where such information
has been put to practical use.[24,45,46]

IV METHODS USED IN SPECTROPHOTOMETRIC STUDIES

Carbanion alkali metal salts, in common with other air and moisture
sensitive compounds, require the use of appropriate techniques in order that
meaningful results be obtained. While monographs describing the manipulation
of air/moisture sensitive compounds are available,[47] the methods described
therein are generally applicable to larger scale preparative sequences. For
quantitative studies by electron absorption spectroscopy, where typically
carbanion concentrations of the order of 10^{-4} - 10^{-5} M are used, these methods
require considerable modification. Suitable methods have thus been developed
in a number of laboratories where acidities of very weak acids have been
routinely determined with reliability and precision.[37,38, 48-51]

In our own laboratory we have developed methods in which the use of a
dry box is minimal; simultaneously, contact between solutions and grease or
rubber septum is eliminated. A description of the apparatus and procedures
used is given below and is followed by an account of some typical experiments.
These correspond in fact to the preparation of arylmethyl carbanions as used
in the spectrophotometric studies described in Sections II and III(2,3).

1. Apparatus and procedures

The centrepiece is the reaction vessel used in preparation of the
majority of the carbanion alkali metal salts and which is also adapted for
performing most of the spectrophotometric measurements. Ancillary components
include storage vessels, various adaptors and vessels for dissolution of
reactive metals.

The reaction vessel, shown in Figure 7, consists of a cylindrical tube of capacity ~120 ml, made of pyrex brand glass. It is equipped with one side-arm to which a 1 mm (or 10 mm) quartz uv cell is attached via a graded seal, and a second side-arm consisting of a greaseless "Rotaflo" stopcock attached to an 'O' ring joint. The reaction vessel is made to fit into the cell compartment of a Unicam SP800 spectrophotometer in the present work. (A minor modification to the cover of the cell compartment was required in order to increase its effective height.)

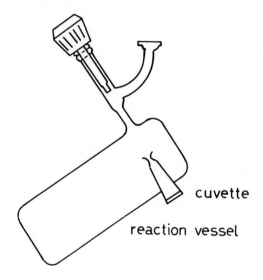

cuvette

reaction vessel

FIGURE 7.   Reaction vessel with attached cuvette used in the spectrophotometric studies of carbanions.

Small samples of compound are introduced into the reaction vessel by weighing into a small glass ampoule, placing this into the arm fitted with the 'O' ring joint, capping the latter with a rubber septum, flushing with nitrogen, and allowing the ampoule to enter the evacuated vessel via the Rotaflo stopcock. For introduction of volatile solvents, the reaction vessel is attached to a vacuum manifold via the 'O' ring joint and the solvent is distilled under vacuo from a storage vessel reservoir. Non-volatile liquids, or solutions of reagents, can be added directly under gravity from a storage vessel via an adaptor (C); these are described below.

The storage vessel, shown in Figure 8(B), is constructed from cylindrical pyrex glass tubing to which a Rotaflo stopper fitted with an 'O' ring
joint is attached. These storage vessels vary in size from ~25 ml (consisting
of a graduated tube) to 500 ml in our own experiments, though 1 ℓ capacity (or
larger) could similarly be constructed.

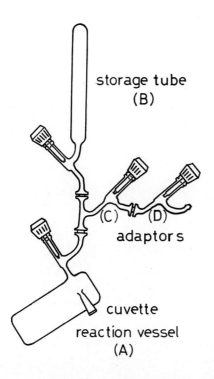

FIGURE 8. Assembled apparatus for transfer of cesium cyclohexylamide/cyclo-
hexylamine for storage tube (B) into reaction vessel (A).[43]

Anhydrous solvents can be kept in these storage vessels for extended
periods. Typically a solvent such as THF is first dried over calcium hydride,
then distilled from lithium aluminum hydride into one of these vessels containing n-butyllithium and TPM. The latter serves as indicator since the
development of color, corresponding to formation of TPM⁻, ensures that the
solvent is anhydrous.

The dissolution of a reactive metal on a gram scale in a given solvent,

118

e.g. the preparation of a stock solution of cesium cyclohexylamide (CsCHA/CHA), can be effected by means of the apparatus shown in Figure 9. It consists essentially of a 50 ml round bottom flask having a long neck fitted with a

FIGURE 9. Apparatus used for preparation of cesium cyclohexylamide/cyclohexyl-
amine solutions showing glass ampoule containing cesium in place
prior to crushing.[43]

Rotaflo stopcock and an attached 'O' ring joint. The metal sealed into a glass ampoule by conventional methods,[47] is introduced into the flask by severing the latter along the cylindrical neck portion, and the parts are then re-sealed. The vessel is evacuated, the ampoule crushed by means of the Rotaflo stopper and, after inverting the flask, solvent (CHA) is distilled in under vacuo. During the ensuing reaction (~36 h), H_2 is vented from time to time through a mercury trap while the vessel is attached to the vacuum manifold. The resulting solution (pale yellow green CsCHA/CHA) is transferred into a graduated storage tube via adaptor C in Figure 8.

2. Preparation of arylmethyllithiums from arylmethanes and n-butyllithium

The arylmethane (~2 mg) was introduced into the reaction vessel in a vial and THF (~20 ml) distilled in under vacuo. A solution of n-butyllithium in hexane (2M) was added in a 10-fold excess aliquot with a syringe through a septum in the 'O' ring joint and the concentration of arylmethyllithium produced was monitored spectrophotometrically.

In the case of TPM in THF the reaction yielding TPM^-Li^+ occurred essentially quantitatively in ~15 min, while in the case of DPM reaction occurred likewise but somewhat slower (~30 min). In the case of the more weakly acidic hydrocarbons DPTM and PPT, however, several aliquots of n-BuLi were required for complete conversion, while attempts to metalate toluene by this method were largely unsuccessful. Apparently, with the very weakly acidic hydrocarbons n-BuLi was reacting competitively with the solvent.[52]

Use of DME or Et_2O as solvents in the reaction between n-BuLi and TPM or DPM led to very much slower reactions and low extents of conversion (<25%). This resulted probably in part from reaction of n-BuLi with solvent (especially DME), and in part from aggregation of n-BuLi (in the case of Et_2O).[53] However, TPM^-Li^+ and DPM^-Li^+ in either DME or Et_2O solution could readily be obtained from the respective THF solutions by removal of THF under vacuum and transfer of the desired solvent to the organolithium. To minimize contamination by traces of remaining THF, this solvent is then removed under vacuo and replaced by fresh solvent, the cycle being repeated a number of times.

3. Preparation of arylmethylcesiums in cyclohexylamine

The arylmethylcesiums were obtained by reaction of the arylmethanes with CsCHA/CHA using the following procedure.

The arylmethane was first introduced into the reaction vessel in an ampoule as described above. CHA was then transferred under vacuum into the reaction vessel by distillation from a stock LiCHA/CHA solution (obtained by adding BuLi to CHA in presence of TPM). The apparatus in Figure 8 was then assembled (adaptor D being included for flexibility in attachment to vacuum manifold) and the CsCHA/CHA introduced from its storage reservoir (graduated tube B), via the adaptor C, which allowed transfer to be made in an evacuated

120

system. Following spectrophotometric measurement of the organocesium, further portions of CsCHA/CHA were added as necessary until the desired concentration of RCs was produced. For equilibrium (pK_a) measurements a deficiency of CsCHA/CHA was present.

4. Preparation of arylmethylpotassiums from arylmethanes and potassium amide or potassium methylamide

A glass ampoule containing a known weight of potassium (25-35 mg), sealed under vacuo, was introduced into the reaction vessel. Following evacuation of the vessel, the ampoule was broken by shaking and 1-2 g of ammonia (or methylamine) was distilled in under vacuo. A small quantity of Fe_2O_3 (1-3 mg) was introduced into the reaction vessel in a vial under nitrogen. A change in color from blue to pale yellow of the ammonia solution after 15-30 min at -30° indicated the formation of KNH_2 (as compared to 4-6 h in the absence of Fe_2O_3), while the methylamine solution changed color after 20 h at 5° (as compared to 72 h in the absence of Fe_2O_3). The reaction vessel was then attached to the vacuum line, the ammonia (or methylamine) distilled back into the storage vessel, and solvent (THF or DME) introduced by distillation under vacuo. A known weight of the arylmethane was then added in a small vial under nitrogen, the vessel shaken for reaction to occur, and placed into the spectrophotometer for intermittent monitoring.

5. Preparation of arylmethylpotassiums from arylmethanes and potassium hydride/18-crown-6

A known weight (~50 mg) of potassium hydride (obtained from the oil suspension by washing with dry petroleum ether under nitrogen in a dry box) was introduced into the reaction vessel. THF (~30 ml) was distilled in, which was followed by addition of 18-crown-6 polyether (0.3-0.4 g) and the arylmethane (2-3 mg). After vigorous shaking of the heterogeneous mixture, the development of the carbanion was followed spectrophotometrically.

If a homogeneous solution of KH/18-crown-6 in THF is desired (e.g. in the solubility measurement of KH/18-crown-6 in THF, required in the acidity determination of H_2, Section III(1)), the procedure given above is modified as follows. The reaction vessel containing the heterogeneous mixture KH/18-crown-6/THF is attached to a cylindrical glass piece with a built-in fritted disc equipped with an 'O' ring joint at either end. The lower end of this piece is connected to a second reaction vessel fitted with a 1 cm quartz cuvette and containing an excess of TPM. Prior to filtration, the lower part of the apparatus (consisting of the fritted disc and the reaction vessel) is evacuated and the fritted disc flamed out. On filtration a red solution of TPM⁻ is obtained and from the measured absorbance and the known extinction coefficient the concentration of KH in solution can be calculated.

ACKNOWLEDGEMENT

We thank the Natural Sciences and Engineering Research Council of Canada and the Atomic Energy of Canada Limited for financial support of the research described herein.

122

REFERENCES

1 H.V. Carter, B.J. McClelland, and E. Warhurst, Trans. Faraday Soc., 56
   (1960) 455.

2 B.J. McClelland, Trans. Faraday Soc., 57 (1961) 1458, 2073.

3 N.S. Bayliss and E.G. McRae, J. Phys. Chem., 58 (1954) 1002.

4 T.R. Griffiths and M.C.R. Symons, Mol. Phys., 3 (1960) 90.

5 D.J. Cram, J.L. Mateos, F. Hauck, A. Langemann, K.R. Kopecky, W.D. Nielsen,
   and J. Allinger, J. Am. Chem. Soc., 81 (1959) 5774; D.J. Cram, "Fundamentals
   of Carbanion Chemistry", Academic Press, New York, 1965.

6 M. Szwarc, Macromol. Chem., 35 (1960) 132.

7 D.J. Worsfold and S. Bywater, Can. J. Chem., 38 (1960) 1891.

8 Ions and Ion Pairs in Organic Reactions, edited by M. Szwarc, Wiley, New
   York (a) Vol. 1, 1972; (b) Vol. 2, 1974.

9 E. Buncel and B.C. Menon, J. Org. Chem., 44 (1979) 317.

10 C.W. Davies, "Ion Association", Butterworths, London, 1962.

11 T.E. Hogen-Esch and J. Smid, J. Amer. Chem. Soc., 88 (1966) 307.

12 J.W. Burley and R.N. Young, J. Chem. Soc. Perkin Trans. II, (1972) 1006.

13 J.-P. Pascault and J. Golé, Bull. Soc. Chim. France, (1974) 362.

14 R.J. Bushby and G.J. Gerber, J. Chem. Soc. Perkin Trans. II, (1976) 1688.

15 C.J. Pedersen and H.K. Frensdorff, Angew. Chem. Int. Ed. Engl., 11 (1972) 16.

16 J. Smid in ref. 8a.

17 J.B. Grutzner, J.M. Lawlor, and L.M. Jackman, J. Amer. Chem. Soc., 94 (1972)
   2306.

18 A. Streitwieser, Jr., C.J. Chang, W.B. Hollyhead, and J.R. Murdoch, J. Amer.
   Chem. Soc., 94 (1972) 5288.

19 E. Buncel, B.C. Menon, and J.P. Colpa, Can. J. Chem., $\underline{57}$, 999 (1979).

20 J.W. Burley and R.N. Young, J. Chem. Soc. B, (1971) 1018; J. Chem. Soc.
   Perkin Trans. II, (1972) 835.

21 D.H. O'Brien, C.R. Russell, and A.J. Hart, J. Amer. Chem. Soc., 98 (1976)
   7427; ibid., $\underline{101}$, 633 (1979).

22 R. Waack, M.A. Doran, and P.E. Stevenson, J. Amer. Chem. Soc., 88 (1966)
    2109.

23 R. Waack and M.A. Doran, J. Phys. Chem., 67 (1963) 148.

24 M. Szwarc, "Carbanions, Living Polymers and Electron Transfer Processes."
    Wiley, New York 1968.

25 R. Waack and M.A. Doran, J. Am. Chem. Soc., 85 (1963) 1651.

26 R. Asami, M. Levy, and M. Szwarc, J. Chem. Soc., (1961) 361.

27 B. Bockrath and L.M. Dorfman, J. Amer. Chem. Soc., 97 (1975) 3307;
    L.M. Dorfman, R.J. Sujdak and B. Bockrath, Acc. Chem. Res., 9 (1976) 352.

28 E. Buncel and B.C. Menon, J. Amer. Chem. Soc., 99 (1977) 4457.

29 E. Buncel and B.C. Menon, J. Organometal. Chem., 141 (1977) 1.

30 J.R. Jones, "The Ionization of Carbon Acids", Academic Press, London 1973.

31 "Proton Transfer Reactions" edited by E.F. Caldin and V. Gold, Chapman and
    Hall, London 1975.

32 E. Buncel, "Carbanions. Mechanistic and Isotopic Aspects", Elsevier,
    Amsterdam 1975; E. Buncel and H. Wilson, Adv. Phys. Org. Chem., 14 (1977)
    133.

33 A.H. Zimmerman, K.J. Reed, and J.I. Brauman, J. Amer. Chem. Soc., 99 (1977)
    7203.

34 J.E. Bartmess, W.J. Hehre, R.T. McIver, Jr., and L.E. Overman, J. Amer.
    Chem. Soc., 99 (1977) 1976.

35 T.B. McMahon and P. Kebarle, J. Amer. Chem. Soc., 98 (1976) 3399.

36 D.K. Bohme, E. Lee-Ruff, and L.B. Young, J. Amer. Chem. Soc., 94 (1972)
    5153.

37 A. Streitwieser, Jr., J.R. Murdoch, G. Häfelinger, and C.J. Chang, J. Amer.
    Chem. Soc., 95 (1973) 4248 and previous papers in the series.

38 W.S. Matthews, J.E. Bares, J.E. Bartmess, F.G. Bordwell, F.J. Cornforth,
    G.E. Drucker, Z. Margolin, R.J. McCallum, G.J. McCollum, and N.R. Vanier,
    J. Amer. Chem. Soc., 97 (1975) 7006.

39 K. O'Donnell, R. Bacon, K.L. Chellappa, R.L. Schowen, and J.K. Lee, J. Amer.
    Chem. Soc., 94 (1972) 2500.

124

40 R.G. Pearson and J. Songstad, J. Amer. Chem. Soc., 89 (1967) 1827.

41 E.A. Symons and E. Buncel, J. Am. Chem. Soc., 94 (1972) 3641; Can. J. Chem.,
    51 (1973) 1673; E. Buncel and E.A. Symons, J. Am. Chem. Soc., 98 (1976) 656;
    E. Buncel, R.A. More O'Ferrall and E.A. Symons, J. Amer. Chem. Soc., 100
    (1978) 1084.

42 E. Buncel and B.C. Menon, Chem. Commun., (1976) 648.

43 E. Buncel and B.C. Menon, Can. J. Chem., 54 (1976) 3949.

44 E. Buncel, A.R. Norris, K.E. Russell, and R. Tucker, J. Amer. Chem. Soc.,
    94 (1972) 1646; E. Buncel, A.R. Norris, K.E. Russell, P. Sheridan, and
    H. Wilson, Can. J. Chem., 52 (1974) 1750; E. Buncel, A.R. Norris, K.E.
    Russell, and H. Wilson, ibid., 52 (1974) 2306.

45 M. Szwarc, A. Streitwieser, Jr., and P.C. Mowery, in ref. 8b.

46 T.E. Hogen-Esch, Adv. Phys. Org. Chem., 15 (1977) 154.

47 D.F. Shriver, "The Manipulation of Air-Sensitive Compounds", McGraw Hill,
    New York 1969.

48 K. Bowden and R. Stewart, Tetrahedron, 21 (1965) 261.

49 J.J. Delpuech and D. Nicole, J. Chem. Soc. Perkin II, (1974) 1025

50 F. Terrier, F. Millot, and R. Schaal, Bull. Soc. Chim. France (1969) 3002.

51 C.D. Ritchie and R.E. Uschold, J. Am. Chem. Soc., 90 (1968) 3415.

52 A. Maercker and W. Demuth, Liebigs Ann. Chem., (1977) 1909.

53 T. Holm, Acta Chem. Scand B 32 (1978) 162.

CHAPTER 4

VIBRATIONAL INFRARED AND RAMAN SPECTROSCOPY OF CARBANIONS

by J. CORSET

Laboratoire de Spectrochimie Infrarouge et Raman - C.N.R.S.

2 à 8 rue Henri Dunant - Thiais 94320 - France

CONTENTS

I. INTRODUCTION

It is rather difficult to make a clear distinction between organometallic compounds and carbanions. Nevertheless, infrared and Raman spectroscopy have provided[1-3] information for characterizing the anionic structure of species such as cyclopentadienyl or allyl metal compounds which may be σ, π and ionic compounds. As will be discussed in Section V, anionic structures are mainly characterized by a strong electron delocalization on the anion skeleton and a rather small metal anion force constant, which compares well with that of alkali metal salts. The σ and π bonding takes place mostly with transition metals or their complexes, while the ionic bonding is principally observed with alkali or alkali-earth metals. This ionic character of the metal-carbon bond may also strongly change with the physical state of the compound. It is indeed well known that even with strongly electropositive metal atoms such as the alkali metals even the simple salts like MCl[4] or MNO_3[5] are effectively covalently bonded through charge transfer in the gaseous state[6] or when trapped in inert gas matrix.[5,7] The ionic character appears mainly through the solvation, as shown by Pimentel and co-workers[7] who have characterized the ionization of the LiCl molecule through solvation in matrix using infrared spectroscopy.

It is easy to understand that a large number of carbanionic species which are known to exist in the solid state as polymeric compounds[8-10] may have a reactivity strongly depending on the structure of the smaller aggregates formed through solvation in solutions. Due to their very short observation time, infrared and Raman spectroscopy are then among the most relevant techniques to characterize the species formed in solution. Unfortunately, probably because of the difficulties involved, very few detailed studies have been undertaken on the structure of carbanionic species in solution. The spectroscopic studies of the structure of ionic solutions have been developed through studies of more stable salt solutions. The reported analyses are often limited to the well defined group frequencies such as $C \equiv N$ stretching vibrations, the other skeletal vibration modes being less easily understood and needing more elaborate treatment.

Since it is not our purpose to give an exhaustive report of all the work done by vibrational spectroscopy on organometallic compounds or even on carbanions, which can be found elsewhere,[3,11] we have chosen to present, after a short description of the experimental techniques focusing on the special care to be taken for the handling of carbanionic compounds, the methods which may give structural information from IR and Raman spectra on the distribution of species in solution as well as their structure. In the basic theory section, we shall focus on the force field calculations which relate the observed spectra to the bond properties and define the other parameters needed for assignment of spectra (intensities, selection rules, polarization ratio). We shall then present the methods used in vibrational spectra assignments and derivation of structural information for solid state compounds as well as for solutions. The examples will then be chosen as close as possible to carbanion chemistry problems. In the last section we shall briefly present some examples of carbanion studies for which vibrational spectroscopy has proven to give useful informations.

II. EXPERIMENTAL TECHNIQUES

We will not describe in detail instruments and methods in infrared and Raman spectroscopy, but will point out the improvement in currently available instruments for the physical chemist and will indicate the special care required for the scanning of good quality spectra, referring the reader to more detailed accounts. The preparation of compounds is generally described in the original papers and monographs.[12,13] Details will only be given on the sample handling.

The absorption of infrared radiation by the sample Figure 1.a. is now currently measured with double beam infrared spectrometers, the different parts of which have been described in many books.[14-23] The monochromators which were first equipped with prism are now most exclusively using gratings. Interferometers have also been developed mainly in the far-infrared (600 to 10 cm^{-1}) with small computers doing on line the Fourier transform of the interferrogram.[22,23]

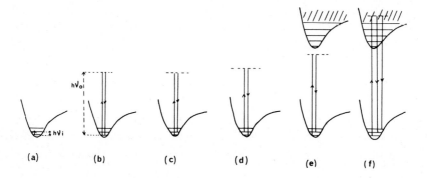

Fig. 1. Infrared absorption (a) and different scattering processes (b to f) depending on the proximity of the exciting line energy $h\nu_o$ to an electronic transition energy : (b) Rayleigh scattering ; (c and d) Normal Raman scattering (c) Stokes lines (d) anti-Stokes lines ; (e) Pre-Resonance Raman scattering ; (f) Resonance Raman scattering.

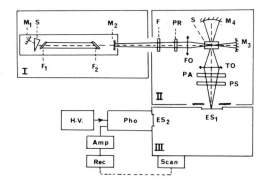

Fig. 2. Raman spectrometer with laser excitation : I – Laser, II – Sample
holder plate, III – Double monochromator

M_1, M_2 mirors of the laser cavity
S selector prism of the laser line
F_1, F_2 Brewster windows
ES_1 monochromator entrance slit
ES_2 monochromator exit slit
Pho photomultiplier
H.V. high voltage supply
Amp. Amplifier
Rec. recorder
Scan. Scanning mechanism

F interference filter
PR polarization rotator
FO focalisation lens
M_3, M_4 mirrors
S sample
TO transfer optic
PA polarization analyser
PS polarization scrambler

Several types of diffusion processes take place when a sample is irradia-
ted with high energy monochromatic radiation of frequency ν_o which is called the
"exciting radiation". Some photons are scattered at the frequency ν_o of the exciting radiation and correspond to the "Rayleigh scattering", while a smaller
portion, less than one photon in 1000, is scattered at frequencies $\nu_o \pm \nu_i$,
where ν_i is the vibrational frequency of the molecules, and correspond to the
"Raman scattering" (see Section III-B and Figure 1). Basic design, indicated in
Figure 2, has been described by several authors.[24-27]

Raman spectrometry has been greatly helped by the development of laser
sources, photomultiplier detectors, as well as improvement of the stray light
rejection of the monochromators.[26,27] Both infrared and Raman spectrometers
are now largely improved through digitalizing the output signal of the detector
as well as the scanning device of the monochromators allowing to interface the
spectrometers with computers.[28,29]

Most of the organometallic compounds are air- moisture sensitive and must
be handled either in a dry-box or glove-bag. This last technique is more convenient when the sample need to be handled under a controlled atmosphere (oxygen
or carbon dioxide free atmosphere for instance).

A. Infrared

The common commercial instruments have most often a resolution limit between 0,1 and 1 cm^{-1} and may be calibrated with standards provided by the "I.U.P.A.C. Commission on Molecular Structure and Spectroscopy".[30] Exact calibration is particularly important in order to measure small frequency shifts due to molecular interactions and to compare infrared and Raman spectra of the same sample. In order to get good quality spectra with accurate position and intensity of bands, the spectral slit width must be smaller than 1/5 or 1/10 of the observed band width[15,16] and correct amplifier gain, response time and scanspeed must be chosen.

Solid compounds are studied as crystalline films, mulls or pressed discs.[17] The most common mulling agent is Nujol. Fluorolube or hexachlorobutadiene are often convenient to examine the frequency ranges where Nujol presents absorptions bands. They cannot always be used for reactive organometallic compounds.[2,31-33]

Spectra of liquids or solutions are usually scanned in sealed fixed thickness cells in order to prevent contact with atmospheric water vapour. The solutions are often prepared directly in the reaction vessel which is often equipped with a slip-on rubber septum cap. The solution is then transferred to the infrared cell with a syringe needle through the cap.

The spectra of gaseous organometallic samples are very difficult to obtain due to their high reactivity and their low vapor pressure. Usually heated gas cells are used, which are carefully evacuated while heating to remove adsorbed water vapor.[34] The monomeric species have been studied with the matrix isolation technique which was first introduced by Pimentel.[35] The species is trapped at very low temperature, 10 to 40°K, on a cold window in an inert gas matrix (N_2, Ar, etc...) see references.[36,37] The organometallic compound is prepared in the matrix through vaporisation of an organic compound and of alkali metal atoms using a Knudsen cell.[38,39]

The most commonly used windows for the mid-infrared region are CaF_2, NaCl, KBr and CsI. With CsI windows which allow all the ranges above 200 cm^{-1} to be covered, only low polarity solvents like benzene or tetrahydrofuran may be used due to the high solubility of this salt in other solvents. Possible reactions with the solute must also be checked. For the solid compounds the mulling agent like Nujol often protect the window against any reaction with the organometallic compound. In the far-infrared, polyethylene, teflon and silicium are used.

Low temperature spectra are obtained either with commercially available thermostated cells or with laboratory made glass-metal cells cooled by liquid nitrogen[40] or more sophisticated thermostated cells.

B. Raman

The spectrometers are usually equipped with double monochromators which are often sufficient for gas or neat liquid studies. Triple monochromators are used for powdered solid sample with high stray-light level or to study the frequency range of the spectrum close to the excitation line. The calibration of the instrument must be carefully checked with standard emission lines available from discharge lamps filled with a noble gas or a metal vapour.[41,42] Its dependence on temperature has also to be checked and measured at each run of a sample through scanning of the laser excitation line and parasite laser lines, for instance by removing the laser line filter.

The handling of sample is easier in Raman than in infrared due to the fact that excellent Raman spectra are obtained with sample placed in sealed glass capillaries or tubes which can be placed in a cryostat or an oven. This procedure may be applied independently of the physical state of the sample. The sample volume necessary to record a spectrum has been highly reduced by the use of laser sources excitation[24,26,27] and is now reduced to a volume of some cubic micrometers when the diffused light collection is made with a microscope like in the Mole Microprobe (I.S.A.).[43-45]

The most common difficulty encountered in obtaining Raman spectra of organometallic compounds is the fluorescence or the laser light absorption by the sample. The fluorescence may often be due to impurities like greases which have high fluorescence and may cause local burning of the sample. The sample must then be purified by usual techniques like distillation, recrystallization, etc. in equipment which eliminates contamination by stopcock grease. The sample may also be treated with a carbon adsorbent. For liquids the presence of dust is very critical and the sample must be carefully filtered when necessary. It may also be necessary to change the excitation line in order to prevent absorption by fluorescent impurities or by the sample itself. With organometallic compounds good results are often obtained with the red lines of an He-Ne laser at 632.8 nm or of a Kr laser at 647.1 nm.

Like in infrared, when the spectrometers are coupled with a computer, the signal to noise ratio may be improved through data accumulation and signal averaging. The use of solution or solid sample spectra may also be greatly facilitated through direct treatment of data such as base line modeling or background corrections.[28,29]

When the laser excitation frequency approaches that of an absorption band of the compound, as with a coloured sample for instance, special methods must be used to prevent heating or burning of the sample.[46-49] For intensity measurement corrections due to absorption of the exciting and diffused light have to be done and the sample concentration adjusted.[47,48] Rotating sample or surface scanning technique have been described.[47,48] A circulation cell which may be sealed under vacuum has been used for carbanion solutions studies.[50]

Fast Raman technique may be useful for kinetic studies purposes[51] or when the compound is too unstable to be studied by ordinary Raman methods. In this last case, the Raman spectrum may be obtained during the time of a very short laser pulse before the compound decomposes.[52] These methods are also promising in order to discriminate the background fluorescence from the Raman spectrum.[47] For a general review see ref. 45.

III. BASIC THEORY

Our purpose is not to give a detailed treatment of theories which are extensively presented elsewhere[53-58] but to summarize some fundamental steps and hypotheses of calculations in order to make understandable the information available from the observation of vibrational modes.

A. Potential function and vibrational modes

1. Internal coordinates

The description of the motions of a polyatomic molecule having N nuclei requires 3N coordinates. Of these 6 for a non linear molecule or 5 for a linear one correspond to translational or rotational motions. The other $3N-6$ or $3N-5$ coodinates are called "internal coordinates". The vibrational energy of the molecule which is the sum of the potential energy V and of the kinetic energy T may be expressed in different ways. Although most of the calculations start with the "cartesian internal coordinates", which make the kinetic energy easier to express, the potential energy is more easily understood when expressed through bond stretching and angle deformations. Their relation with Cartesian displacement coordinates is linear only in the small amplitude motions approximation, "harmonic approximation". The Eliashevich coordinates R_m[54,56,59] which are most often used correspond to the linear part of this relation. They correspond to changes in bond length or in bond angle.

2. Potential function

The potential energy function is most often written as a Taylor series expansion of the internal coordinates. Two types of potential function are generally used to calculate the normal vibration modes.

(a) The "generalized valence force field" G.V.F.F.

$$V = V(o) + 1/2 \; \Sigma_{mm'} f_{mm'} \; R_m R_{m'} + 1/6 \; \Sigma_{mm'm''} f_{mm'm''} \; R_m R_{m'} R_{m''} + \ldots \tag{1}$$

The "harmonic aproximation" means that terms of higher order than quadratic are neglected.

The quadratic force constants are then defined as :

$$f_{mm'} = \partial^2 V / \partial R_m \; \partial R_{m'}) \; R_m = R_{m'} = 0 \tag{2}$$

The coordinates used are only bond stretching Δr_{ij}, and valence angle variations $\Delta \theta_{jk}$. f_{mm} are stretching or bending principal force constants, while $f_{mm'}$ are interaction force constants.

(b) The "Urey-Bradley force field" U.B.F.F. [60]

This force field uses not only bond length and valence angle variations, but also the variations Δq_{jk} of the q_{jk} distances between non bonded atoms,

$$V = \Sigma_i \; V \; (\Delta r_i) + \Sigma_{i>j} \; V \; (\Delta \theta_{jk}) + \Sigma_{ij} \; V \; (\Delta q_{jk}) \tag{3}$$

where : $V \; (\Delta r_i) = K'_i r_{ij} \; \Delta r_{ij} + 1/2 \; K_i \; (\Delta r_{ij})^2$

$$V \; (\Delta \theta_{jk}) = H'_{jk} \; r_{ij} \; r_{jk} \; \Delta \theta_{jk} + 1/2 \; H_{jk} \; r_{ij} \; r_{ik} \; (\Delta \theta_{jk})^2$$

$$V \; (\Delta q_{jk}) = F'_{jk} \; q_{jk} \; \Delta q_{jk} + 1/2 \; F_{jk} \; (\Delta q_{jk})^2$$

and K_i, K'_i are stretching force constants ; H_{jk}, H'_{jk} are bending force constant ; F_{jk}, F'_{jk} are repulsive force constant ; F' is usually taken as 0.1 F.

3. Equations of motion

Using the Wilson method, [54] which defines a G matrix with elements $g_{mm'}$ the kinetic energy matrix can then be written :

$$2\,T = \overset{\cdot}{R}{}^{\dagger}\,G^{-1}\,\overset{\cdot}{R} \qquad\qquad \text{or} \qquad 2\,T = \Sigma_{mm'}\,g^{-1}_{mm'}\,\overset{\cdot}{R}_m\,\overset{\cdot}{R}_{m'} \qquad\qquad\qquad (4)^{*}$$

and the potential energy

$$2\,V = R^{\dagger}\,F\,R \qquad\qquad \text{or} \qquad 2\,V = \Sigma_{mm'}\,f_{mm'}\,R_m R_{m'} \qquad\qquad\qquad (5)$$

The Lagrange equations of motion are then written :

$$\frac{d}{dt}\,\left(\frac{\partial U}{\partial \overset{\cdot}{R}}\right) + \left(\frac{\partial U}{\partial R}\right) = 0 \qquad\qquad \text{with} \quad U = T - V \qquad\qquad (6)$$

We get 3N-6 second order differential equations of the form

$$\Sigma_m\,g^{-1}_{mm'}\,\overset{..}{R}_m + \Sigma_m f_{mm'}\,R_m = 0 \qquad\qquad\qquad (7)$$

The solutions are :

$$R_{ms} = a_{ms}\,\cos.\,(\lambda_s^{1/2}\,t + \phi_s) \qquad\qquad\qquad (8)$$

where a_{ms} is the maximum vibration amplitude corresponding to the coordinate R_{ms}, λ_s the phase factor and $\lambda_s = 4\,\pi^2\nu_s^2$ the frequency factor.
After derivation of R_m and replacing $\overset{..}{R}_m$ in equation (7) we get the homogeneous linear equations :

$$\Sigma_m\,(f_{mm'} - \lambda_s\,g^{-1}_{mm'})\,a_{ms} = 0 \qquad\qquad\qquad (9)$$

or written under a matrix form and after multiplying by G :

$$|FG - E\lambda_s|\,A_s = 0 \qquad\qquad\qquad (10)$$

where A_s is the column matrix of maximum vibrations amplitudes a_{ms} corresponding to the ν_s frequency. The frequency factors λ_s are then the solutions of the secular determinant :

$$|FG - E\Lambda| = 0 \qquad\qquad\qquad (11)$$

$*$ $\overset{\cdot}{R}{}^{\dagger}$ means the transpose matrix of the $\overset{\cdot}{R}$ and $\overset{\cdot}{R}_m = \partial_m/\partial_t$

where E is the identity matrix and Λ the diagonal matrix of frequency parameters λ_s. The equation (10) can be written :

$$|FG - E\Lambda|\ A = 0$$

where A is the square matrix of the 3N-6 over 3N-6 amplitudes vectors A_s from
equation (10) for each λ_s ; the a_{ms} values may be calculated, assuming their
normalization such as :

$$\sum_m (a_{ms})^2 = 1 \tag{12}$$

The normalized vibrations amplitudes x_{ms} are then :

$$x_{ms} = a_{ms}/(\sum_m (a_{ms})^2)^{1/2} \tag{13}$$

4. Vibrational normal modes and potential energy distributions (P.E.D.)

In the harmonic approximation, all the vibration mode are orthogonal, which
mean that they do not exchange energy. A system of coordinates Q_s called "normal
coordinates" may then be found such that the kinetic and potential energy may be
written :

$$2\ T = \sum_{s=1}^{3N-6} (\dot{Q}_s)^2 \qquad\qquad 2\ T = \dot{Q}^\dagger E \dot{Q} \tag{14}$$

or with the matrix notation

$$2\ V = \sum_{s=1}^{3N-6} \lambda_s (Q_s)^2 \qquad\qquad 2\ V = Q^\dagger \Lambda Q \tag{15}$$

The Lagrange equations of motion correspond then to the 3N-6 independent equations :

$$\ddot{Q}_s + \lambda_s Q_s = 0$$

Their solutions being written :

$$Q_s = Q_s^o \cos(\lambda_s^{1/2} t + \phi_s) \tag{16}$$

If we call L the transformation matrix from normal to internal coordinates,

$$R_m = \sum_s L_{ms} Q_s \qquad or \qquad R = LQ \tag{17}$$

it may then be shown that :

$$Q_s^o = \Sigma_m \; L_{ms}^{-1} \; a_{ms} \tag{18}$$

This means that considering the preceeding normalization condition equation (12),

$$Q_s^o = 1 \text{ and } L_{ms}^{-1} = a_{ms}$$

The L_{ms}^{-1} elements are the vibration amplitudes of the R_m internal coordinates for the vibration mode ν_s. The potential energy for the normal mode ν_s will be written according to equation (15) :

$$V_s = 1/2 \; \lambda_s \; Q_s^2 = \lambda_s$$

The equation (8) may then be written :

$$\lambda_s = \Sigma_m \; L_{ms}^2 \; f_{mm} + \Sigma_{m'\neq m} \; L_{ms} \; L_{m's} \; f_{mm'}$$

$$\text{or } \Sigma_m \; (L_{ms}^2/\lambda_s) \; f_{mm} + \Sigma_{m'\neq m} \; (L_{ms} \; L_{m's}/\lambda_s) \; f_{mm'} = 1 \tag{19}$$

The terms L_{ms}^2/λ_s and $2 \; L_{ms}L_{m's}/\lambda_s$ are called "potential energy distribution". The first correspond to the contribution to the potential energy of the normal mode ν_s of the principal force constant f_{mm} ; the second represent the contribution of the interaction force constant f_{mm}'. In general the L_{ms}^2/λ_s terms are larger than the others and provide a reasonable measure of the contribution of the internal coordinate R_m to the normal coordinate Q_s.

5. Symmetry coordinates

The difficult computational problem[55,61,62] encountered in calculating force constants directly from vibrational frequencies may be simplified with symmetry coordinates. These coordinates S_i take into account the fact that vibrational modes belonging to different symmetry classes of the symmetry point group of the considered molecular entity are orthogonal to each other. The secular determinant equation (11) using these coordinates may be factored in subdeterminants of lower dimensions, corresponding to the different symmetry classes :

$$|FG - E\Lambda| = 0$$

These "symmetry coordinates" are linearly related to the internal coordinates through the matrix U :

$$S = UR \qquad\qquad (20)$$

The F and G matrices expressed with symmetry coordinates are then related to the F and G matrices by the relations :

$$F = UFU' \qquad\qquad (21)$$

$$G = UGU' \qquad\qquad (22)$$

The symmetry force constants F_{ij} are sometimes used in place of f_{mm}, in order to reduce the number of force constants to adjust for the calculation of a given frequency.

For a bent XY_2 molecule of C_{2v} symmetry, the symmetry coordinates are :

$$S_1 = 2^{-1/2} (\Delta r_{12} + \Delta r_{13})$$
$$\qquad\qquad\qquad\qquad A_1$$
$$S_2 = \Delta\theta_{23}$$
$$\qquad\qquad\qquad\qquad\qquad\qquad\qquad (23)$$
$$S_3 = 2^{-1/2} (\Delta r_{12} - \Delta r_{13}) \qquad B_1$$

where S_1 and S_2 correspond to species A_1 and S_3 to species B_1, Δr_{12}, Δr_{13} and $\Delta\theta_{23}$ being the three internal valence coordinates corresponding to variation of bonds lengths r_{12} and r_{13} and valence angle θ_{23}.

The F and G matrix elements are :

$$F_{11} = f_r + f_{rr} \qquad\qquad\qquad\qquad G_{11} = \mu_y + \mu_x (1 + \cos\theta)$$

$$F_{12} = 2^{1/2} f_{r\theta} \qquad\qquad A_1 \qquad G_{12} = -2^{1/2} \mu_x \sin\theta$$

$$F_{22} = f_\theta \qquad\qquad\qquad\qquad\qquad G_{22} = 2 |\mu_y + \mu_x (1 - \cos\theta)| \qquad (24)$$

$$F_{33} = f_r - f_{rr} \qquad\qquad B_1 \qquad G_{33} = \mu_y + \mu_x (1 - \cos\theta)$$

The secular determinant is then factored in two sub-determinants for vibrations of species A_1 and B_1, and it is readily seen that calculation of ν_3 needs the adjustement of only one force constant F_{33} with symmetry coordinates, instead of two f_r and f_{rr} with internal coordinates. The number of L elements is also considerably reduced. This advantage may also be kept for more complicated molecules using local symmetry coordinates[55] for groups like CH_3 or CH_2.

B. Intensities

1. Selection rules

Using the normal coordinates Q_s, the Schrodinger equation may be solved for the harmonic approximation, by means the Hamiltonian $H = T + V$. The vibrational energy levels E_s and vibrational wave functions ψ_{vs} are then obtained :

$$E_s = h \nu_s (v_s + 1/2) \tag{25}$$

The intensity of the vibrational bands in IR and Raman spectra is then proportional to the square of the matrix elements :

$$\left| M \right|_{v'v''} = \int \psi_{v'} \, M \, \psi_{v''} \, d\tau \tag{26}$$

where M is the molecular dipole moment μ for infrared or the amplitude of the dipole moment P induced by the exciting radiation for the Raman ; $\psi_{v'}$ and $\psi_{v''}$ are the vibrational wave functions of the states involved characterized by their quantum vibrational numbers v' and v''. The integral is over normal vibrational coordinates .

The molecular dipole moment may be related either to the charges on atoms or to the bond moments.[53,63] It may be expanded in a series in powers of the normal coordinates.

$$\mu_u = \mu_u^o + \Sigma_s \left(\frac{\partial \mu_u}{\partial Q_s} \right)_o \, Q_s + 1/2 \, \Sigma_{s,s'} \left(\frac{\partial^2 \mu_u}{\partial Q_s \partial Q_{s'}} \right)_o \, Q_s \, Q_{s'} + \ldots \tag{27}$$

where μ_u indicates a component (u = x, y, z) of the molecular dipole moment vector.

The molecular induced dipole moment vector P is :

$$\left| P \right| = \left| \alpha \right| \left| E \right| \tag{28}$$

where E is the electric field of the exciting radiation of frequency ν_o and $\left| \alpha \right|$ the molecular polarizability tensor.

$$|\alpha| = \begin{vmatrix} \alpha_{xx} & \alpha_{xy} & \alpha_{xz} \\ \alpha_{yx} & \alpha_{yy} & \alpha_{yz} \\ \alpha_{zx} & \alpha_{zy} & \alpha_{zz} \end{vmatrix} \qquad (29)$$

The components of the polarizability tensor may also be series-expanded :

$$\alpha_{\rho\sigma} = \alpha_{\rho\sigma}^{\circ} + \sum_s (\frac{\partial \alpha_{\rho\sigma}}{\partial Q_s}) \, Q_s + \ldots \qquad (30)$$

Simple selection rules may then be derived from the harmonic approximation, both mechanical (see Section III-2-a) and electro-optical (the dipole moment and the polarizability are assumed linear functions of the vibration coordinates). In this case, each normal mode satisfies the selection rule $\Delta v = \pm 1$ and only transitions $\Delta v_s = v'_s - v''_s = 1$; $\Delta v'_s = 0$ are allowed. They correspond to the fundamental frequencies v_s of the normal modes. Other selection rules are linked with the symmetry properties of the vibration modes[53,54,63,64] and derived through group theory. They may be summarized in the following way for the activity of fundamentals ; a vibration mode v_s will be infrared active if the normal coordinate Q_s belongs to the same symmetry species as at least one of the dipole moment components μ_u ; it will be Raman active if the normal coordinate Q_s belongs to the same symmetry species as at least one of the polarizability components for the particular point group of the molecule.

2. Intensities

The intensities of the fundamental modes in infrared and Raman are determined according to equations (26) to (30) by the first derivatives of the dipole moment and polarizability components, $(\partial \mu_u/\partial Q_s)_{\circ}$ and $(\partial \alpha_{\rho\sigma}/\partial Q_s)_{\circ}$.

(a) Infrared

The absolute (integral) intensity of a fundamental IR absorption band is given by :

$$A_s = \int_b k_s(v)\,dv = \frac{N\pi}{3c} (\frac{\partial \mu}{\partial Q_s})^2 = \frac{N\pi}{3c} \left| (\frac{\partial \mu_x}{\partial Q_s})^2 + (\frac{\partial \mu_y}{\partial Q_s})^2 + (\frac{\partial \mu_z}{\partial Q_s})^2 \right| \qquad (31)$$

where $k_s(v)$ is the molecular absorption coefficient, N is the number of molecules in unit volume, C is the velocity of light.

140

(b) <u>Raman</u>

In order to define the intensity of Raman lines, it must be considered that the molecular induced dipole depends on the respective orientation of the molecular axis x, y, z and on the orientation of the electric field vector of the incident light. If X, Y, Z be the laboratory fixed system of axis, then with the geometry described on Figure 3, the induced dipole component P_x will be :

$$P_x = \alpha_{xx} E_x + \alpha_{xy} E_y + \alpha_{xz} E_z$$

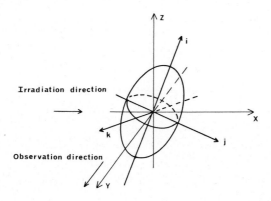

Fig. 3. Relative orientation of the laboratory fixed system of axis : X Y Z and of the molecular fixed system of axis : i j k.

The molecular tensor α' is related to the space fixed tensor α by the matrix relation :

$$\alpha = T \alpha' T^{-1} \tag{32}$$

where T is a transformation matrix the components of which are the director cosines of the two systems of axis. In infrared, the random orientation of molecules in a fluid averages the oscillating dipole to zero. In Raman, as a consequence of the tensor properties of the polarizability, the average over all orientations is not zero. Two factors remains invariant over the transformation T, the isotropic part a and the anisotropic part b of the polarizability :

$$a = 1/3 \; (\alpha_{ii} + \alpha_{jj} + \alpha_{kk})$$

$$b^2 = 1/2 \; \left| (\alpha_{ii} - \alpha_{jj})^2 + (\alpha_{jj} - \alpha_{kk})^2 + (\alpha_{kk} - \alpha_{ii})^2 + 6 \; (\alpha_{ij}^2 + \alpha_{jk}^2 + \alpha_{ki}^2) \right| \tag{33}$$

where i, j, k refer to the principal axis of the polarizability ellipsoid of the molecule.

According to the classical elementary treatment of scattering processes, the incident electromagnetic field E varies with time at frequency ν_o, and α varies with time with frequencies ν_s :

$$E = E_o \cos (2 \pi \nu_o t)$$

After replacing in equ.(28) E and α, which is time dependent, by Q_s, and on rearrangement the induced dipole moment is found to be :

$$P = \alpha_o E_o \cos (2 \pi \nu_o t) + \Sigma_s (\frac{\partial \alpha}{\partial Q_s})_o Q_s^o \{\cos |2\pi(\nu_o+\nu_s)t + \phi| + \cos |2\pi(\nu_o-\nu_s)t - \phi|\} \quad (34)$$

The first term corresponds to the Rayleigh scattering without change of frequency and in phase with the incident light. The second and third terms correspond to dipoles which scatter with frequencies $\nu_o + \nu_s$ and $\nu_o - \nu_s$, i.e. Raman scattering. The high frequency term corresponds to anti-Stokes lines and the low frequency term to Stokes lines. The phase factor ϕ being different for each scattering molecule, the observed emission which is the sum of those for all the scatterers will be incoherent.

The classical electromagnetic theory shows that an oscillating dipole radiates energy at a rate given by :

$$I = \frac{16\pi^4 \nu^4}{3 c^2} |P|^2 \quad (35)$$

The scattered intensity for a Raman line will then depend on the nature of the irradiating light and on the polarization of the scattered light. If we consider that the direction of the incident light is parallel to the x axis (Figure 4), and that the scattered light is observed along the Y direction of the laboratory space fixed axis, the scattered light polarized along the Z or X direction for an incident unpolarized light will be :

$$I_z \simeq |P_z|^2 \simeq a^2 + (7/45) b^2$$

$$I_x \simeq |P_x|^2 \simeq (6/45) b^2 \quad (36)$$

Thus the ratio of the radiated light polarized in the X and Z direction, that is to say parallel or perpendicular to the direction of irradiation, is expressed by :

$$\rho_n = \frac{I_x}{I_z} = \frac{I_y}{I_\perp} = 6 \; b^2 / (45 \; a^2 + 7 \; b^2) \tag{37}$$

If the irradiation is made with a polarized radiation (laser beam for instance), the polarization direction being the Z direction, the depolarization ratio will be :

$$\rho_p = 3 \; b^2 / (45 \; a^2 + 4 \; b^2) \tag{38}$$

The α_{ii} components of the molecular polarizability tensor are related to the symmetry properties of the molecule. The totally symmetrical part of the polarizability changes only when the molecule is distorted in a totally symmetric manner. This means that only vibrations which belong to the totally symmetric species will have depolarization ratios such as : $0 < \rho_n < 6/7$ or $0 < \rho_p < 3/4$
The other modes not belonging to the totally symmetric species will have

$\rho_n = 6/7$ or $\rho_p = 3/4$.

We now return to the expression of the intensity derived from the quantum mechanical treatment of the Raman effect (equ. 26). For a Stokes line the intensity of Raman line corresponding to a transition from an initial state v' to a final vibrational state v" belonging to the same electronic state is expressed as :

$$I_{v'v"} = \frac{2^7 \pi^5}{3^2 c^4} \; I_o \; (\nu_o + \nu_{v'v"})^4 \; \Sigma_{\rho 6} \; |(\alpha_{\rho 6})_{v'v"}|^2 \tag{39}$$

where I_o is the intensity of the incident light and the summation is over all the orientations ρ and σ. According to the Placzek theory[53,66] and the Kramers Heisenberg dispersion relations, $(\alpha_{\rho\sigma})_{v'v"}$ is written :

$$(\alpha_{\rho 6})_{v'v"} = \frac{1}{h} \Sigma_r \; | \; \frac{(M_\rho)_{rv"} \; (M_6)_{v'r}}{\nu_r - \nu_{v'} - \nu_o + i\Gamma_r} + \frac{(M_\rho)_{v'r} \; (M_6)_{rv"}}{\nu_r - \nu_{v"} + \nu_o + i\Gamma_r} \; | \tag{40}$$

where $(M_\rho)_{v'r}$ is the electronic dipole transition moment along the ρ direction

$$(M_\rho)_{v'r} = \int \psi_r \; M_\rho \; \psi_{v'} \; d\tau$$

and the summation takes place over all the vibronic states r of the molecule ; ν_r is the frequency of the intermediate state r, and Γ_r a damping factor representing the finite lifetime and "sharpness" of this intermediate state.

(c) Resonance Raman effect

Depending on the relative position of the electronic levels e of the molecule and the energy of the exciting radiation ν_o, several types of Raman effect have been considered :

(i) "off Resonance" or ordinary Raman effect, $\nu_o << \nu_e$, then $(\alpha_{\rho\sigma})_{vv}$' may be considered as independent of ν_o.

(ii) "Pre-Resonant or Resonant Raman effect", when ν_e becomes close to ν_o, then $\nu_e - \nu_o$ becomes very small and one of the terms in the summation over r in the equ. (40) may become very large. The Raman scattered intensity may then be strongly increased. The theory of the Raman effect in the "Resonance" or "Pre-Resonance" conditions has been developed by several authors[67-69] in order to get information as to which vibrations of a molecule are subject to resonance enhancement. For an introduction and review on this subject see for instance refs. 49,69,70.

(d) Intensities and bond properties

The intensity of both infrared and Raman bands may be related to the bond properties through the following relations

$$\frac{\partial \mu_\rho}{\partial Q_s} = \Sigma_m \frac{\partial \mu_\rho}{\partial R_m} \frac{\partial R_m}{\partial Q_s} = \Sigma_m L_{ms} \frac{\partial \mu_\rho}{\partial R_m}$$

$$\tag{41}$$

$$\frac{\partial \alpha \rho 6}{\partial Q_s} = \Sigma_m \frac{\partial \alpha \rho 6}{\partial R_m} \frac{\partial R_m}{\partial Q_s} = \Sigma_m L_{ms} \frac{\partial \alpha \rho 6}{\partial R_m}$$

where L_{ms} are defined through equ. (17) and may be calculated from the molecular geometry and the observed frequencies.

IV. ASSIGNMENT OF SPECTRA AND STRUCTURE

A. Physical State

Infrared and Raman spectra may be very different depending on the physical state. In the gaseous state, molecules or molecular units may be considered as isolated and information may be gained from the vibration-rotation or pure rotation band structure analysis for light molecules,[53,71] or from the band contour analysis for heavier molecules.[72] From these studies, information is obtained on the symmetry of the molecule, on its vibrational modes and on its geometry through moments of inertia calculations. Nevertheless, few studies have been reported for carbanions in the gaseous state,[34,73] due to their low vapor pressure and stability. Furthermore, there may be association in the vapour as for instance with the alkali halides which are known to dimerize.[74] For this type of compound, monomer units may be studied through isolation in an inert gas matrix at temperatures between 10 and 40 K,[36,37] or through direct preparation in the matrix of the organometallic compound as has been done for CH_3Li.[39]

In the solid state, molecules or ions are usually ordered and may strongly intereact with each other. When the crystalline structure is known from X-ray diffraction studies or assumed from comparison with parent compounds, selection rules may be derived from both the site symmetry group of the carbanion and the Bravais unit cell factor group (see e.g. refs. 75-77). If there are several carbanions in the unit cell ($Z \neq 1$), intermolecular couplings between vibrations of the molecular entities in the Bravais cell may be observed. These couplings can produce splittings of the infrared or Raman bands ; for centrosymmetric crystals the infrared and Raman bands appear at different frequencies. This phenomenon is called the Davydov effect[78] or "correlation field splittings". For carbanions, extensive vibrational spectroscopic studies on single crystals, as in inorganic chemistry,[76] or molecular crystals,[77] are very seldom performed due to their strong reactivity, which makes their handling very difficult. An infrared polarized light study has been performed for the lithium acetylacetonate[79,80] in relation with its X-ray structure,[10] but most of the relevant studies of carbanionic compounds are done on powdered samples.

As an example for the complex of the acetylacetoacetate potassium enolate with 18-6 crown ether, $C_6H_9O_3^- K^+ C_{12}H_{24}O_6$, the X-ray structure[81] shows a monoclinic unit cell of space group $P_{2_1/n}$ isomorphous of the C_{2h}^5 point group with four entities per unit cell, $Z = 4$. The four complex units are related in the unit cell through a symmetry center and a screw axis parallel to the b axis (Figure 4). The anions related through the screw axis are far apart and separated from each other by a crowned K^+ cation. The distance between the two anions related through the center of symmetry is shorter than the others and it is not surprising to observe for the more polar vibrational modes of the carbanion infrared absorption and Raman scattering bands at different frequencies (Figure 5). These "correlation field splittings" are expected to be generally strong for polar vibrational modes and largely depend on the distance between units.[82] The bands observed in infrared for each mode correspond to the Au and Bu while the Raman bands correspond to the Ag and Bg components of the factor group C_{2h}. The A-B splitting is too small to be observed while the u-g splitting was observed to be 5 to 10 cm^{-1} depending on the vibrational mode considered.[31] On the

other hand, the allylpalladium chloride complex $(C_3H_5PdCl)_2$ crystallizes with
the $P_{2_1/n}$ space group with four allyl units per cell corresponding to two molecular dimers $(C_3H_5PdCl)_2$ each being located on a site symmetry C_i.[83] The allyl
vibrational modes appear in the infrared and Raman at the same frequency but
the A-B splitting is seen on both infrared and Raman components due to the coupling between anions of two dimers related through the C_2 screw axis.[94]

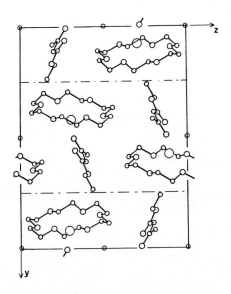

Fig. 4. Orthogonal projection of the unit cell of the crystallized ethylacetoacetate potassium enolate complex with 18-6 crown-ether $C_6H_9O_3^-K^+C_{12}H_{24}O_6$. Symmetry
elements in the YZ plane are indicated : ₒ inversion center, -.-.- diagonal glide
plane. Others symmetry elements, screw axis and inversion center (1/2, 1/2, 1/2),
are not shown.

In the liquid state or in solution, the interpretation of spectra is more
complicated. In a pure liquid, molecular or ionic interactions are usually similar to those encountered in the solid state, but disorder may strongly broa-
den the observed bands. Davydov effects may still be observed showing the
persistence of a short range order as in polar solvents[85,86] or proton donor
solvents.[87] In solutions only the vibrational modes which appear in the trans-
parency regions of the solvent may be observed. For the very strongly absorbing
or scattering vibrational modes of the compounds, very dilute solutions may be
examined and then only the interactions with the solvent have to be taken into
account. For inert molecules in non-polar solvents, spectra close to those observed in the gaseous state are usually obtained and band profile analysis gives
information on the motion of the molecule in the solution.[88] Because of the importance in chemistry of the structure of carbanions in solution, the informa-

tion obtained from vibrational spectroscopy will be considered in Section IV-C.

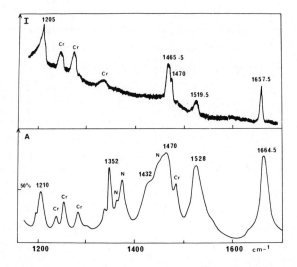

Fig. 5. Infrared and Raman spectra of the crystallized ethylacetoacetate potassium enolate complex with 18-6 crown ether $C_6H_9O_3^-k^+C_{12}H_{24}O_{26}$. Powder in Raman and Powder Nujol (N) mull in infrared. Cr indicates absorptions of the crown ether.

B. Assignment of spectra

Assignment of spectra is the most difficult part of the work in vibrational spectroscopy. These assignments are usually obtained through derivation of the selection rules in infrared and Raman for the site symmetry group of the anion.

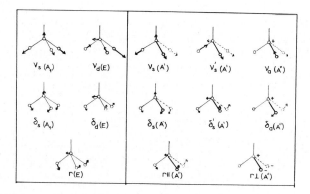

Fig. 6. Vibrational normal modes of a methyl group R-CH$_3$ along its local symmetry C_{1h} or C_{3v}.

The separation between the totally symmetric vibrational modes and the other modes may be obtained by measuring the depolarization ratio of the Raman bands for the molten, liquid or dissolved sample, provided its structure does not change with the physical state. The assignments are usually done qualitatively in terms of local symmetry motions which correspond to "group vibrations". These are illustrated for a methyl group with symmetry C_{3v} or C_{1h} (Figure 6) where ν, δ and r refer respectively to stretching, bending and rocking motions. The assignments are usually greatly helped when isotopic derivatives are available, or through comparison with the spectra of parent molecules or groups for which the assignment is well interpreted.[89-91] The assignments are generally easy for vibrational modes above 1600 cm^{-1} which usually correspond to stretching vibrations of characteristic vibrators such as XH, - C≡N, C=O or to XH bending vibrations. Below 1600 cm^{-1} skeletal stretching modes are expected as well as bending vibrations ; they may be coupled with CH_3 or CH_2 bending vibrations and the description of normal modes is less easy. When H/D isotopic substitution is available, these couplings may be brought in sight through comparison of the frequency shifts ratios with those reported[92] for the uncoupled motions of isolated CH_2 or CH_3 groups. Normal modes involving skeletal stretching or bending coordinates are less easy to make precise and a normal coordinate calculation may be needed (see Section III.A.4).

Another difficulty, often encountered in the assignment of spectra, is the occurrence of anharmonic resonances such as Fermi resonances[93] or Darling and Dennisson resonances,[94] which can make an overtone or combination mode as intense as a fundamental one. These resonances between a fundamental and an overtone or combination level are often observed, for instance with carbonyl groups,[95,96] and may be analyzed through the "solvent variation method".[95]

As an example, we shall summarize the evolution of assignments of the vibrational spectra of the acetylacetonate anion (Acac). If we include some works on the infrared spectra of solutions such as that of Bellamy and Branch[97] on chloroform (Acac)$_2$Cu solutions or those more recent[98-100] on Na$^+$Acac$^-$ and K$^+$Acac$^-$ in dissociating media (DMSO, MeOH, $H_2$0), most of the work on acetylacetonates has been done by infrared spectroscopy on solids. Since the pionnering work of Morgan[101] and Lecomte et al.[102] stretching vibrations of the $C_3O_2^-$ group bonded to a metallic cation have been located between 1200 and 1700 cm^{-1}. Their assignment was first precised by Nakamoto et al.[103,104] through a normal coordinate calculation with a simple Urey-Bradley force-field. This calculation was based for (Acac)$_2$Cu on the approximation of a 1:1 (metal-ligand) complex, which ignores the interaction between ligands because of the lack of Raman data, the copper atom being located on an inversion center of the unit cell (space group $P_{2_{1/n}}$).[105] This calculation has been repeated by Mikani et al.[106] and extended taking into account metal-ligand vibrations which had been ignored in the first calculation. The assignments given for the bands at 1580, 1554, 1534 and 1274 cm^{-1} of $(Acac)_2Cu$ were then respectively $\nu_a(C...C)$, $\nu_s(C...O)$, $\nu_a(C...O)$ + $\delta(CH)$ and $\nu_s(C...C)$ + $\nu(C-CH_3)$, as described in Table 1 for the Acac⁻ anion of C_{2v} symmetry. These assignments, although based on the spectra of 24 compouds[107] allowing to locate these vibration modes between 1630 and 1567 cm^{-1}, 1560 and 1517 cm^{-1}, 1486 and 1431 cm^{-1}, 1429 and 1357 cm^{-1} independently of the nature of the metallic atom, were further questioned. Through use of $^{16}O/^{18}O$, Pinchas et al.[108] have revised the assignment of vibrational modes involving the oxygen atom for chromium (III) and manganese (III) acetylacetonates. This isotopic substitution shows a frequency shift of 12 cm^{-1} for the higher frequency band while the other band above 1500 cm^{-1} is not significantly affected by this isotopic exchange, indicating that the higher frequency component is to a large extent a $\nu(C...O)$ stretching vibration, while the other is almost a pure $\nu(C...C)$ stretching mode. Some other assignments were also revised and further precised by Junge and Musso[109,110] using $^{12}C/^{13}C$, $^{16}O/^{18}O$ and $^1H/^2H$ substitutions. An infrared polarized light study of a single crystal of LiAcac[80,111] has shown that the bands at 1602 and 1263 cm^{-1} belong to the A_1 vibrations of the C_{2v} local symmetry point group of the anion with the transition moment parallel to the z axis of the crystal ; the bands at 1520 and 1455 cm^{-1} with their transition moment parallel to the x axis have the B_1 symmetry.

TABLE 1

Potential energy distribution for dichloro(acac)platinate (II) ion and description of symmetry coordinates and group vibrations;[112] r_1, r'_1, r_2, r'_2, δ_1, δ'_2 correspond respectively to C...O and C...C bonds and C-C-H angle of the C_{2v} symmetry Acac⁻ anion.

	P.E.D				Symmetry coordinates Group vibration	
Sym. Coord.	S_1	S_3	S_5	S_{15}	Species A_1	
Obs. Freq.						
1563	1.00	0.13	0.04	0.01	$S_1 = 2^{-1/2}(\Delta r_1 + \Delta r'_1)$	$\nu_s(C...O)$
1288	0.02	1.00	0.33	0.02	$S_3 = 2^{-1/2}(\Delta r_2 + \Delta r'_2)$	$\nu_s(C...C)$
952	0.27	0.37	1.00	0.54	$S_5 = 2^{-1/2}(\Delta r_3 + \Delta r'_3)$	$\nu_s(C\_\_R)$
					S_{15}= ring deformation	
	S_3	S_4	S_6	S_{14}	Species B_1	
1538	0.20	1.00	0.03	0.27	$S_4 = 2^{-1/2}(\Delta r_2 - \Delta r'_2)$	$\nu_a(C...C)$
1380	1.00	0.17	0.01	0.19	$S_3 = 2^{-1/2}(\Delta r_1 - \Delta r'_1)$	$\nu_a(C...O)$
1212	0.16	0.04	0.13	1.00	$S_{14}= \Delta\delta_1 - \Delta\delta'_1$	$\delta(C\_\_H)$
941	0.07	0.05	1.00	0.05	$S_6 = 2^{-1/2}(\Delta r_3 - \Delta r'_3)$	$\nu_a(C\_\_R)$

The potential energy distribution of the normal modes of the acetyl acetonate anion was reinvestigated by Behnke and Nakamoto[112] for AcacPd(II)Cl$_2$K using deuterated compounds. The monomeric enolate structure of this anion prevents the difficulties due to possible interactions between ligands as in (Acac)$_2$Cu. The calculation also involves vibrations due to metal-Acac interactions ; only methyl groups were included as point mass. The results of this calculation for C$_3$O$_2^-$ skeleton stretching vibrations are shown in Table 1. The assignments of low frequency motions involving metal oxygen vibrations were further precised using ^{16}O/^{18}O substitution[110,113] or metallic atom substitution, ^{6}Li/^{7}Li,[111] ^{50}Cr/^{53}Cr,[114] ^{24}Mg/^{26}Mg[115] and Raman spectroscopy.[113,115]

C. Structure of carbanions in solutions

The structure of carbanion solutions is of extreme importance to the organic chemist. It is well known that carbanion reactivity is strongly dependent on concentration, nature of the solvent, presence of salts or additives like crown-ethers[116,117] and cryptates,[117] which are strong complexing agents of cations. For alkali or alkali earth metal ions, especially, vibrational spectroscopy has proved to be one of the most powerful techniques to visualize the distribution of species in solution. We shall summarize these possibilities referring to examples on simple salts or to reviews of other works relevant to electrolytes solutions in non-aqueous solvents.[118,119] In spite of the importance of the knowledge of the nature and the structure of carbanionic species in solutions in order to explain the orientation or the stereospecificity of their alkylation reaction, very few studies have been done in that field.

1. Ion-Ion interactions

(a) Detection by the internal vibrations of polyatomic anions

A large number of studies have been devoted to bulky anions of high symmetry (see 118 and references therein). For the hypothetical free anion some vibrations are degenerate, or only infrared or Raman active, and its interactions with solvent molecules or cations may lower the symmetry. The appearance of new bands due to the breaking of the degeneracy may then be used to detect such associations.[119]

With more basic carbon- containing anions or carbanions as shown through the $\Delta\nu$(AH) frequency shift of an hydrogen bonding solvent (Table 2), the ionic associations are often very large even in dissociating media. For instance with alkali cyanides we were able[120] to detect the formation of free anions, ion-pairs, triple cations and higher aggregates, even in a dissociating medium like

N,N-dimethylformamide. The vibrational modes of the free anion are usually observed using salts of a large cation like tetraalkylammonium[121,122] or tetraphenylarsonium,[120] which are dissociated in high dielectric constant solvents. The vibrations of free anions may also be identified through addition of strongly complexing agents like crown ethers or cryptates[117] of a specific cation. Addition of a large excess of a crown-ether may be needed to shift equilibrium (44) to the right.

$$M^+X^- \rightleftarrows M^+ + X^- \tag{42}$$

$$M^+ + Cr \rightleftarrows M^+Cr \tag{43}$$

$$M^+X^- + Cr \rightleftarrows M^+Cr + X^- \tag{44}$$

Free ions and ion pairs may also be identified through dilution effects. Concentration range as low as 10^{-4} M may be reached with data accumulation and the results may then be compared with those obtained from conductance or other techniques.[119,129]

TABLE 2

Basicities of some anions characterized through $\Delta\nu$ (XH) frequency shifts of proton donors

Proton donor	CCl_3CD	CH_3OH	$(CH_3)_3COH$	C_6H_5OH	Ref
ν (XH) free	2253 (b)	3644 (b) 3622 (b)	3620 (b)	3614 (b)	
Anions X$^-$					
NO_3^-	37 (a, b")	215 (a', b)			125, 126
SCN^-	48 (a",b')	296 (a", b)		494 (a",b)	128
I^-	67 (a",b)	255 (a", b) 238 (a", b')		360 (a',b")	123, 124
CF_3COO^-		285 (a", b)			122
Br^-	75 (a',b) 63 (a',b")	304 (a", b) 291 (a", b')		472 (a',b)	123, 124
F^-		349 (a", b) 338 (a", b')		564 (a', b)	123, 124
Cl^-	82 (a, b") 85 (a',b)	371 (a", b) 348 (a",b')		566 (a', b)	123 to 125
CN^-		410 (a",b')			120
$CH_3COCHCOOC_2H_5^-$			440 (a"',b"')		127

cation : $a = As\emptyset_4^+$, $a' = NBu_4^+$, $a'' = NHept_4^+$, $a''' = (K^+Cr222)$
solvent : $b = CCl4$, $b' = CH_2Cl_2$, $b'' = CHCl_3$, $b''' = THF$
$\Delta\nu$ (XH) $= \nu$ (XH)$_{free}$ $- \nu$ (XH)$_{complex}$, usually for 1:1 complexes with the aggregated salt of a tetraalkylammonium cation (a) in a low polarity medium (b). Numbers are given in cm^{-1} units.

Higher order ionic associations are more difficult to analyze. The formation of triple cation $M^+X^-M^+$ (Tc) or triple anion $X^-M^+X^-$ (Ta) may be studied through the common ion salt effect.[120,121,130,131]

$$M^+X^- + M^+ \rightleftharpoons M^+X^-M^+ \tag{45}$$

$$M^+X^- + X^- \rightleftharpoons X^-M^+X^- \tag{46}$$

For instance, very stable triple anions are often formed with bidentate salts of lithium such as trifluoroacetate,[143] or enolates of acetylacetoacetate.[145] These ions are usually formed by mixing a lithium salt solution with a solution of a dissociated salt of the same anion (NR_4^+ or K^+Cr222).

The formation of aggregates (A) such as dimers (D) of ion-pairs or tetrameric species according to equilibrium (47) may be shown through

$$nM^+X^- \rightleftharpoons (M^+X^-)_n \tag{47}$$

comparison of infrared and Raman spectra of such solutions. For these species involving several anions by entity, couplings between vibrational modes of different anions may indeed be observed as in the solid state.[132,133]

(b) Far infrared studies

Many studies have been done, mainly by Popov[134] or Edgell[135] and coworkers, in the far infrared region, where strong absorptions are observed. They were first assigned to "vibrations of the ion in a solvent cage" and were further shown to be due to ion-solvent ν ($M^{Z+}...S$) stretching vibrations ; the bending vibrations of the $M^{Z+}S_n$ structure absorb at lower frequencies with a smaller intensity.[136] The frequency of the maximum of this rather wide band depends on the nature of the solvent and is usually located around 400 cm^{-1} for Li^+, 200 cm^{-1} for NH_4^+, 180 cm^{-1} for Na^+, 150 cm^{-1} for K^+, 125 cm^{-1} for Rb^+ and 110 cm^{-1} for Cs^+. The frequency of this band has also been shown to be shifted to lower frequency when contact ion-pair are formed.[137] It was further shown through studying the ion-ion associations simultaneously in the mid-infrared and in the far-infrared regions, that this broad band must correspond to the enveloppe of the ion-ion

vibrations and of the ion-solvent vibrations which may be strongly coupled.[121]
It is then very difficult to use these absorptions to detect different types of
ionic associations (see Section V-C-2).

2. Solvation of ionic species

Solvation of ionic species may also be observed through vibrational spectrometry. It is usually difficult to distinguish the spectrum of the molecules
in the ion first solvation shell from that of the pure solvent for two reasons
the frequency shift of the vibrational modes of the ions or solvent molecules
bonded to ions are relatively small, and the number of molecules belonging to
the first solvation shell of ions is also small compared to the unperturbed
solvent molecules in binary salt-solvent mixtures unless the salt concentration
is rather high. These studies are better done in mixtures of two solvents where
preferential solvation takes place for the solvent of interest, the other solvent
acting as a diluent. The solvation of simple ions has been studied using either
salts of large cations such as tetraalkylamonium or cryptated potassium cation
K^+Cr222, and salts of large anions such as ClO_4^-, BPh_4^-, $Co(CO)_4^-$ which are usually dissociated. The solvation of ionic associated species has a very important influence on ionic association equilibria. It can be shown through ion-ion
vibration observation[124] or through the internal vibrations of ions, that the addition of a strongly solvating molecule breaks the ion-ion associations.[121,130,31]
Very few studies of this type are concerned with carbanionic species, except to
our knowledge that of the solvation of the acetylacetoacetate anion by t-butanol ;[127] examples for other salts will be found in monographs.[118,119]

D. Structure of the species

Through examination of the spectra, the problem of the existence of several
non-equivalent molecular entities in the unit-cell of the crystal or of the
existence of equilibria between different species in the liquid or in solution
may be solved. We shall now deal with spectra of defined entities and we shall
consider two steps : the determination of a basic structure and the refinement
of this structure. The structure of the molecular or ionic species is both the
starting and the end point of the spectral assignment. The assumed geometrical
structure is first used to calculate the number of the vibrational modes and to
derive the selection rules to be compared with the observed spectra. When a complete assignment of the spectra has been achieved, the geometrical structure is
used to calculate the G matrix elements and to calculate the force field of the
entity (see Section III.A), which gives information on the electronic structure
of the molecule and on the bond lengths and hybridization angles.

Several cases may be encountered. In the easiest one the compounds studied, or closely related ones, are crystalline solids for which X-ray structures are available. For isotopically different compounds an identical structure is generally assumed but this assumption must be checked ; a phase change for instance may occur through deuteration when strong hydrogen bonds are involved (lithium acid oxalate[138]) or through temperature change if the spectra are not recorded at the same temperature as the X-ray diagram (β-naphthol[139]). A closely related compound may, for instance, be the carbanion of a different metal whose structure is known. The planar C_{2v} structure of the acetylacetonate anion with a chelated C_3O_2M ring structure is found in a large number of compounds and is very often inferred for unknown compounds.[104,115] Nevertheless the close relation between the compounds must be checked through careful comparison of the spectra in order to distinguish them for instance from carbon metallated anions[140] as evidenced by the high frequency of the ν (C = O) vibration compared to those of the chelated compound. This structure of the carbanion has also been successfully extended to acetylacetonate enolates,[141] through observation of the characteristic vibration modes of the chelated cycle C_3O_2M.[31,142] These structural similitudes are no longer possible if different types of bonding take place between the metal and the carbanion as in σ-bonded,[143] π-bonded[144] and ionic allylic compounds.[145]

When there is no structure known of even parent compounds, a structure may often be proposed using the spectral characteristics of the starting molecules such as $C_6H_5SO_nCH_3$ for the study of carbanions α to sulfur,[146,147] or $(C_2H_5O)_2POCH_2X$ for the study of phosphonate carbanions.[148,149] For these compounds only some skeleton vibrations show strong perturbations when compared to the carbanion. A large number of the other vibrational modes are observed at frequencies very close of those of the starting molecule (see Section V, D and E). A simplified analysis of these strongly perturbed vibrational modes often supports the proposed structure.

The spectra of carbanionic species observed in solution may often be difficult to analyze when several vibrational modes of the carbanion are hidden by the solvent absorptions, even when using different kinds of solvents or deuterated solvents in order to increase the number of observable vibrational modes.[121,136,141] For these reasons, it is very important to obtain the spectrum of the pure solid compound or of the solid solvated compounds which may crystallize from the solution. The spectra of the pure solid are indeed often very close to those of the aggregated species in low polarity media.[147-149]

The structure of the species may be deduced in different ways, one of the most interesting being to compare through their spectra the structure of the species in the solid state and in solution. This procedure gives direct information on structure ; bond length and angle. The frequencies of internal vibrations of the ions are indeed most often strongly affected by small changes in these parameters as will be shown later on. In other cases, a thorough analysis of frequency shifts through a complete force field calculation or through simplified force field calculations may also provide important information on the values of bond length or angle variations, which may also be checked through intensity variations.

1. Comparison of structures in the solid state and in solution

This method is used either for strongly aggregated species which may compare well with the "polymeric structure" of pure solid compounds, or for solvated species which may be isolated through shifting equilibria ; equations (42) to (47) of this section. These shifts are most often obtained through addition of a strongly complexing agent of cations such as triethylenediamine,[150-152] quinuclidine,[153] crown-ethers[31] and cryptands.[142] An externally solvated ion-pair may then be crystallized from the solution and its X-ray structure analyzed. The spectra of the solid compound and of the isolated species in solution may then be compared. This procedure was first used by Stucky and coworkers[150] to establish the structure of the benzyllithium ion-pair through its near-UV spectrum. A much more accurate comparison may be made through vibrational spectroscopy as found possible for externally crown-solvated ion-pairs of K^+ and Na^+ salts of acetylacetate in low polarity media like THF or benzene.[31,141] The structure of Li^+ triple anion of acetylacetate enolate has recently been demonstrated through this method and is illustrated in Figure 7. In spite of the existence of four molecular entities in the unit cell, very small coupling may be observed between the different entities of $(E_2Li)^- K^+ Cr222$. As shown in Figure 7, part 2 and 3, only one band is observed for each stretching normal mode of the enolate ring C_3O_2M and the infrared and Raman frequencies are very close to each other. On the other hand, for the pure solid lithium enolate large differences are observed between infrared and Raman, the ν_s (C...O) mode being located at 1621 cm^{-1} in the infrared and at 1645 cm^{-1} in Raman. Furthermore, some infrared and Raman modes are split as for instance the stretching mode ν (C - O) of the C - O band α to the ester carbonyl group at 1176-1180 cm^{-1} (Figure 7, parts 4 and 5). These couplings may be indicative of a polymeric structure of ELi similar to that reported for LiAcac.[10] The spectrum of the 0.05 M solution of $(E_2Li)^- K^+ Cr222$ in CH_2Cl_2 is very similar to that of the pure solid

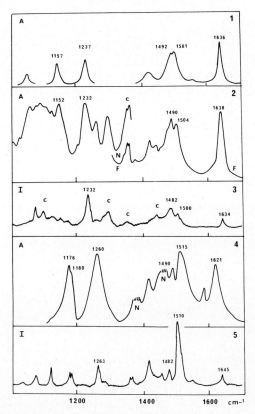

Fig. 7. Infrared and Raman spectra of $\left|(CH_3COCHCOOEt)_2Li\right|^- K^+Cr222$: 1 to 3 and of pure $CH_3COCHCOOEtLi$: 4 and 5.
1- Infrared spectra of a 0.05 M.CH_2Cl_2 solution after substraction of the spectra of a 0.05 M CH_2Cl_2 solution of Br^-K^+Cr222. Cell thickness 0.011 cm.
2-Infrared spectra of $(E_2Li)^-K^+Cr222$ in nujol N or fluorolube F mull.
3-Raman spectra of $(E_2Li)^-K^+Cr222$ powder. $\lambda_0 = 647.1$ nm of a krypton laser.
4-Infrared spectra of pure ELi in nujol N mull.
5-Raman spectra of ELi powder. $\lambda_0 = 647.1$ nm of a krypton laser. E = $(CH_3COCH\ COOEt)$ and C means an absorption or diffusion band of the cryptand 222.

compound as shown by the very close frequencies of the main vibrational modes[142] (Figure 7, parts 1 and 2). This very small sensitivity of the frequencies to the environmental change is well understood if it is considered that the Li^+ cation is fully insulated by the four oxygens of two enolate anions as in $(CF_3COO)_2Li)^{[-130]}$ where the inter- ion forces are very little affected by the surrounding solvent. This is no longer true when triple anions $(E_2Na)^- (K^+Cr222)$ are considered and a frequency shift of the vibrational modes is observed when comparing CD_2Cl_2 and THF solutions, the THF molecules being able to take part in the Na^+ solvation even when surrounded by four oxygens of two enolate anions.[141]

156

2. Use of force field calculations

As was summarized in Section III, significant force field may be derived using several isotopic species. Nevertheless, in most cases not all of the 1/2 n (n+1) force constants may be determined because of the lack of observed frequencies, and assumptions must be made to restrict the choice of a priori force constants. This choice may be guided by calculation of the more significant force constants using semi-empirical quantum chemical calculation methods,[154] or by comparison with the force field of related molecules for which the same basic assumptions have been made ; for instance interaction force constants are only taken into account when the considered vibrators have a common atom and may be transferred in a series of compounds.[155,156] The structure of the cis and trans conformers of t-butylformate were confirmed through a calculation of their vibrational mode frequencies,[157] from transferred force field.

Most of the time, simplified force field calculations are used and take into account either the evolution of the main force constants or their variations. The assumption of the separation of low and high frequency motions[54] is often used for the calculation of stretching frequencies. For instance, the k_{AB} force constant of an $(AB)_x$ group or molecule having x equivalent AB bonds may be obtained from the average ν (AB) frequency :[158,159]

$$k_{AB} = 4 \pi^2 \nu^2_{AB} \mu_{AB} \qquad \nu(AB)_{av} = \frac{1}{x} \left| \nu_s(AB_x) + (x-1) \nu_{as}(AB_x) \right|$$

where $\mu_{AB} = m_A m_B/(m_A + m_B)$ and ν_s and ν_{as} are the symmetric and antisymmetric vibrations modes of the AB_x group. This approximation is especially valuable for XH vibrations for which the bending force constant is much smaller than the stretching force constant.[160] With this approximation, and assuming that interaction force constant may be neglected, the 2α angle of an AB_2 molecule is given by the relation :

$$\nu_s/\nu_{as} = (1 + \cos^2\alpha)/(1 + \sin^2\alpha)$$

or by more elaborate expressions (ref. 71, p. 170).

The force constant may then be related to the bond length or bond-orders for which correlation curves have been established[160-163] through the known structures of a series of parent compounds. Very short bond length variation may be determined from correlations with frequencies, as for example : $\Delta\nu(OH)/\Delta r(OH) \simeq 11000$ cm^{-1}/Å,[164] $\Delta\nu(CH)/\Delta r(CH) \simeq 10800$ cm^{-1}/Å[165] or $\Delta\nu(C-O)/\Delta r(CO) \simeq 3300$ cm^{-1}/Å.[164] However, these relations may not be always linear.[162] Usually these approximations are only relevant for large frequency variations. For $\nu(CH)$

vibrations the $\nu(CH_x)$ frequencies may be perturbed by resonances with overtone of bending vibrations ; the CH vibrators of a CH_x group may have different CH bond lengths and then be nonequivalent.[165,166] These relations may be checked through comparison between $\nu_{av}(XH_3)$ and $\nu(XHD_2)$, for instance, which allows one to detect nonequivalent CH bonds.[167*]

For highly symmetric groups like XY_2 (C_{2v}), XY_3 (D_{3h}), XY_4 (T_d), XY_6 (O_h) perturbation calculations are often used to get information on the structure of the species found in solution (Section IV.C). Generally, the force field is first calculated for the "free species" which has the highest symmetry. One or two main force constants are then perturbed to correlate the frequency shifts and the splitting of the degenerate frequencies with the spectrum of the species.[104,169] This was applied to determine the structure of complexes formed by XH_2 or XH_3 groups through hydrogen bonding.[169] An XH_2 group or molecule may form 1:1 or 1:2 complexes through hydrogen bonding with basic solvents where only one XH force constant, or both, are perturbed. An XH_3 group or molecule may be perturbed either dissymetrically on only one XH bond, or symmetrically on its three XH bonds, as was shown for the ammonia molecule solvating an halogenide anion[170] or a methyl group solvating such an ion[171] in solution. This method has also been applied to the solvation and ionic associations of polyatomic anions such as XY_3^-, XY_4^-, and equations have been derived by Creighton for the frequency shifts of their vibrational modes.[172]

3. Use of intensity measurements

Although much information is contained in the intensity of infrared or Raman bands since they are directly related to the electronic charge motions during the associated vibrational quantum transition, they are not currently used to derive structural information.[173,174] Intensity measurements have usually been applied to well characterized vibration modes such as ν (C ≡ N) or ν (C = O) and it is known that the infrared intensity of the ν (C = O) stretching vibration band increases strongly when going from ketones to amides and may be related to other bond properties.[175] The covalent character of the magnesium dicyclopentadienyl has been demonstrated[176] by measuring the infrared intensity of the anti-symmetric ring metal stretching vibration which is approximatively seventy times smaller than that calculated from a point charge

---

* It is rather difficult to obtain an accurate force field for $\nu(XH_x)$ stretching frequencies due to the large amplitude of the proton motion which prevents using the harmonic approximation, see Section III. Calculating an accurate force field would require taking into account anharmonicity corrections which differ for $\nu(CH_x)$ and $\nu(CD_x)$ through vibration amplitudes.[168]

model. On the other hand the ionic character of the alkali metal ion bonding to solvent molecules has been inferred to be merely of the ion-dipole type from the strong infrared intensity of the ion-solvent vibration[121] and its very small Raman intensity.[177,178]

Using the bond moment approximation (see Section III.B) the infrared intensity may be used to measure bond angle variations. For a bent AB_2 molecule with C_{2v} symmetry, the bond moment of the molecule has no component along the z axis perpendicular to the plane of the molecule and we then have :

$$\left(\frac{\partial \mu}{\partial Q_s}\right) = \left| \left(\frac{\partial \mu x}{\partial Q_s}\right)^2 + \left(\frac{\partial \mu y}{\partial Q_s}\right)^2 \right|^{1/2}$$

If we use the high and low frequency motions separation for the AB_2 molecule, which is equivalent to writing $Q_1 \simeq S_1$ and $Q_3 \simeq S_3$ (S_1 and S_3 being given by equations (23)), it may be shown through application of equations derived in Section III that :

$$A_1/A_3 = (\partial \mu/\partial Q_1)^2/(\partial \mu/\partial Q_3)^2 = tg^2 (\theta/2)$$

where θ is the angle between the two AB bonds, A_1 and A_3 the integrated intensity of the symmetric and antisymmetric stretching mode. An angle of 145° has thus been determined between the two (C ≡ N) bonds of the dicyanamide ion $N(CN_2)^-$.[173] This relation has been also applied to the determination of the angle between carbonyl groups in dicarbonylated molecules and was checked on molecules of known structure.[179,180]

V. SPECTROSCOPIC STUDIES OF ORGANOALKALI OR ALKALINE-EARTH COMPOUNDS

A. Alkyl and alkenyl compounds

1. Alkyl compounds

(a) Spectra formed by organo alkalimetal compounds. Due to the strong reactivity of n-alkyl alkali compounds of sodium, potassium and ceasium for which there are no known inert solvents, there are very few studies on the structure of these organometallic compounds.[9] Very early, infrared spectroscopy had been used to study CH_3Li, C_2H_5Li.[36,73,181] After some misassignments of the ν (C-Li) vibrations, these vibrations were clearly observed through their isotopic shift $^6Li/^7Li$ and were located between 340 and 530 cm^{-1} for solid compounds.[182] The presence of impurities like EtOLi have also been detected through their IR spectra[183] and the spectra of the solutions have been shown to have very little dependence on the concentration of RLi and on the solvent nature (C_6H_{14}, C_6H_6, $(C_2H_5)_2O$, $(n-Bu)_2O$.[182,183] This is in agreement with the aggregation state of organolithium compounds in solution :[184]

$$(LiR)_2 \rightleftarrows (LiR)_4 \rightleftharpoons (LiR)_6$$

Unfortunately, there are very few detailed assignments of the spectra. Such a study has only been done for the MeLi monomer through isolation in an argon matrix.[39] Through use of isotopic substitutions H/D, $^6Li/^7Li$ and $^{13}C/^{12}C$ a valence field has been calculated as well as the potential energy distribution of normal modes, which correspond almost exactly to the C_{3v} symmetry group frequencies (see FIGURE 6).

The aggregation state most often met for organolithium species is the tetrameric one similar to that found in the solid state for MeLi, where each methyl group is interacting with three Li atoms forming one face of the Li tetrahedron. Large differences are observed for the methyl group frequencies in the tetrameric and in the monomeric species, mainly for the bending and rocking vibrations (Table 3). The lack of Raman data for MeLi makes it difficult to determine precisely the part due to the symmetry change of the methyl group (the three Li-C bonds are nonequivalent),[185] and that due to the increase of the repulsion between the hydrogens and Li atoms. This also makes difficult the comparison between Li-C bondings in monomeric and tetrameric species. It has indeed be shown for t-BuLi in benzene solutions that at least two infrared bands and one polarized Raman band have an $^6Li/^7Li$ isotopic shift.[32] The presence of this strong polarized Raman band at 563 cm^{-1} (^6Li) and 521 cm^{-1} (^7Li) makes a tetrameric arrangement (T_d symmetry) of the four units more probable than an eight-membered cyclic structure of C_{4v} symmetry for which this band should also be infrared active.

More recently a detailed vibrational study of $(t-C_4H_9Li)_4$ has been undertaken.[186] Raman frequencies and intensities in methylcyclohexane solution and infrared frequencies in Nujol mull have been obtained and assigned using H/D and $^6Li/^7Li$ isotopic shifts. A normal coordinate analysis neglecting hydrogen atoms has been performed which leads to a k(Li-C) force constant of 0.77 mdyne/Å, in agreement with the one obtained for CH_3Li monomer. The weak k(Li-Li) force constant of 0.27 mdyne/Å and the low bond polarizability derivative obtained for this bond from the set of values which gives reasonable bond polarizability derivatives for C-C stretching and C-C-C bending coordinates, suggest that Li-Li bonding is small in that tetrameric structure.

TABLE 3

Comparison of vibration frequencies of some metal bonded methyl group and metal-carbon force constant.

	$(CH_3)_2Mg$	$CH_3MgBr\ 2Et_2O$	CH_3Li	CH_3Li	CH_3K
Phys. State	N. Mull	Liquid	N. Mull	Ar Matrix	KBr Pellets
Structure	Polymer	Monomer	Polymer	Monomer	Monomer
Ref.	8	188	9	39	
ν_a or ν_d (CH_3)	2908		2840	2820	2810
ν'_s (CH_3)	2877				
ν_s (CH_3)	2827		2780	2780	2745
ν_m (CH_3) [a]	2871	2851	2810	2800	2777,5
δ_a (CH_3) [b]	1459	1419	1453.5	1387	
δ_o (CH_3) [b]	1198	1109	1078.5	1158	
r (CH_3)		518	446	410	
$k(M-C)$ [c]	1.05	1.40		0.78	
$l(M-C)$	2.24	2.15	2.31	(2.10)	
Ref.	187	188	34	39	

a ν_m is defined $\nu_m = (\nu_a + \nu'_s + \nu_s)\frac{1}{3}$ or $\nu_m = (2\nu_d + \nu_s)\frac{1}{3}$ along its local symmetry (see Fig. 6).

b The average of the observed frequencies has been used each time that several bands are observed due to intermolecular couplings.

c $k(M-C)$ is given in mdyne/$\mathring{A}$ and $l(M-C)$ in $\mathring{A}$.

(b) Species formed by organomagnesium compounds

(i) In the solid state

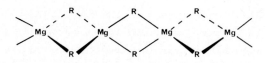

Fig. 8. Schematic structure of R_2Mg compounds.

Both $(CH_3)_2Mg$[187] and $(C_2H_5)_2Mg$[189] have been extensively studied by vibrational spectrometry ; they form infinite chains in which the neighbouring rings are almost orthogonal (Fig. 8).[8] The normal modes analysis gives more support to a C_{2h} factor group than to the D_{2h} factor group proposed for $(CH_3)_2Mg$ by X-ray analysis.[8] For ethylmagnesium the vibrational spectroscopic results agree with a C_{4h} factor group for the chain. The spectra at liquid nitrogen temperature show a noticeable structure change, which is interpreted by a conformational change of the chains. In these compounds, Mg atoms are almost tetrahedrally surrounded by four alkyl groups, each bridging two magnesium atoms.

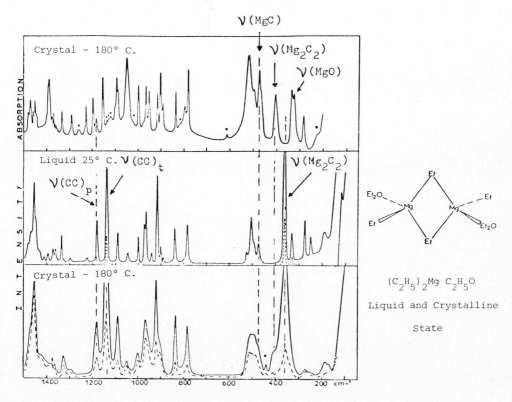

Fig. 9. Infrared and Raman spectra of solid and liquid $(C_2H_5)_2Mg \cdot 2(C_2H_5)_2O$ showing its dimeric structure.

From the ethyl ether solution of $(C_2H_5)_2Mg$ a monosolvated compound has been crystallized, $(C_2H_5)_2Mg \cdot (C_2H_5)_2O$.[190] The structure of this compound is shown to be that of a dimer through the observation of both the infrared and Raman spectra where Mg-C vibrations characteristic of terminal ethyl group (t) and bridged ethyl groups (p) have been located, respectively : ν (Mg-C) at 473 cm^{-1} and

and $\nu_a(Mg_2C_2)$ at 403 cm^{-1} in infrared, and $\nu_s(Mg_2C_2)$ at 333 cm^{-1} in Raman. The $\nu(MgO)$ vibrational mode due to coordinated ether-ligand was observed at 323 cm^{-1}. The $\nu(C-C)$ internal vibrations of these two types of ethyl groups are also distinguished at 1180 cm^{-1} $\nu(C-C)_p$ and 1140 cm^{-1} $\nu(C-C)_t$ in the Raman spectra (Fig. 9).

TABLE 4

Influence of ether solvation on metal-ligand bond properties in organomagnesium compounds[a]

	Mg-C	Mg-Br	Mg-O	Ref.
MgBr$_2$ (gas)		1.48		196
		2.34		198
MgO (gas)			2.34	71
			1.749	71
MgEt$_2$	399			199
	1.05			199
	2.26			197
MgBr$_2$.2 Et$_2$O		184.5	3.03	200
		0.48	0.57	200
		3.06	2.13	201
EtMgBr.2 Et$_2$O	485	250	308	
	1.40	0.85	0.6	
	2.15	2.48	2.04	193
MgEt$_2$.2 Et$_2$O	473		323	190
	403(ν_a)			
	333(ν_s)			

a In each column the numbers mean : average $\nu(Mg-X)$ stretching frequency in cm^{-1}, k (Mg-X) in mdyne/Å and r (Mg-X) in Å.

In order to interpret the structure of organomagnesium ether solutions, mixed type compounds RMgX.n(C$_2$H$_5$)$_2$O were studied with n = 1 or 2, R = Me[189] or Et[189,191] and X = Cl[189] or Br, I.[191,192] The X-ray studies[193] of the solid compound C$_2$H$_5$MgBr. 2(C$_2$H$_5$)$_2$O shows the existence of monomeric units having a quasi tetrahedral arrangment of ligands (C$_2$H$_5$, Br, (C$_2$H$_5$)$_2$O) around the central magnesium atom. A detailed assignment of the normal vibrational modes of this monomeric unit was done through the examination of IR and Raman spectra of five isotopic species : C$_2$H$_5$MgBr.2 Et$_2$O, C$_2$H$_5$MgBr.2 Et$_2$O-d$_{10}$, CH$_3$CD$_2$MgBr.2 Et$_2$O CD$_3$CH$_2$MgBr.2 Et$_2$O and C$_2$D$_5$MgBr.2 Et$_2$O, and of C$_2$H$_5$MgI.2 Et$_2$O. Much care has been given to the assignment of metal ligand vibrations of this monomeric unit, (TABLE 4). Examination of metal ligand vibrations of CH$_3$MgX.2 Et$_2$O with X = Br, I[188] leads to the assignment of a similar monomeric structure to these compounds.

For these RMgX.2 Et$_2$O crystallized compounds, a comparison (TABLE 3) of r (CH$_2$) and δ(CH$_3$) vibrations of Et and Me ligands with those of the same groups in the symmetric polymeric compound R$_2$Mg shows a large frequency perturbation of these bending vibrations of the CH$_n$ groups bonded to the metal atom, as for the Li compounds. This frequency shift is probably due to a decrease in repulsive forces between the electrons of CH bonds and the valence electrons of metal atoms but may also be related to the strengthening of the M-C bond (TABLES 3 and 4).

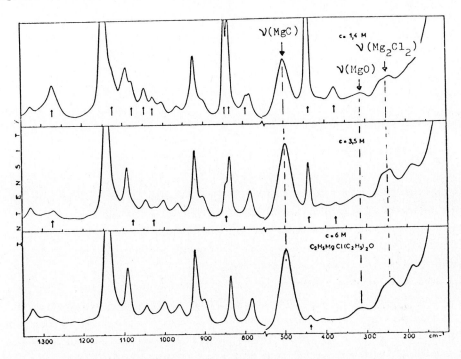

Fig. 10. Raman spectra of C$_2$H$_5$MgCl solutions in (C$_2$H$_5$)$_2$O. Arrows indicate solvent ether diffusion bands.

(ii) Liquid state and ether solutions

The spectra of the RMgX.2 Et$_2$O compounds (R = Me or Et and X = Br or I)[191,192] in the solid or liquid state and in solution are very similar. The spectra of solutions of EtMgBr.2 Et$_2$O between 1 and 4 molar may be interpreted as an overlapping of C$_2$H$_5$MgBr.2 Et$_2$O and pure ether spectra (FIGURE 10). The observation of ν(MgBr), ν(MgC) and ν$_s$ (MgO$_2$) scattering lines shows that the species formed in these solutions are monomeric units with a tetrahedral surrounding of Mg atoms by ligands (Br, C$_2$H$_5$ and 2 Et$_2$O). Bands due to Et$_2$Mg or MgBr$_2$ such as ν$_s$(MgC$_2$) or ν$_s$(MgBr$_2$)are barely visible and are consequently present to less than

3 %, if any. Schlenk's equilibrium is thus shifted strongly toward mixed species.

The infrared and Raman spectra of C_2H_5MgCl solutions in Et_2O differ noticeably from those of C_2H_5MgBr and a liquid monoetherate $C_2H_5MgCl.(C_2H_5)_2O$ has been isolated from these solutions.[189] The observation of four MgCl bands, two of which are infrared active and two Raman active, and $\nu(MgC)$ and $\nu(MgO)$ bands at frequencies close to those observed for $EtMgBr.2\ Et_2O$, suggests a cyclic dimer model with C_{2h} symmetry for this mono etherate (FIGURE 11).

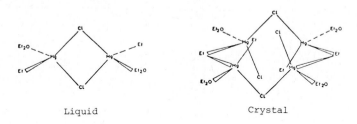

Liquid   Crystal

Fig. 11.   Structure of $CH_3\ MgCl(C_2H_5)_2O$ in liquid and crystalline forms

The spectra of 1 to 6 M solutions show the overlapping of the spectra of this species and of pure solvent ether, which confirms that Schlenk's equilibrium is strongly shifted toward mixed species. The spectra of the species crystallizing from these solutions are far more complicated and both involve chlorine and ethyl bridging groups between Mg atoms.

The Raman spectra of diethylmagnesium in diethylether solutions at different concentrations and at different temperatures have also been investigated.[194] By examination of the intensity changes of the bands corresponding to pure solvent and of characteristic metal ligand vibrations modes an equilibrium between a monomer unit and a dimer unit has been found (FIGURE 12) :

$$\left| (C_2H_5)_2Mg.(C_2H_5)_2O \right|_2 + 2\ (C_2H_5)_2O \ \rightleftarrows \ 2\ (C_2H_5)_2Mg.\ 2\ (C_2H_5)_2O$$

A thermodynamic study of this equilibrium has been performed[194] and the structure of the monomer and dimer units have been deduced through examination of the crystallized monomer and dimer spectra.[190]

These studies have also been extended to some other organomagnesium compounds dissolved in ethyl ether, isopropyl ether or THF.[195]

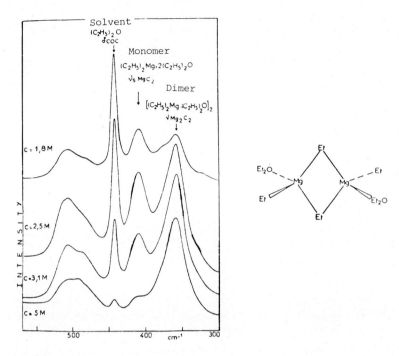

Fig. 12. Raman spectra of $(C_2H_5)_2Mg$ solutions in $(C_2H_5)_2O$ at 25°C.

2. Allyl compounds

(a) Solid state

Allyl compounds are known to form different kinds of compounds in which the metal atom may be bonded in three different ways to the allyl group : σ, π or ionic. Starting with a precise assignment of the IR and Raman spectra of allyl chloride and bromide followed by a force field calculation or normal vibrations modes,[202] Sourrisseau and coworkers have investigated these different types of bonding through vibrational study of σ bonded allyl mercury compounds,[143] π bonded palladium and nickel complexes[144] and ionic allyl magnesium, lithium and sodium compounds.[2] The IR and Raman spectra of solid compounds which have been carefully assigned show very different spectral features.

In TABLE 5 and FIGURE 13, we have summarized some characteristic spectra and assignments of some important vibrational modes. While σ allyl mercury has vibrational modes rather close to those of the other substituted allyl compounds with bands assigned to ν(C-C) and ν(C=C), this distribution is no longer valid for π allyl complexes $(C_3H_5PdCl)_2$, where the bands at 1383 and 1023 cm^{-1} are

TABLE 5

Skeletal and CH stretching vibrations frequencies of some allylmetal compounds

Compound	$\nu(C = C)$	$\nu(C - C)$	$\delta(CCC)$	$\nu(CH)_m^a$	Ref
C_3H_5Cl	1642	938	409	3009	202
$\sigma\text{-}C_3H_5HgCl$	1627	936	385	3000	143
	$\nu_a(C\text{-}C\text{-}C)$	$\nu_s(CCC)$	$\delta(CCC)$		
$(\pi\ C_3H_5PdCl)_2$	1383	1023	511	3049	144
C_3H_5Na	1527	1022	608	2987	2

^{a} $\nu(CH)_m$ average frequency of the five $\nu(CH)$ fundamentals

assigned to the ν_a (CCC) antisymmetrical and ν_s (CCC) symmetrical stretching
vibrations of the planar C_s allyl group, in agreement with the X-ray structure. [83]
In this structure, the C...C bond lengths are found very close to each other
and intermediate between a single and a double bond. For allylmagnesium compounds C_3H_5MgCl $(C_3H_5)_2Mg$ as well as for alkalimetal allyl compounds[2], the
strong IR band observed around 1530 cm^{-1} is assigned to ν_a (CCC), in agreement
with previous studies,[203-206] while the ν_s (CCC) mode is assigned to the
strong Raman band around 1000 cm^{-1}. The δ (CCC) mode is observed in IR and Raman
around 600 cm^{-1}. From these three skeletal vibration frequencies a k(C...C)
force constant of 6.6 mdyne/Å and a CCC angle of 140° are calculated (see Section IV-D) which confirms the strong ionic delocalization in this anion,

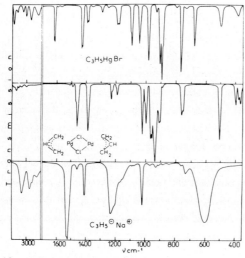

Fig. 13. Infrared spectra of (a) C_3H_5HgBr, (b) $(C_3H_5PdCl)_2$, (c) C_3H_5Na compounds
in the solid state.[208]

in excellent agreement with the calculated SCF value of 133°,[207] and reflects the repulsion between the non-bonded negative centers of this anion. A detailed spectroscopic study has also be done for the ionic potassium salt of 2-methyl-allyl[33] for which a force field calculation shows results in excellent agreement with those obtained for the other alkali metal allyl compounds (FIGURE 14).

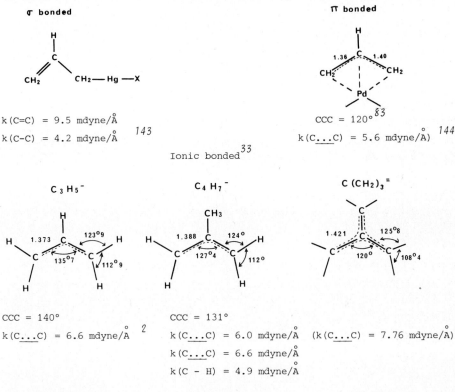

σ bonded

k(C=C) = 9.5 mdyne/Å
k(C-C) = 4.2 mdyne/Å [143]

π bonded

CCC = 120°[83]
k(C...C) = 5.6 mdyne/Å) [144]

Ionic bonded[33]

$C_3H_5^-$

CCC = 140°
k(C...C) = 6.6 mdyne/Å [2]

$C_4H_7^-$

CCC = 131°
k(C...C) = 6.0 mdyne/Å
k(C...C) = 6.6 mdyne/Å
k(C - H) = 4.9 mdyne/Å

$C(CH_2)_3^=$

(k(C...C) = 7.76 mdyne/Å)

Fig. 14. Comparison of σ, π and ionic bonded structure of organoallyl compounds deduced from X-ray[83] or MINDO/3 calculations[33] with spectroscopic data. Values bracketed are obtained through XY, XY_2 or XY_3 approximations.

The trimethylenemethane potassium salt has also been investigated,[33] and assuming an XY_3 planar skeleton for this anion, a k(C...C) = 7.76 mdyne/Å force constant is obtained. All these structural results are in excellent agreement with the calculated geometry of these anions using the MINDO/3 method (FIGURE 14). The large intensity increase of the δ(CH_2) vibration is also in agreement with the strong negative charge calculated on the terminal carbons, while the ν(CH)$_m$ frequency decrease (TABLE 5) may be related to the repulsion between negative charges on hydrogen and on these carbons atoms.

(b) Solutions

Solutions of allyllithium and allylmagnesium chloride in THF or ethyl ether between 0.3 and 3 M have been investigated by infrared spectroscopy. They had previously been examined only between 1600 and 1500 cm^{-1} where the strong ν_a(CCC) band is observed.[205,209] The main absorptions of the allyl anion ν_a(CCC), ν_s(CCC), δ(CCC) and ν(M-C), are observed in solution at frequencies very close to those observed for the solid state, but the existence of two bands in THF and possibly three bands in $(C_2H_5)_2O$ for the δ(CCC) mode show the probable existence of several anionic entities in the solution.

The Grignard reagent C_3H_5MgCl is very soluble in THF (3 M) but only slightly soluble in Et_2O (0.3 M). The allyl anion bands are also observed at frequencies close to those of the solid compound, the ν_a(CCC) and δ(CCC) vibration frequencies are increased due to Mg solvation, but the anion structure remains close to that of a $C_3H_5^-$ anion.

TABLE 6

Comparison of metal carbon and CH stretching force constants of alkyl and aryl organometallic compounds

Ref.	k(M-C)	K(C-H)	Ref.	k(M-C)[a]		k(M-C)[a]
208 $Hg(CH_3)_2$	2.45	4.63	143 $Hg(C_3H_5)_2$	2.6	$Hg(C_5H_5)_2$	1.70
210 $BrHgCH_3$	2.60	4.93	143 $BrHg(C_3H_5)$	2.62		
			144 $(C_3H_5PdCl)_2$	2.8		
187 $Mg(CH_3)_2$	1.05	4.56	2 $Mg(C_3H_5)_2$	0.8	$Mg(C_5H_5)_2$	1.3
188 $BrMgCH_3 \cdot 2Et_2O$	1.40					
39 $Li(CH_3)$	0.78	4.32	2 $Li(C_3H_5)$	0.45	$Li(C_5H_5)_2$	1.1
			2 $Na(C_3H_5)$	0.30	$Na(C_5H_5)_2$	1

[a] Calculated with the approximation of a XY or XY_2 model

3. Cyclopentadienyl compounds

Cyclopentadiene may also form σ, π and ionic organometallic compounds, as has been reviewed by Fritz.[1,211] Few detailed studies have been performed for cyclopentadienyl ionic compounds in solutions. The observation of only four strongly infrared active normal vibration modes as expected for the planar D_{5h} cyclopentadienyl anion has been considered characteristic of ionic bonding in solution ; this observation was made for K, Rb, Cs, Ca, Sr, Ba cyclopentadienyl compounds and, surprisingly, for Cp_2Mn. More than four infrared active vibrations are expected for σ and π bonded cyclopentadienyl compounds. They have either C_{5v}

symmetry (one sided compounds) or the D_{5h} and D_{5d} symmetry for sandwich compounds like ruthenocene and ferrocene, depending on whether the molecules are staggered or eclipsed or not. Li, Na and Mg cyclopentadienyl compounds seem to behave like the σ bonded compounds with C_{5v} symmetry. More recent studies on alkaline-earth cyclopentadienyl compounds show that the calcium salt has some covalent character in the solid state, while it is essentially ionic in solution.[212,213] Cyclopentadienylmagnesium is supposed to form triplet ions in THF solution, while C_5H_5MgCl probably forms ion pairs.[214]

4. Metal carbon bonds and structure of alkyl carbanions

In order to distinguish between organometallic and carbanionic compounds, we shall compare the behaviour of alkyl and allylic organometallic compounds. For the alkyl compounds, it may be seen from TABLE 5 and 7 that the metal- carbon force constant decreases with electronegativity of the metal atom : Hg 1.44, Mg 1.14 and Li 0.97. It is known that the $\delta_s(CH_3)$ symmetric bending vibration of an XCH_3 molecule with X atoms of a given row of the Periodic Table is a linear function of the electronegativity[39,215] of the X atom. Andrews[39] has shown that in spite of a small deviation from linearity, this curve may be extrapolated to $\delta_s(CH_3) = 970$ cm^{-1} when the electronegativity becomes 0. This frequency must represent that of a CH_3^- anion and was noticed to be very close to that of its isoelectronic NH_3 molecule for which the $\delta_s(CH_3)$ frequency is observed at 950 cm^{-1}. The $\delta_s(CH_3)$ frequency observed for CH_3Li at 1158 cm^{-1} (TABLE 3) fits this correlation but is considerably higher than that observed at 1061 and 1096 cm^{-1} for the solid MeLi which is tetrameric.

For organomagnesium compounds $\delta_s(CH_3)$ is observed at 1198 cm^{-1} for solid $(CH_3)_2Mg$ which is polymeric (TABLE 3). The $\delta_s(CH_3) = f$ (electronegativity) correlation curve gives an estimated value of 1160 cm^{-1} for the $(CH_3)_2Mg$ monomer.[216] The frequency decrease observed from polymeric to monomeric units is in the reverse sense of that observed for CH_3Li ; for this latter molecule the frequency increase of δ_sCH_3 when going from polymeric (tetramer units) to monomeric CH_3Li is probably due both to the decrease of electronic repulsions between CH and metal atoms electrons and to the shortening of the metal-carbon bond in the monomer. The frequency decrease observed for $Mg(CH_3)_2$ may be related to the metal-carbon distance shortening when going from bridged to terminal methyl groups like that observed in $Al_2(CH_3)_6$[217] where the Al-C distance varies from 2.13 to 1.96 Å for bridged and terminal methyl groups, respectively, the C-Al distance becoming closer to the sum of covalent radii of atoms 1.95 Å for the terminal methyl group. This trend is also observed when comparing solid $Mg(CH_3)_2$, where only bridged methyl groups are found, and monomeric solvated species like

170

$CH_3MgBr.2Et_2O$. In this latter species, the strong frequency decrease may be
due to both the shortening of the Mg-C bond (TABLE 3), which makes the Mg-C
distance closer to the sum of covalent radii 2.07 Å, and also to the solvation
of the Mg atom, which makes the $\delta_s(CH_3)$ frequency becoming closer to the hypothetical $\delta(CH_3^-) = 970$ cm^{-1} frequency. The $\delta_s(CH_3)$ frequency may thus reflect
several factors. The decrease of the k(M-C) force constant when the metal atom
becomes more electropositive may also be correlated with the decrease of the
k(C-H) stretching force constant (TABLE 6), which makes the hydrogen of the methyl group of organometallic compounds more acidic.

For allylic compounds (TABLE 6), while the metal carbon force constant is
close to that observed for solvated alkyl compounds where the metal atom is
less electropositive like Hg, the force constant becomes very different from
that observed for saturated alkyl compounds when the electronegativity of the
metal atom becomes closer to 1. For instance, for C_3H_5Li the k(Li-C) force
constant is approximatively half that of monomeric CH_3Li and becomes even smaller than that observed for $\nu(Li^+..S)$ ion-solvent vibrations : the calculated
k(M^+-DMSO) force constant for a single X-Y model being 0.69 mdyne/Å for Li$^+$
and 0.42 mdyne/Å for Na$^+$.[218] This low metal carbon force constant is indicative of the strongly ionic character of the alkali metal allyl compounds, the
anion charge being stabilized through delocalization. This large difference in
behaviour between alkyllithium compounds and allyllithium is also consistent
with the large intensity of the ν(M-C) band in infrared, while the band is hardly seen in Raman[2] for allyllithium. The ν(C-Li) band has easily been observed
in Raman for t-BuLi solutions in benzene,[32] showing a covalent character for the
metal- carbon bond in these compounds.

B. Nitro and nitrile organometallic compounds

1. Nitro compounds

Due to the strong acidity of the nitromethane hydrogens, this compound is
known to form salts in the presence of alkali bases. The earliest studies of
the sodium salt by infrared spectroscopy[219-221] had suggested a planar structure with delocalization of the six π electrons of this anion (FIGURE 15).

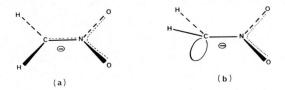

(a)   (b)

Fig. 15. Possible structures for sodium nitromethane anion

Mathieu and Massignon[219] had first noticed the disappearance in the Raman spectra of sodium methanenitronate and propanenitronate of the assymetric and symmetric stretching vibrations of nitromethane and nitropropane at 1560 and 1360 cm^{-1}. Jonathan,[24] and Feuer and coworkers,[221] observed that the infrared spectra of sodium alkanenitronates had four characteristic bands in the regions 1605-1587 cm^{-1}, 1316-1225 cm^{-1}, 1175-1140 cm^{-1} and 734-700 cm^{-1}. By analogy with the ν(C=N) vibration of alkylimines and oximes, which usually appear between 1680 and 1620 cm^{-1},[221] they assigned the higher frequency band to ν(C=N) and the three others to ν_a(NO$_2$), ν_s(NO$_2$) and δ(NO$_2$) respectively. The structure shown in FIGURE 15(a) was thus proposed. Considering the overall spectra of sodium nitromethane, Yardwood and Orville-Thomas,[222] by taking into account the low frequency of the ν_a(CH$_2$) and ν_s(CH$_2$) which appear at 2923 and 2851 cm^{-1}, have favoured the structure shown in FIGURE 15(b), where the CH$_2$ carbon has hybridization close to sp^3. The higher frequency band is then assigned to ν_a(NO$_2$), this frequency being close to that in nitromethane and the three others to ν_s(NO$_2$), ν(C-N) and δ(NO$_2$) respectively. It was impossible to observe the Raman spectra of sodium nitromethane in aqueous solution, since in this solvent it becomes transformed into sodium methazonate :[223]

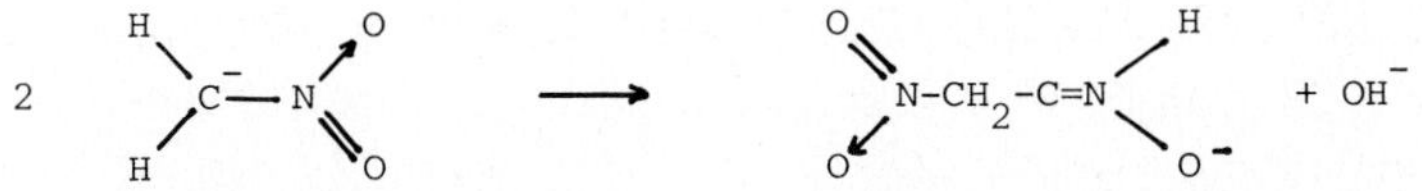

By comparison with the Raman spectra of aqueous solutions of sodium 2-nitropropane,[220] Brooks and Jonathan[224] observed that the band at 1616 cm^{-1} is strong and polarized in Raman. This confirms the assignment of this band to an A$_1$ mode of the C$_{2v}$ symmetry anion like ν(C=N) and disagrees with its assignment to ν_a(NO$_2$), see TABLE 7. These authors have also modified some other assignments through comparison with CD$_2$NO$_2^-$Na$^+$. It is interesting to note that in this strongly delocalized anion the mean ν(CH) frequency observed at 2887 cm^{-1} is lower than that observed for ν(CH)$_m$ of allylsodium, indicating probably a large delocalization of charge on to the hydrogen atom of this anion.

The potassium dinitromethane salt has also been examined through Raman spectroscopy but no detailed assignment is given[225] and structural conclusions are less obvious.

TABLE 7

Different assignments of vibrational modes proposed for the main absorptions of nitronate anion and parent molecules

$CH_2NO_2^-Na^+$	$CD_2NO_2^-Na^+$	220	221	222	224
2920	2308	ν_a (CH$_2$)		ν_a (CH$_2$)	ν_a (CH$_2$) or CD$_2$
2847	2124	ν_s (CH$_2$)		ν_s (CH$_2$)	ν_s (CH$_2$) or CD$_2$
1582	1553	ν (C=N)	ν(C=N)	ν_a (NO$_2$)	ν (C=N)
1437	1205	δ (CH$_2$)		δ (CH$_2$)	δ (CH$_2$) or CD$_2$
1272 1261	1233 1217	ν_a (NO$_2$)	ν_a (NO$_2$)	ν_s (NO$_2$)	ν_a (NO$_2$)
1185 1032 1018	 884 876	r (CH$_2$) ν_s (NO$_2$)	νs (NO$_2$)	w (CH$_2$) ν (C-N)	(comb) r (CH$_2$)
983	899	w (CH$_2$)		t (CH$_2$)	ν_s (NO$_2$)
736	728	w (NO$_2$)	δ (NO$_2$)	w (NO$_2$)	w (NO$_2$)
691 679	547 536	δ (NO$_2$)		δ (NO$_2$)	w (CH$_2$)
649	640				δ (NO$_2$)
538	511	r (NO$_2$)		r (NO$_2$)	r (NO$_2$)

2. Nitriles

(a) Alkyl nitriles

Sodium acetonitrile salt and related compounds have been postulated to exist as intermediates in various reactions of nitriles containing α-hydrogen atoms, but they are difficult to characterize.[226-228] The infrared study of the evolution with time of metallated acetonitrile in DMSO (FIGURE 16) led[229] to characterizing the formation of diacetonitrile (FIGURE 17.b) through dimerization of the carbanion.

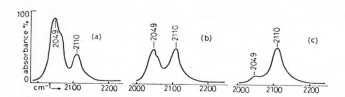

Fig. 16. Infrared spectra of acetonitrile metalated by dimsylsodium in DMSO taken at 5 min intervals. (After Jucnovski and Binev[229])

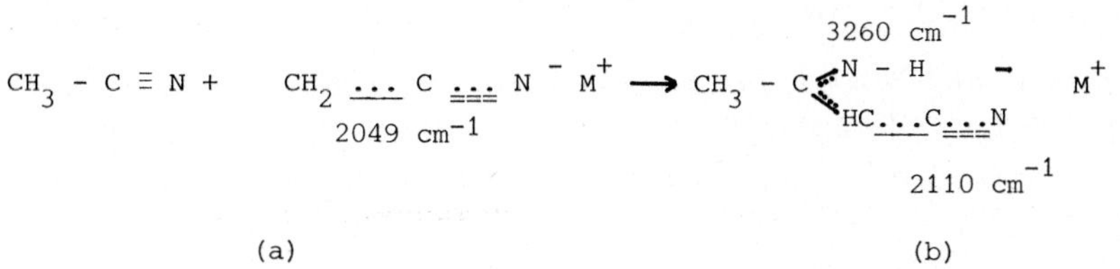

$$CH_3 - C \equiv N + \quad CH_2 \overset{...}{} C \overset{...}{} N^- M^+ \longrightarrow CH_3 - C \overset{\overset{3260\ cm^{-1}}{N-H}}{\underset{HC...C\underset{===}{...}N}{}} - M^+$$

$$2049\ cm^{-1} \qquad\qquad\qquad 2110\ cm^{-1}$$

(a) (b)

Fig. 17. Dimerization reaction of acetonitrile carbanion.

The addition of a proton donor transforms the diacetonitrile anion into enaminonitrile.[230] The bands between 2049 and 2075 cm^{-1} are assigned to the ν (C≡N) vibrations of the metal nitrile ion-pair and the bands above 2100 cm^{-1} to the dinitrile anion or, after protonation, to the starting nitrile and the enaminonitrile. The ν (C...N) frequency of the metallated acetonitrile ion-pair is very close to that observed for alkali cyanide ion-pairs[120] which were located at 2060 and 2070 cm^{-1} respectively for Na^+ and Li^+ salts in DMF solution. The diacetonitrile carbanion has been characterized by the ν (C...N) and ν (NH) bands at 2110 and 3260 cm^{-1}. Although the deuterated and ^{15}N substituted species of acetonitrile were available,[231] only the ν (C...N) vibration of the acetonitrile anion has been examined in different solvents like HMPT or THF, allowing assignment of the absorption of the "free anion" at 2050 cm^{-1}. This frequency is very close to that of the "free cyanide anion" observed at 2054 cm^{-1}.[120] It is not possible to confirm the anion delocalization because a study of the ν (C-C) region is lacking ; nevertheless a CNDO/2 calculation shows the k (C-C) force constant to increase from 6.18 mdyne/Å for CH_3CN to 6.64 mdyne/Å, while k (C ≡ N) decreases from 18.87 mdyne/Å to 15.19 mdyne/Å.[232] The large intensity increase of the ν (C≡N) vibration in the carbanion seems in agreement with ionic bonding in the ion-pair.

The tricyanomethanide ion has also been studied through vibrational spectroscopy,[233-235] but although its planar D_{3h} structure is known through X-ray structure,[237] its force field calculation is made difficult due to the scarcity of observed frequencies. Three sets of force constants which fit the observed frequencies have been determined.[234] Some electron delocalization must nevertheless take place in this anion due to the short C-C bond length found between 1.145 and 1.164 Å.

(b) Aryl nitriles

The phenylacetonitrile carbanions are more stable than those of acetonitrile and their ν (C ≡ N) vibration has been characterized for the lithium[195,229]

and sodium salts.[238] They are located at slightly higher frequencies than in
alkyl compounds ; $C_6H_5CHCNLi$ 2089-2070 cm^{-1} and CH_2CNLi 2062-2051 cm^{-1} in THF
solution. The ν (C...N) integrated intensity is also strongly increased
$(A(C...N) \simeq 10^5$ L.mol.$^{-1}$ $cm^{-2})$ by a magnitude of one or two orders of magnitude
when compared to the A (C ≡ N) of the starting molecule. This ν (C...N) frequency depends strongly on the nature and position of the substituent in substituted
phenylacetonitrile. The best linear correlation is found with the Hammett σ^{-236}
constant, while for the starting molecule the best correlation is found with
the Hammett σ^+.[232] The ratio of the slopes of these two correlation lines,
ν (C...N) = f (σ), which is equal to 3.2, has been called a "transmission coefficient". This larger influence of the substituent on the ν (C...N) frequency in
the carbanion reflects the more important delocalization. Similar observations
have been made for carbanions of polyphenylacetonitrile where the ν(C...N) frequency has been correlated with the bond order of the C ≡ N group.[239] More recently these studies were extended[240] to mono-and dimetallated derivatives of
aryldiacetonitrile compounds. In the mono-metallated derivatives, there is a
small frequency change of the non-metallated nitrile group compared to the starting molecule : 2246 to 2239 cm^{-1} for phenyldiacetonitrile, while the change is
from 2096 to 2047 cm^{-1} when comparing the metallated ν (C...N) frequency of the
mono-and dimetallated derivatives. This is in accord with a larger delocalization for the -C...N⁻ group than for the - C ≡ N group.

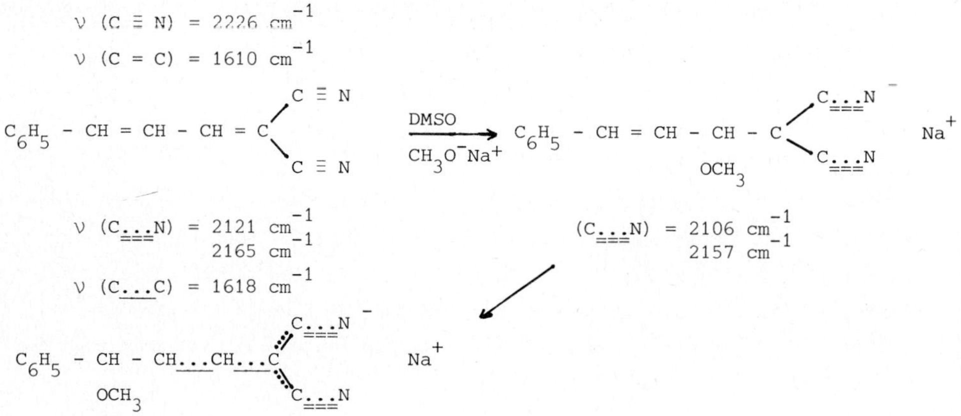

ν (C ≡ N) = 2226 cm^{-1}
ν (C = C) = 1610 cm^{-1}

$$C_6H_5 - CH = CH - CH = C \begin{array}{c} C \equiv N \\ \\ C \equiv N \end{array} \xrightarrow[CH_3O^- Na^+]{DMSO} C_6H_5 - CH = CH - CH - C \begin{array}{c} C...N \\ \\ OCH_3 \quad C...N \end{array} Na^+$$

ν (C...N) = 2121 cm^{-1} (C...N) = 2106 cm^{-1}
                 2165 cm^{-1} 2157 cm^{-1}
ν (C...C) = 1618 cm^{-1}

$$C_6H_5 - CH - CH...CH...C \begin{array}{c} C...N \\ \\ C...N \end{array} Na^+$$
$$OCH_3$$

Fig. 18. Metallation reaction of 1,1 -dicyano-4-phenylbutadiene followed by
isomerization.

The infrared study of the evolution with time of the metallation reaction of cyano-polyenes has also shown that the metallation reaction takes place at the β carbon atom (FIGURE 18).[241] The 1,2 carbanionic adduct formed further isomerizes into the more stable 1,4 adduct for butadiene derivatives, or into the 1,6 adduct for the substituted hexatrienes (FIGURE 18).

C. Enolates carbanions

1. Simple enolates

Very few vibrational spectroscopy studies have been devoted to the metal enolates of monocarbonylated compounds such as aldehydes and ketones. Zook et al. have shown that the $\nu(C=O)$ stretching frequency of pinacolone at 1710 cm^{-1} is replaced by a band at 1575 cm^{-1} in its sodium salt.[242] House and Trost[243] have observed a different behaviour of mercury and alkali enolates : α-chloro-mercury acetone shows a $\nu(C=O)$ band at 1650 cm^{-1}, while the lithio and sodio phenylacetone in DME solution show strong absorptions at 1565-1585 cm^{-1} and 1550-1575 cm^{-1} respectively. This seems to indicate that mercury is bonded to the α carbon atom, as confirmed by NMR, while bonding with alkali metals takes place at the oxygen site.

Maroni and coworkers have tried to distinguish between O-metallated, C-metallated and mesomeric carbanide-enolate anion structures of magnesium derivatives of ketones[244] and of Li, K, Zn, Mg and Hg derivatives of 2,2 dimethyl-3-pentanone.[245] The $\nu(C=O)$ = 1710 cm^{-1} of 2,2 dimethyl-3-pentanone disappears after metallation and new bands appear between 1660 and 1580 cm^{-1}, in agreement with preceeding observations, but assignment to a $\nu(C=C)$ band or to a $\nu(C\ldots O)$ band remains an unsolved problem.[244,245] More recently Lochmann et al.[246] have studied the IR spectra of lithium salts of different ketones in THF or heptane solutions and that of acetone in the solid state. They have also examined the spectra of 2,5 dimethyl-3-butanone Li, Na or K salts in differents solvents and report characteristic frequencies for these metallated compounds between 3050 and 3150 cm^{-1}, 1500-1650 cm^{-1} and 650-850 cm^{-1}. The first two groups of bands are shown to depend on the nature of the solvent and of the metal atom ; they are assigned to the $\nu(CH)$ and $\nu(C=C)$ vibrations of the O-metallated species,

$$(CH_3)_3C \diagdown C = CH_2$$
$$M - O \diagup$$

the low frequency bands are assigned to the wagging motion of the CH bonds. However, nothing has been said so far about the C-O stretching motion,[246] probably because the complete spectra of the solid compounds are lacking. These authors had previously observed the vibrational spectra of sodium and potassium-t-butoxides[247] in the solid state and in solution and proposed an assignment of the observed bands through comparison with those of t-butanol and t-butyl chloride. The ν (O-M) vibrations have been located respectively at 170 and 228 cm^{-1} for K and Na salts, but the C-O stretching vibrations are strongly coupled with ν(C-C) stretching vibrations and with rocking CH_3 vibrations, as shown through examination of the t-butoxide-d_9 spectra. Comparison of the solid state and solution spectra shows that potassium t-butoxide remains tetrameric in solution as in the solid state, whereas sodium t-butoxide seems to form more complicated aggregates in nonpolar solvents and in the solid state.

2. β-Dicarbonylated enolates

β-Dicarbonylated enolates have been extensively studied by vibrational spectroscopy. The infrared and Raman spectra of a large number of acetylacetone (Acac) metal compounds have been studied in the solid state and their assignment (see Section IV-B) has shown the formation of a delocalized and planar C_3O_2M ring, whatever the metal atom (M) may be. The observation of low frequency spectra has allowed characterization of metal-oxygen bonding in these compounds.[107] The k(M-O) force constants are found between 1.30 and 1.95 mdynes/Å for Cu(Acac)$_2$, Pd(Acac)$_2$, Fe(Acac)$_3$, Cr(Acac)$_3$, Co(Acac)$_3$.[107] Although a detailed analysis of ν(Li-O) vibrations of lithium 1,3 dionates has been performed[79] the calculation of the k(Li-O) force constant is made difficult by the polymeric structure of this compound.[10] From study of the monomeric compound Li HFA-TMED which is a 1:1 adduct of lithium hexafluoroacethyl acetonate (LiHFA) and tetramethylenediamine (TMED) a k(Li-O) force constant of 0.5 mdyne/Å has been calculated.[152] This exhibits once again ionic bonding with the alkali metal, although the delocalization inside the enolate ring does not seem to depend strongly on the nature of the metal atom.[104]

Recently Arnett and De Palma[248] have examined the low frequency spectra of dibenzoylmethide and dipivaloylmethide in THF and DMSO solutions. Their infrared results are insufficient to allow a relevant assignment of cation-anion vibrations in this region. Difficulties pertaining to this region of the spectra have indeed been pointed out in Section IV-C-1-b and care must be taken in order to prevent confusion with internal vibrations of the anion or of the solvent (bending or torsion motions).

Cambillau et al.[31,141,142] have undertaken a detailed study of the structure of the alkaliacetylacetoacetate enolate solutions and of their complexes
with crown-ethers or cryptands. A few examples have already been presented in
Section IV for illustration of the method and we merely summarize here the results. In low dielectric constant aprotic solvents like THF, DME and pyridine,
alkali acetylacetoacetate enolates form "aggregates" which dissociate into
"contact ion pairs" on dilution. Through crown-ether (Cr) additions, equilibria
(47) and (48) are progressively shifted to ion pair and "externally crown solvated ion-pair" formation.

$$M^+E^- + Cr \rightleftharpoons CrM^+E^- \tag{48}$$

The shift of equilibrium (48) depends on the solvent, the nature of the cation
and of the crown-ether used.[31,141] The similarity of the infrared spectra in the
solid and in the solution state show that the species retain a structure very
close to that found by X-ray analysis. The small frequency shifts observed in
solution when comparing K^+ and Na^+ compounds (TABLE 8) are due to changes in
delocalization inside the chelated ring, in agreement with the X-ray structures
and reactivity differences.

TABLE 8

Infrared frequencies of externally crown solvated ion pairs in the solid state
and in solution.

	ν_s (C...O)	ν_a (C...C)	ν_a (C...O)	ν_s (C...C)
E^-K^+18Cr6 (solid)	1664,5	1528	1470	1210
(Sol. THF)	1660	1521	1471	1210
E^-Na^+15Cr5 Solid)	1663	1525	1476	1214
(Sol. THF)	1657	1518.5	1473	1217

When cryptates (Crp) are added to these solutions, "cryptate separated ion-
pairs" are formed in which the anion has a structure very close to that of the
"transoid free anion"[31] equn. (49), but also triple anions may be formed as intermediates species according to equn. (50).[141]

$$M^+E^- + Crp \rightleftharpoons (CrpM^+)E^- \tag{49}$$

$$M^+E^- + (CrPM^+)E^- \rightleftharpoons E^-M^+E^-(CrpM^+) \tag{50}$$

TABLE 9

Infrared frequencies of triple anions of acetylacetoacetates enolates

	$\nu_s(C...O)$	$\nu_a(C...C)$	$\nu_a(C...\Theta)$	$\nu_s(C...C)$
$E_2Li(K^+Crp\ 222)$ (Solid)	1638.5	1506	1494	1234
Solution CH_2Cl_2	1636	1501	1492	1237
Solution DMSO	1639	1502	1487	1235
$E_2Na(K^+Crp\ 222)$ (Solid)	1641	1510	1480	
Solution CH_2Cl_2	1647	1512	1481	1223
Solution THF	1654	1523	1470	1221

For the Li^+ cation, the frequencies of the vibration modes of the triple anion depend very little on the nature of the surrounding media (TABLE 9 and FIGURE 7), but for the Na^+ cation an appreciable frequency change is noticed when comparing the CH_2Cl_2 and THF solutions. This solvent effect is interpreted[141] by THF participation to the Na^+ cation solvation in the triple anion, while the Li^+ cation is no longer accessible to the solvent in the triple anion.

In high dielectric constant aprotic solvents like DMSO, the enolates form solvated ion-pairs which dissociate through dilution, equn. (42). Through comparison of the infrared spectra of the free transoid anion[31] in this solvent with that of potassium enolate solutions, a dissociation coefficient of 0.80 is found, in excellent agreement with the 0.85 value measured by conductimetric titration.

In protic solvents of low dielectric constant such as methylene chloride or chloroform, enolate carbanions disappear progressively by reaction with the solvent, as shown for the lithium triple anion in the presence of an excess of cryptate (211). Small amounts of "cryptate separated ion pairs" may be formed, equn. (51), which react with the solvent regenerating the starting acetylacetoacetate :

$$(E_2Li)^- (Li^+Crp211) + Crp211 \rightleftharpoons 2\ E^-\ (Li^+Crp211) \qquad (51)$$

The spectra obtained by Markov et al.[249] for magnesium acetylacetoacetate enolate in chloroform solution also show a reaction of the enolate with the solvent which regenerates the acetylacetoacetate. In stronger proton donor solvents like t-butanol, alkali acetylacetoacetate enolates have been shown to exist as aggregates in equilibrium with ion-pairs, as in DME or THF.[127] Whereas in THF or DME cryptated (Crp222) or crowned (18Cr-6) potassium enolate forms different species, in t-BuOH they both form solvated anions. The measure of the $\Delta\nu$(OH) frequency shift of t-butanol bonded to these quasi free anions show the high basicity of the enolate anion (TABLE 2). From study of the ν_s(C...O) and ν(OH) absorption bands, the dissociation of the externally crown-solvated ion-pair has been shown to take place in THF-t-BuOH solvent mixtures through the formation of an inter-mediate species.[127]

D. Phosphonate carbanions

Cotton and Schun[250] have published the spectra of sodium, zinc, cobalt (II) and chromium (III) salts of diethoxyphosphonylacetylmethane and dimethoxyphos-phonylacetylmethane in the solid state. They have shown that the ν(C=O) band of the carbonyl group located at 1710 and 1717 cm^{-1} as well as the ν(P=O) stret-ching vibrations located at 1260 cm^{-1} in these β-ketophosphonates disappear in the metal complexes, while three strong bands appear in the metal complexes at about 1530, 1415 and 1170 cm^{-1}. The lower frequency band is assigned to the ν(P...O) band. The other two bands, by analogy with acetylacetonates, are assigned to coupled C...O and C...C stretching vibrations of a planar chelated ring, FIGURE 19. The existence of this planar ring was further demonstrated by the X-ray structure of the trinuclear Co(II) complex of the diethoxyphosphonylace-tylmethane anion.[251] Subsequently, Kirilov and Petrov[252] reported the spectra of Li, Ca and Mg salts of diethoxyphosphonylethoxycarbonylmethane. Probably, because of an incomplete metallation of their product, the ν(P=O) band was mi-sassigned and the authors have favoured a structure in which metallation takes place on the ester oxygen and the P=O group is coordinated to the metal atom.

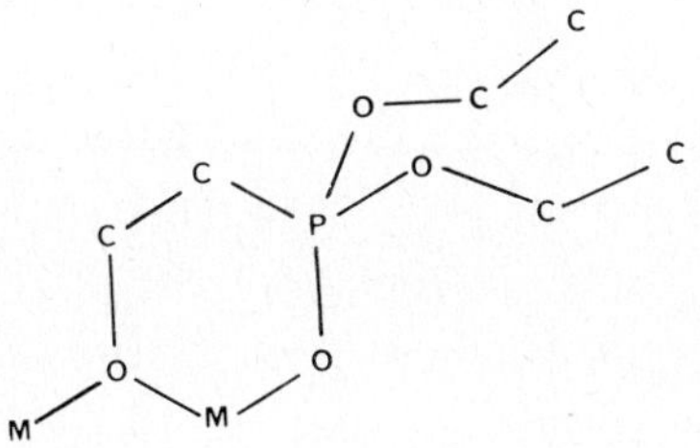

Fig. 19. Structure of the diethoxyphosphonylacetylmethane anion of the trinuclear Cobalt(II) complex of this anion.[272]

We have recently undertaken a detailed vibrational spectroscopic study of several phosphonate (EtO)$_2$POCH$_2$X carbanions in the solid and solution state. The vibrational spectra of the starting phosphonates (EtO)$_2$POCH$_2$X with X = CO$_2$CH$_3$, - PO(OC$_2$H$_5$)$_2$ and -C≡N, have been assigned through comparison with parent molecules, and it is shown that while most of the bands may be assigned in terms of group frequencies, the bands below 900 cm^{-1} are less easily assigned. The (PC_1) and (PO_1) stretching vibrations expected between 600 and 900 cm^{-1} are probably strongly coupled,[148] see SCHEME on FIGURE 20.

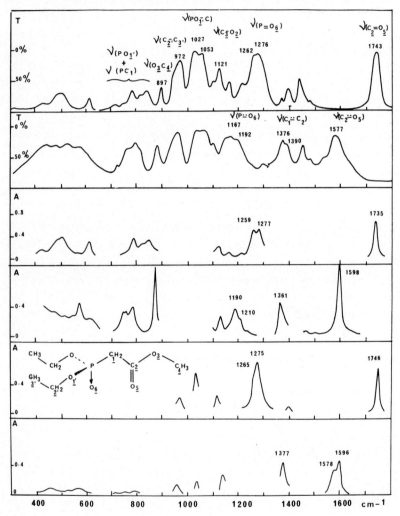

Fig. 20. Infrared spectra of $(EtO)_2POCH_2COOCH_3$ liquid (1) or in THF (5) and DMSO (3) solutions and of its lithium salt solid in nujol mull (2) or in DMSO (4) and THF solutions. Concentration of solutions : 0.37 M. ; cell thichness : 0.0030 cm.

Comparison of the spectra for the lithium salt of carbomethoxymethyl-phosphonate and the starting phosphonate (FIGURE 20) readily shows that both the $\nu(C_2=O_5)$ and $\nu(P=O_6)$ bands have disappeared as in the β ketophosphonates.[250] Through metallation new bands appear at 1577, 1376-1390 and 1167-1192 cm^{-1}, and are respectively assigned to $\nu(C_2\cdots O_5)$, $\nu(C_1\cdots C_2)$ and $\nu(p\cdots O_6)$. This shows the formation of a chelated cyclic carbanion, in agreement with the results of Cotton and Schunn.[250] It has also be shown that other bands involving ethoxy group motions are shifted by the electron delocalization of the carbanion.

TABLE 10

Comparison of $\nu(C\cdots O)$ and $\nu(C\cdots C)$ frequencies of phosphonates carbanions and phosphorus ylids.

Phosphonates	Frequency cm^{-1}	Ylids	Frequency cm^{-1}
			$\nu(C\cdots O)$[255]
		(Ph)$_3$P-CH-COMe	1542
$\underset{\text{(EtO)}_2\text{POCHCCH}_3}{\overset{\text{O} \quad \text{O}}{\ \ }}$ Na$^+$	$\nu(C\cdots O)$[250] 1540	(Ph)$_3$P-CHCO(Ph)	$\nu(C\cdots O)$[254] $\nu(C\cdots O)$[255] 1516 1526 1529
	$\nu(C\cdots C)$[250] 1425		$\nu(C\cdots C)$[254] 1401 1387
$\underset{\text{(EtO)}_2\text{POCHCOOCH}_3}{\overset{\text{O} \quad \text{O}}{\ \ }}$ K$^+$	$\nu(C\cdots O)$[148a] 1611 $\nu(C\cdots C)$[148] 1359	(Ph)$_3$P-CH-COOPh	$\nu(C\cdots O)$[295] $\nu(C\cdots O)$[253] 1620 1614 $\nu(C\cdots C)$[253] 1334

[a] Frequencies of the solid compound measured in nujol mull

Only a few vibrations of the carbanion are observable in DMSO or THF solutions (FIGURE 20), but the spectra of the species in solution appear very close to those of the solid compound. This means that the species in solution retain an ion pair structure with a delocalized U-shaped phosphonate ester group, analogous to acetylacetoacetate enolate carbanions. Furthermore, while only externally solvated contact ion-pairs are formed in DMSO, both ion-pairs and aggregates are observed in THF as shown through a dilution effect on the two $\nu(C_2=O_5)$ bands observed at 1578 and 1596 cm^{-1}.[148] For the potassium salt, the ion-pair may be partially dissociated in DMSO solution where the free ions have two conformational isomers, as better seen by NMR methods.[148] Conformational changes are indeed usually seen through frequency perturbations of the bending vibrations,[157] which are difficult to assign in these solutions. Upon cryptation (Crp222) of the potassium salt in DMSO, the spectrum of the free anion is observed. The characteristic vibration modes $\nu(C_2\ldots O_5)$, $\nu(C_1\ldots C_2)$, $\nu(P\ldots O_6)$ are observed at frequencies very close to those of the chelated potassium salt, indicating a similar delocalization in the free anion and in the chelated ring (FIGURE 20).

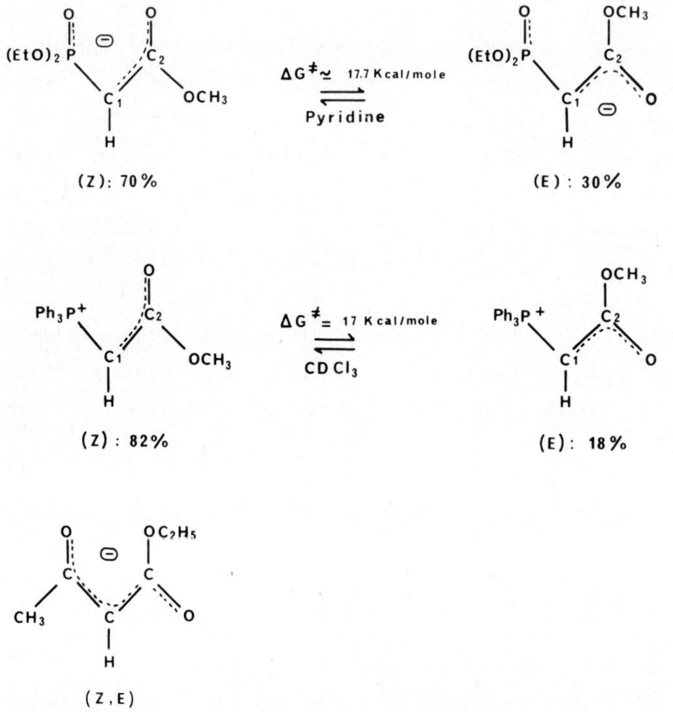

Fig. 21. Comparison of structures of free anions of acetylacetoacetate, of phosphorus ylid and of phosphonoester.[148]

As shown in FIGURE 21 and TABLE 10, comparison of $\nu(C_1\ldots C_2)$ and $\nu(C_2\ldots O_5)$ frequencies shows the strong structural similarity between the anionic species of the phosphonate ester and the phosphorus ylid, which are shown through NMR to exist as (Z) and (E) conformers in equilibrium, with the population ratios indicated on FIGURE 21. While phosphonate ester and acethylacetate carbanions ion-pairs have a very similar chelated structure, the free anion differs noticeably ; the

acetylacetoacetate anion has only the (Z, E) conformation[141] like the acetylacetonate anion,[256] the analogous conformation of the phosphonate ester anion being
less populated.

E. Carbanions α to sulfur

Carbanions α to sulfur are important intermediates in organic synthesis due
to the high stereoselectivity of many reactions in which they are involved. The
origin of this stereoselectivity is still a matter of contraversy; the structure
of these carbanions is indeed not yet solved.[257] The ab initio calculations of
Wolfe et al.[257] on $^-CH_2SH$, $^-CH_2SOH$, $^-CH_2SO_2H$ have shown that the preferred configuration of the carbanion is a pyramidal one in all cases, with the most stable orientation corresponding to the maximum of gauche interactions between lone
pairs and polar bonds. In a more recent study of $^-CH_2SH$ and $^-CH_2SCH_3$, Lehn et
al.[258] reached the same conclusions. In a ^{13}C NMR study of a series of sulfur
compounds with different oxidation states : $C_6H_5SO_nCH_3$ with n = 0, 1, 2 and of
their lithium and potassium salts in different solvents, Chassaing and Marquet[259]
have interpreted the J^1_{C-H} coupling constant of these species as due to hybridization changes ; they have also shown that the metallated carbon is nearly
planar in the sulfoxide (n = 1) and nearly pyramidal in the sulfide (n = 0), while
it is intermediate for the sulfone (n = 2). A chelated structure was then proposed for $C_6H_5SOCH_2^-Li^+$ where the Li^+ atom is bonded to both carbon and oxygen
atoms (FIGURE 22).

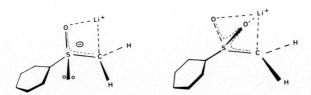

Fig. 22. Proposed structures for the lithio-phenylsufoxide and the lithio-phenyl-
sulfone carbanions.

In order to verify this hypothesis we have undertaken an infrared and Raman study of these compounds[146] and of their Li^+ and K^+ salts.[147] A detailed assignment
of the $C_6H_5SO_nCH_3$ molecules has been done using $C_6D_5SO_nCH_3$, $C_6H_5SO_nCD_3$ and
$C_6H_5SO^{13}CH_3$ isotopic molecules and a force field calculation is in progress in
order to determine precisely the normal modes involving the CH_3-S stretching
motion. The Li^+ and K^+ salts spectra have been scanned for $C_6H_5SOCH_3$ derivatives
as nujol mulls and the spectra of both salts show the disappearance of the bands

assigned to $\nu(S=O)$ (1048-1065 cm^{-1}), $\nu(CH_3-S)$ (620-700 cm^{-1}) modes and of those corresponding to the bending and rocking modes of the methyl group. Two intense bands appear between 830 and 940 cm^{-1} in the IR which are assigned to the pro- bably strongly coupled $\nu(C...S)$ and $(S...O)$ stretching vibrations of the delo- calized carbanion. The C-S bond has indeed gained a partial double bond charac- ter, which increases its frequency, and the S=O bond has lost a part of its double bond character. Furthermore for the compound $C_6D_5SOCH_2^-Li^+$ a $\nu(C-H)$ band of low intensity is observed at 3076 cm^{-1}, in excellent agreement with the non planar character of the CH_2^- carbon. The vibrations of the monosubstitued phenyl ring show only very slight frequency perturbations when comparing the starting mole- cule with the carbanion. Thus the NMR and infrared results are in excellent agreement with the carbanion structure of FIGURE 22 where the Li^+ ion interacts with the delocalized charge on both the oxygen and carbon atoms.

The spectra of the lithium salts of phenyl methyl sulfone and phenyl methyl sul fide have also be examined. FIGURE 23 shows for instance the spectra of a solid film of phenyl methyl sulfone and of its lithium salt. The $\delta(CH_3)$ and $r(CH_3)$ absorptions disappear in the carbanion spectra and strong perturbations of the SO_2 group vibrations as well as of the $\nu(CH_3-S)$ stretching vibration are obser- ved. Phenyl ring vibrations show only very small frequency perturbations. The $\nu_a(SO_2)$ and $\nu_s(SO_2)$ vibrations are decreased by 78 and 45 cm^{-1}, respectively, while the bending motion $\delta(SO_2)$, $w(SO_2)$, $\nu(SO_2)$ have increased frequency, the vibrational mode which involves mainly the CH_3-S stretching motion increases by 106 cm^{-1}. These features indicate that the Li^+ cation interacts with the two oxygen atoms of the SO_2 group and with the CH_2^- carbon (FIGURE 23).

The hybridization state of the latter is intermediate between pyramidal and planar, with probably less double bond character of the $^-CH_2...S$ bond than in sulfoxide. For the methyl phenyl sulfide, while absorptions of the CH_3 group disappear in the spectra of the lithium salt, only very small perturbations are observed for the modes involving the CH_3-S stretching vibrations. This indicates that the metallation takes place only at the $^-CH_2$ carbon atom, the hybridization of which is probably close to pyramidal. It is thus shown that the hybridization state of the $^-CH_2$ carbon is strongly dependent on the delocalization of the ne- gative charge on the oxygen atoms.

These results confirm the NMR observations, and while they agree with ab initio calculations for the sulfide carbanion structure, they are in disagreement for the sulfoxide and sulfone, probably due to the inadequacy of the orbital basis used. A more detailed analysis of the spectra and a force field calculation are in progress in order to determine precisely the evolution of the k(C-S) force constant in these compounds.

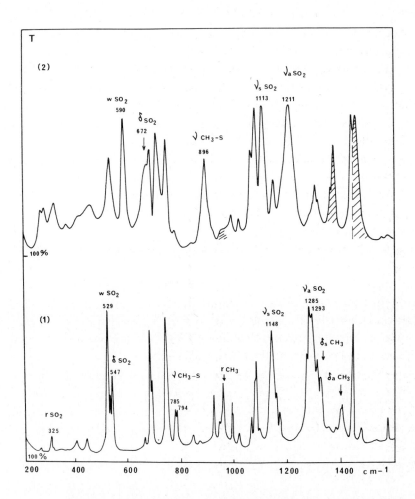

Fig. 23. Infrared spectra of phenyl methyl sulfone (solid film) (1) and of its lithium salt (nujol mull) (2) ; shaded absorptions are due to nujol.

F. Aromatic carbanions

Most of the studies of the aromatic hydrocarbon negative ions, resulting from the reaction of the hydrocarbons with alkali metals, have been undertaken through visible or UV spectrophotometry.[265] In spite of the importance of vibrational spectra in elucidating the electronic structure, very few studies have been reported except an IR study on polyacene anions,[260] the study by Li and Devlin[261] on potassium salts of anthracene in the solid state, and some preliminary Raman results on anion radicals and dianions of anthracene, diphenyl, terphenyl, diphenylbutadiene, perylene and benzophenone.[262]

More recently Takahashi and Maeda[263,264] have shown that Raman spectroscopy through the resonance Raman effect could be a very powerful tool to look at the structure of aromatic carbanions and of the species formed in solutions, even at concentrations as low as 10^{-3} to 10^{-4} M in THF. Using argon laser lines at 457.9, 488.0 and 514.5 nm they have obtained excellent spectra of anthracene mono- and dinegative ions[263] at concentrations of 10^{-2} to 10^{-3} M in THF, showing a pre-resonance effect. When using the He-Ne laser line at 632.1 nm, a strong resonance effect is observed, getting closer to the absorption maxima at 730 nm in the monoanion and 610 nm in the dianion, and solutions of concentration close to 10^{-4} M must be used. The intensity enhancement of Raman line is mostly observed for totally symmetric Ag modes corresponding to the aromatic ring vibrations. As an example, the most intense Ag line of anthracene at 1403 cm^{-1} is observed at 1360 cm^{-1} for the monoanion and at 1350 cm^{-1} for the dianion. For this latter species, almost rigorous resonance conditions are reached with the 532.8 nm excitation line, while overtones of this mode are observed at 2690 and 4045 cm^{-1}.

A similar study has been done for biphenyl (BP) negative ion[263] where the optical absorptions at 625 nm comes close to rigorous resonance with the 632.8 He-Ne laser line and the 647.1 Kr laser line. The frequency shifts $\Delta\nu = \nu(BP^-)$ - $\nu(BP)$, as well as the Raman intensity enhancement through resonance, is discussed in relation to molecular orbital calculations. The 625 nm absorption is thus confirmed to be due to an allowed transition polarized along the long molecular axis ; the BP 1287 cm^{-1} band, which is mainly due to the inter-nuclei C-C bond stretching vibration, is therefore strongly enhanced through resonance and its frequency is increased by $\Delta\nu = 39$ cm^{-1}. The other ring stretching vibra-

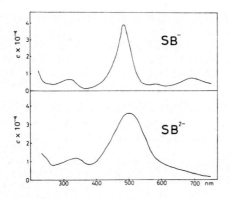

Fig. 24. Absorption spectra of SB^- and SB^{2-} (After Takahashi and Maeda.[264])

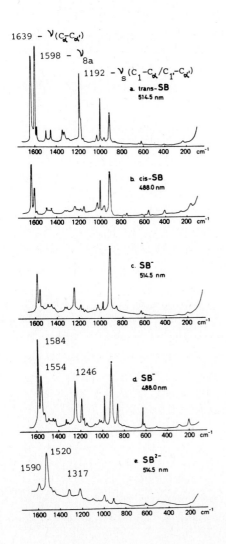

$1639 - \nu(C_\alpha\text{-}C_{\alpha'})$

$1598 - \nu_{8a}$

$1192 - \nu_s(C_1\text{-}C_\alpha/C_{1'}\text{-}C_{\alpha'})$

a. trans-SB
514.5 nm

b. cis-SB
488.0 nm

c. SB⁻
514.5 nm

1584
1554   1246   d. SB⁻
488.0 nm

1590   1520   e. SB²⁻
514.5 nm
1317

Fig. 25. Raman spectra of trans and cis stilbene SB, SB⁻ and SB²⁻. (a) Trans-SB in THF, 0,5 M ; (b) cis-SB in THF uncertain concentration ; (c, d) SB⁻, 2,6 10⁻⁴M ; (e) SB²⁻, 1.8 10⁻³M. ＊ THF lines. (After Takahashi and Maeda[264])

tions have negative $\Delta\nu$ frequency shifts, showing a larger delocalization in the BP⁻ anion and an increase of the bond order of the internuclear C-C bond compared to the BP molecule.

As shown on FIGURE 25, the cis and trans stilbene Raman spectra are different. For instance, the $\nu(c_\alpha = c_{\alpha'})$ band at 1639 cm⁻¹ is more intense than the ν_{8a} band (phenyl C-C ring vibration) in the cis and not in the trans stilbene. The symmetric stretching vibration of the C_1C_α and $C_1,C_{\alpha'}$ bonds appears as an intense band at 1192 cm⁻¹ only in the trans stilbene. The 488.0 and 514.5 nm lines of an

188

Argon laser due to the large molar extinction coefficient of the absorption spectra of both SB^- and SB^{2-} allow one to obtain resonance Raman spectra at very low
concentrations of these species (10^{-4} M). It is shown that when the carbanion is
prepared from trans or cis stilbene, the spectra of SB^- and SB^{2-} are the same,
which means that the "stiffness" of the $C_\alpha C_{\alpha'}$ double bond is appreciably reduced
in the ions, allowing isomerization. The spectra of the SB^- anions, and mainly
the 1246 cm^{-1} intense band due to the symmetric stretching vibration of the $C_1 C_\alpha$
and $C_1, C_{\alpha'}$ bonds, ($\nu_S(C_1 C_\alpha/C_1, C_{\alpha'})$, seem to indicate that this anion has the
trans conformation. Furthermore the negative and positive shift $\Delta\nu = \nu(SB^-) -$
ν(trans-SB) respectively for $\nu(C_\alpha C_{\alpha'})$ and $\nu_S(C_1 C_\alpha/C_1, C_{\alpha'})$ vibrations indicate
that π bonding in the anion is more delocalized than in the parent molecule.
This effect seems more important for the SB^{2-} anion, as suggested by the assign-
ment of the 1317 and 1520 cm^{-1} bands to the $\nu_S(C_1 C_\alpha/C_1, C_{\alpha'})$ and $\nu(C_\alpha C_{\alpha'})$ vibrations (FIGURE 25). This behaviour is compared with that of anthracene and is
discussed in terms of electronic structures.

VI. CONCLUSION

While the UV spectrometry is often limited to the study of very dilute solutions and the NMR technique to the observation of an average signal due to exchange phenomena between species, vibrational spectrometry has proven to be
a very powerful tool to analyze the structure of carbanionic species in solutions.
Vibrational spectrometry has shown that carbanions form a special class of organometallic compounds where the electron of the metal atom is transferred to
the organic anion with an almost purely ionic bond between anion and metal. Nevertheless to obtain a precise analysis of the structure of carbanionic species
it is necessary to make a thorough comparison of the spectrum of the solid compound with that of the dissolved compound. Very often a detailed analysis of
vibrational normal modes which is not familiar to the the organic chemist is
needed to get the most interesting information on the extent of electron delocalization in the carbanion.

ACKNOWLEDGEMENTS

The author thanks Miss M.L. JOSIEN Honorary Professor to the University
Pierre et Marie Curie - Paris VI for help and encouragement and all the members
of the laboratory for their collaboration. He is much indebted to G. BRAM,
C. CAMBILLAU, P. SARTHOU, J. SEYDEN-PENNE and T. BOTTIN-STRZALKO of the Research
Group N° 12 of C.N.R.S. and to G. CHASSAING and A. MARQUET of the C.E.R.C.O.A.
for their collaboration and help in the bibliography.

REFERENCES

1 HP. Fritz, "Advances in Organometallic Chemistry", vol.1, Academic Press, London (1964), p.309.
2 C. Sourisseau, B. Pasquier and J. Hervieu, Spectrochim. Acta, 31 A(1975)287.
3 E. Maslowsky Jr., "Vibrational Spectra of Organometallic Compounds", Wiley, New York, (1977).
4 A. Snelson and K. Pitzer, J. Phys. Chem., 67(1963)882.
S. Shick and O. Schnepp, J. Chem. Phys., 41(1964)463.
R.C. Miller and P. Kusch, J. Chim. Phys., 25(1956)860.
5 D. Smith, D.W. James and J.P. Devlin, J. Chem. Phys., 54(1971)4437.
6 J. Franck, H. Kuhn and G. Rollefson, Z. Physik, 43(1927)155.
7 B.S. Ault and G.C. Pimentel, J. Phys. Chem., 79(1975)621.
8 E. Weiss, J. Organometal. Chem., 2(1964)314.
9 E. Weiss and G. Sauermann, J. Organometal. Chem., 21(1970)1.
10 F.A. Schroder and H.P. Weber, Acta Cryst., B 31(1975)1745.
11 N.N. Grenwood et al. A Specialist Periodical Report "Spectroscopic properties of Inorganic and Organometallic compounds" The Chemical Society, Burlington House, London.
12 G.E. Coates, M.L.H. Green and K. Wade, "Organometallic Compounds", Methuen, London (1967).
13 F.G.A. Stone and R. West Ed., "Advances in Organometallic Chemistry", Academic Press, New York.
14 W. Brugel, "An Introduction to Infrared Spectroscopy", translated by A.R. Katritzky, and A.D. Katritzky, Methuen, London (1962).
15 H.A. Szymanski, "Progress in Infrared Spectroscopy", vol.1, Plenum Press, New York (1962).
16 W. West, "Chemical Applications of Spectroscopy", vol. IX, Wiley, New York (1956).
17 A.D. Cross, "Introduction to Practical Infrared Spectroscopy", Butterworths (1964).
18 C.N.R. Rao, "Chemical Applications of Infrared Spectroscopy", Academic Press, New York (1963).
19 D.H. Anderson, N.B. Wooddall and W. West, "Technique of Organic Chemistry - Physical methods" ch. XXIX, vol. 1, Part III, Weissberger (1960), Interscience, New York.
20 C.K.T. Conn and D.G. Avery, "Infrared Methods", Principles and Applications, Academic Press, New York (1960).
21 A.L. Martin, "Infrared Spectroscopy and Molecular Structure", Ed. M. Davies, Elsevier, Amsterdam (1963).
22 P. Bousquet, "Spectroscopie Instrumentale", Dunod, Paris (1969).
23 J.E. Stewart, "Infrared Spectroscopy", Experimental Methods and Techniques, M. Dekker, New York, (1970).
24 H.A. Szymanski, Ed., "Raman Spectroscopy", vol.1, Plenum Press, (1967), vol.2, Plenum Press, (1970).
25 J. Loader, "Basic Laser Raman Spectroscopy", Heyden and Sons, London (1970).
26 M. Delhaye, "Spectrométrie Raman", Techniques de l'Ingénieur, p. 2865, 2, (1975).
27 F. Wallart, Spectra 2000, (1975), 19.
28 J.T. Bulmer, D.E. Irish, F.W. Grossman, G. Herriot, M. Tseng and A.J. Weerheim, Appl. Spectrosc., 29-6(1975)506.
29 J.R. Downey and G.J. Janz, Ch. 1, Vol.1 in "Advances in Infrared and Raman Spectroscopy", R.J.H. Clark and R.E. Hester Ed., Heyden, London (1975)
30 A.R.H. Cole, "Tables of Wavenumbers for the Calibration of Infrared Spectrometers" I.U.P.A.C., "Commission in Molecular Structure and Spectroscopy" Second Edition, Pergamon (1977).
31 C. Cambillau, G. Bram, J. Corset, C. Riche and C. Pascard-Billy, Tetrahedron 34(1978)2675.
32 M. Weiner, C. Vogel and R. West, Inorg. Chem. 1(1962)654.

190

33 C. Sourrisseau, J. Mol. Struct., 40(1977)167.
34 R. West and W. Glaze, J. Am. Chem. Soc., 83(1961)3580.
35 E. Whittle, D.A. Dows and G.C. Pimentel, J. Chem. Phys., 22(1954)1943.
36 H.E. Hallam, "Vibrational Spectroscopy of Matrix isolated Species", Ch. 13 in
    "Molecular Spectroscopy", Ed. by A.R. West, Heyden, London (1977)
37 H.E. HALLAM, "Vibrational Spectroscopy of Trapped species", Wiley, (1973)
38 W.L.S. Andrews and G.C. Pimentel, J. Chem. Phys., 44(1966)2361
    J. Chem. Phys., 47(1967)3637.
39 L. Andrews, J. Chem. Phys., 47(1967)4834.
40 E.L. Wagner and D.G. Hornig, J. Chem. Phys., 18(1950)296.
41 I.U.P.A.C., Tables of Wavenumbers, Butterworths, London, (1961)
42 "Handbook of Chemistry and Physics", 46th Edition, Ed. R.C. Weast, The Chemical
    Rubber and Co. (1965-66).
43 M. Delhaye and P. Dhamelincourt, J. Raman Spectrosc., 3(1975)33.
44 P. Dhamelincourt, Thèse de Doctorat n° 441, Lille, (1979).
45 M. Bridoux and M. Delhaye in "Advances in Infrared and Raman Spectroscopy"
    Vol. 2, R.J.H. Clark and R.E. Hester Ed., Heyden London (1976) ch. 4.
46 H.J. Bernstein in "Advances in Raman Spectroscopy" vol.1, J.P. Mathieu,
    Ed. Heyden London, (1973), p.305.
47 R.J.H. Clark in "Advances in Raman Spectroscopy", vol.1, R.J.H. Clark and
    R.E. Hester, Ed. Heyden (1975), ch.4, p.143.
48 J. Behringer, in "Raman Spectroscopy", vol.1, H.A. Szymanski Ed., Plenum Press
    (1967), Ch.6, p.168.
49 R.J.H. Clark and B. Stewart, in "Structure and Bonding", vol.36, Ed. J.D. Dunitz
    et al., Springer Verlag, Berlin, (1979).
50 C. Takahashi and S. Maeda, Chim. Phys. Letters, 22(1973)364.
51 M. Crunelle-Cras and J.C. Merlin, J. of Raman Spectroscopy, 6(1977)261.
52 M. Delhaye, in Phys. Chem. Biophys. Proc., 27 th., Int. Meet. Soc. Chim. Phys.,
    Ed. J. Joussot-Dubien, Elsevier, Amsterdam (1975) p.213.
53 G. Herzberg, "Infrared and Raman spectra of Polyatomic Molecules", D. Van Nostrand
    New York (1945).
54 E.B. Wilson, J.C. Decius and P.C. Cross, "Molecular Vibrations", McGraw Hill,
    New York, (1955).
55 T. Shimanouchi in "Physical Chemistry an Advanced Treatise", Vol.IV. Molecular
    properties, Ed. D. Henderson, Academic Press, New York, (1970), ch. 6.
56 L.M. Sverdlov, M.A. Kovner and E.P. Krainov, "Vibrational Spectra of Polyatomic
    molecules" Halsted Press, Wiley, New York (1974).
57 P. Barchewitz, "Spectroscopie Infrarouge", Gauthier Villars, Paris (1961), vol.1,
    (1967), vol.2.
58 S.J. Cyvin, "Molecular Vibrations and Meansquare amplitudes", Elsevier, Amsterdam
    (1968).
59 M. Eliashevich, C.R. Acad. Sci., U.S.S.R., 28(1940)605.
60 H.C. Urey and C.A. Bradley, Phys. Rev., 38(1931)1969.
61 D.E. Munn, T. Shimanouchi, J.H. Meal and L. Fano, J. Chim. Phys., 27(1957)43.
62 J.H. Schachtschneider and R.G. Snyder, Spectrochim. Acta, 19(1963)117.
63 L.A. Gribov, "Intensity Theory for Infrared Spectra of Polyatomic molecules",
    Translation from the Russian Consultants Bureau, New York, (1964).
64 F.A. Cotton, "Chemical Applications of Group Theory", Interscience, New York
    (1963).
65 S. Bhagavantam and T. Vankataravudu, "Theory of Groups and its application to
    physical problems", Andhra University, Waltair, Bangalore (1962).
66 G. Placzek, Handbuch der Radiologie, Vol.6 (E. Marx Ed)., Leipzig (1974).
67 A.C. Albrecht, J. Chem. Phys., 34(1961)1476.
68 J. Behringer, Z. Physik, 229, (1969), 209.
69 J. Tang and A.C. Albrecht, in "Raman Spectroscopy", Vol.2, H.A. Szymanski Ed.
    Plenum Press, New York (1970), ch.2.
70 R.J.H. Clark in "Advances in Infrared and Raman Spectroscopy", vol.1.
    R.J.H. Clark and R.E. Hester, Ed. Heyden, London (1975), ch.4.

71 G. Herzberg, "Spectra of Diatomic Molecules", D. Van Nostrand, New York (1950).
72 R.M. Badger and L.R. Zumwalt, J. Chem. Phys., 6(1938)711.
73 D. Shigorin, Spectrochim. Acta, 14(1959)198.
    A.N. Rodionov, D. Shigorin, T. Talalueva and K. Kocheshkov, Izvest Akad. Nauk.
    U.S.S.R., Otdel Khim. Nau. (1958) 120.
74 R.C. Miller and P. Kusch, J. Chem. Phys., 25(1956)860.
75 W.G. Fateley, N.T. Mc.Dewitt and F.F. Bentley, Appl. Spectrosc., 25(1971)155.
76 I.R. Beattie, Chem. Soc. Rev., 4(1975)107
77 G. Turrell, "Infrared and Raman Spectra of Crystals" Academic Press, London,
    (1972).
78 A.S. Davydov, J. Exptl. Theoret. Phys., U.S.S.R., 18(1948)210.
79 E. Funck and A. Jungermann, Spectrochim. Acta, 30 A(1974)1247.
80 E. Funck, A. Jungermann, J. Kaiser and F.A. Schrödder, Z. Naturforsch B 26
    (1971)528.
81 C. Riche, C. Pascard-Billy, C. Cambillau and G. Bram, J. C. S. Chem. Comm. (1977)
    183.
82 R.M. Hexter, J. Chem. Phys., 33(1960)1833.
83 A.E. Smith, Acta Cryst. 18(1965)331.
84 C. Sourisseau and B. Pasquier, Can. J. Spectrosc., 18(1973)91.
85 M.L. Josien, Molecular Spectroscopy of Dense Phases, Proceedings of the 12th
    European Congress on Molecular Spectroscopy, Strasbourg 1975, Elsevier (1976)
    p. 583.
86 P. Mirone and G. Fini, J. Chem. Soc.Faraday Trans II, 70(1974)1777.
87 C. Perchard and J.P. Perchard, Chem. Phys. Letters, 27(1974)445.
88 J. Lascombe, Ed. "Molecular Motions in Liquid", D. Reidel, Dordrecht (1974).
89 L.J. Bellamy, "The Infrared Spectra of Complex Molecules" Wiley, New York, (1964)
90 L.J. Bellamy, "Advances in Infrared Group Frequencies", Methuen, (1968).
91 F.R. Dollish, W.G. Fateley and F.F. Bentley, "Characteristic Raman frequencies
    of Organic Compounds", Wiley, New York (1974).
92 S. Krimm, J. Chem. Phys., 32(1960)1780.
93 E. Fermi, Z. Physik, 71(1931)250.
94 B.T. Darling and D.M. Dennison, Phys. Rev., 57(1940)128.
95 J.F. Bertran, L. Ballester, I. Dobrihalova, N. Sanchez and R. Arricta, Spectro-
    chim. Acta, 24 A, (1968)1765.
96 R.M. Moravie, Thèse de Doctorat, Université Pierre et Marie Curie, Paris VI,
    (1975), CNRS n° AO 9437.
97 J. Bellamy and R.F. Branch, J. Chem. Soc., (1954)4491.
98 K.L. Wierzchowski and D. Shugar, Spectrochim. Acta, 21(1965)943.
99 W.O. George and F.V. Robinson, J. Chem. Soc. (A), (1968)1950.
100 E.E. Ernstbrunner, J. Chem. Soc., (A), (1970)1558.
101 Morgan, U.S. Atomic Energy Commission n°12569 (1949), 16.
102 C. Duval, R. Freymann and J. Lecomte, C.R. Acad. Sci., 231(1950)272.
103 K. Nakamoto and A.E. Martell, J. Chim. Phys., 32(1960)588.
104 K. Nakamoto, "Infrared Spectra of Inorganic and Coordination Compounds", Wiley,
    New York (1963).
105 E.G. Cox and K.C. Webster, J. Chem. Soc., (1935)731.
    H. Koyama, Y. Saito and K. Kuroya, J. Inst. Polyt., Osaka, 46(1953)43.
106 M. Mikami, I. Nakagawa, and T. Shimanouchi, Spectrochim. Acta, 23 A,(1967)1037.
107 K.E. Lawson, Spectrochim. Acta, 17(1961)248.
108 S. Pinchas, B.L. Silver and S. Laulicht, J. Chem. Phys., 46(1967)1506.
109 B. Bock, K. Flatau, H. Junge, M. Kuhr and H. Musso, Angew. Chem. Internat Edit.
    10(1971)225.
110 H. Musso and H. Junge, Chem. Ber. 101(1968)801.
    H. Junge and H. Musso, Spectrochim. Acta, 24 A(1968)1219.
111 E. Funck and A. Jungermann, Spectrochim. Acta, 30 A(1974)1247.
112 G.T. Behnke and K. Nakamoto, Inorg. Chem., 6(1967)433.
113 S. Pinchas and J. Shamir, J. Chem. Soc. Perkin II,(1975)1098.
114 K. Nakamoto, C. Udorich, and J. Takemoto, J. Am. Chem. Soc., 92(1970)973.

115 M. Kirszenbaum, Thèse Doctorat ès Sciences, Université de Paris VI, (1976) CNRS n° AO 12172.
116 C.J. Pedersen and H.K. Frensdorff, Angew. Chem. Intern. Ed. 11, (1972), 16.
117 J.M. Lehn in "Structure and Bonding", vol.16 Springer Verlag, Berlin, (1973).
118 D.E. Irish and M.H. Brooker, "Advances in Infrared and Raman Spectroscopy", vol.2, R.J.H. Clark and R.E. Hester, Ed., Heyden London (1976), ch.6.
    D.E. Irish in "Physical Chemistry of Organic Solvent Systems", A.K. Covington and T. Dickinson Eds. Plenum Press, London (1973), p.433.
119 A.K. Covington and T.H. Lilley, "Electrochemistry, Specialist Periodical Report" Vol.1, The Chemical Society, Burlington House, London, (1969), 1.
120 A. Loupy and J. Corset, J. Sol. Chem. 5(1976)817.
121 A. Regis, Thèse de Doctorat d'Etat, Université Pierre et Marie Curie, Paris VI, CNRS n° AO 10313 (1977)
122 A. Regis and J. Corset, J. Chim. Phys., 76(1979)107.
123 A. Allerhand and P.V. Schleyer, J. Am. Chem. Soc., 85(1963)371 ; ibid. 85 (1963)1233.
124 P. Bacelon, J. Corset and C. de Lozé, Chem. Phys. Letters, 32(1975)458.
125 A.R. Davis, J.W. Macklin and R.A. Plane, J. Chim. Phys., 50(1969)1478.
126 T.J.V. Findley and M.C.R. Symons, J. Chem. Soc. Farad. Trans., II 72(1976)820.
127 P. Sarthou, F. Guibe, G. Bram and J. Corset, Tetrahedron, in press.
    P. Sarthou, thèse de Doctorat, Université Paris XI, Orsay (1978).
128 P. Bacelon, to be published.
129 J.D. Ridell, D.J. Lockwood and D.E. Irish, Can. J. Chem. 50(1972)2951.
130 A. Regis and J. Corset, Chem. Phys. Letter., 32(1975)462.
131 P. Bacelon, C. de Loze and J. Corset, Euchem Conference on Ion-molecule interactions in Nonaqueous media, Leuven Belgique, (1978).
132 D. Paoli, M. Lucon and M. Chabanel, Spectrochim. Acta, submitted
133 M. Chabanel and M. Lucon, "Sixth International Conference on Non aqueous solution", Waterloo, Canada, 7-11 August 1978.
134 A.I. Popov, Pure Appl. Chem., 41(1975)275.
135 W.F. Edgell, "Ions and Ions-pairs in Organic Reactions", vol.1, (M. Szwarc Ed.) Wiley, Interscience New York, (1972), ch.4.
136 A. Regis and J. Corset, Can. J. Chem. 51(1973)3577.
137 P.R. Handy and A.I. Popov, Spectrochim. Acta, 28 A (1972)1545.
138 J. de Villepin and A. Novak, J. Mol. Struct., 30(1976)256.
139 F. Buumgorth, N.B. Chanh, R. Gay, J. Lascombe and N. le Calve, J. Chim. Phys., 66(1969)862.
140 G.T. Behnke and K. Nakamoto, Inorg. Chem., 6(1967)440.
141 C. Cambillau, Thèse de Doctorat, Université Paris XI, Orsay, (1978).
142 C. Cambillau, G. Bram, J. Corset and C. Riche, Nouveau J. Chim., 3(1979)9.
143 C. Sourisseau and B. Pasquier, J. Organometal. Chem. 39(1972)51 ; ibid. 39(1972)65.
144 C. Sourisseau and B. Pasquier, Can. J. Spectrosc., 18(1973)91 ; ibid. 19(1974)1.
145 C. Sourisseau, Thèse de Doctorat, Université Paris VI, (1972), CNRS n° AO 6316.
146 G. Chassaing, A. Marquet and J. Corset, to be published.
147 G. Chassaing, A. Marquet and J. Corset, to be published.
148 T. Bottin-Strzalko, J. Corset, F. Froment, M.J. Pouet, J. Seyden-Penne and M.R. Simonin, J. Org. Chem., submitted.
149 T. Bottin-Strzalko, J. Corset, F. Froment and J. Seyden-Penne, to be published.
150 S.P. Patterman, I.L. Karle and G.D. Stucky, J. Am. Chem. Soc., 92(1970)1150
151 R. Zerger,W. Rhine and G.D. Stucky, J. Am. Chem. Soc. 96(1974)5441.
152 K. Shobatake and K. Nakamoto, J. Chem. Phys., 49(1968)4792.
153 J.J. Brooks, W. Rhine and G.O. Stucky, J. Am. Chem. Soc. 94(1972)7339.
154 B. Silvi, J. Chim. Phys., 76(1979)21.

155 P. Labarde and M.T. Forel, J. Chim. Phys., 70(1973)180.

156 M.T. Forel and M. Fouassier, C.R. Acad. Sci., Paris, 274 B(1972)73.

157 Y. Omura, J. Corset and R.M. Moravie, J. Mol. Struct., 52(1979)175.

158 J.W. Linnett, Trans Faraday Soc., 6(1954)129.

159 W.J. Lehmann, J. Mol. Spectrosc., 7(1961)261.

160 H.J. Bernstein, Spectrochim. Acta, 18(1962)161.

161 J.O.S. Goulden Spectrochim. Acta, 6(1954)129.

162 R.J. Gillepsie and E.A. Robinson, Can. J. Chem., 41(1963)2074.

163 C.A. Coulson, "Valence", 2nd Ed. Oxford University Press, (1961), 270.

164 A. Novak, in Structure and Bonding, vol. 18, Springer Verlag, Berlin, (1974).

165 D.C. Mc Kean, J.L. Duncan and L. Batt, Spectrochim. Acta, 29 A(1973)1037.

166 D.C. Mc Kean, Spectrochim. Acta, 29 A(1973)1559.

167 O. Saur, J.C. Lavalley and R. Romanet, C.R. Acad. Sc. Fr., 269 B(1969)816.

168 A. Burneau, Spectrochim. Acta, 30 A(1974)1861.

169 J. Lauransan, J. Corset and M.T. Forel, Ann. Chim., 3(1968)109.

170 J. Corset and J. Lascombe, J. Chim. Phys., 64(1967)665.

171 J.P. Roche, Thèse de Docteur Ingénieur, Université de Bordeaux I, (1971), n° 150.

172 J.A. Creighton, J.C.S. Dalton Trans, (1974), 2289.

173 D. Steele, Quart. Rev., 18(1964)21.

174 D. Sreele, Advances in Infrared and Raman Spectroscopy, vol.1, R.J.H. Clark and R.E. Hester Ed., Heyden, London (1975), ch.6.

175 T.L. Brown, Chem. Rev., 58(1958)581.

176 E.R. Lippincott, J. Xavier and D. Steele, J. Am. Chem. Soc., 83(1961)2262.

177 D.E. Irish and T. Jary, Faraday Discussions Chem. Soc., 64(1977)95 and 124.

178 L.A. Woodward and D.A. Long, Trans Faraday Soc., 45(1949)1131.

179 C. Fayat and A. Foucaud, Bull. Soc. Chim., 12(1970)4491.

180 C. Fayat and A. Foucaud, Bull. Soc. Chim., 12(1970)4505.

181 T.L. Brown and M.T. Rogers, J. Am. Chem. Soc., 79(1957)1859.

182 T.L. Brown, "Advances in Organometallic Chemistry" Ed. F.G.A. Stone and R. West, vol.3, Academic Press, New York, (1965).

183 T.L. Brown, D.W. Dickerhoof and D.A. Bafus, J. Am. Chem. Soc. 84(1962)1371.

184 J.P. Oliver, in "Advances in Organometallic Chemistry", vol.15, Ed. F.G.A. Stone and R. West, Academic Press, New York, (1977).

185 E. Weiss and E.A.C. Lucken, J. Organometal. Chem., 2(1964)197.
    E. Weiss and G. Hencken, J. Organomet. Chem., 21(1970)265.

186 V.M. Sovell, B.Y. Kimura and T.G. Spiro, J. Coord. Chem., 1(1971)107.

187 J. Kress, D. Bougeard and A. Novak, Spectrochim. Acta, 33 A(1977)161.

188 J. Kress and A. Novak, J. Organometal. Chem., 99(1975)199.

189 J. Kress and A. Novak, J. Organometal. Chem., 99(1975)23

190 J. Kress and A. Novak, Zh. Strukhim, 18(1977)852.

191 J. Kress and A. Novak, J. Organometal. Chem., 81(1975)281.

192 J. Kress and A. Novak, J. Organometal. Chem., 99(1975)199.

193 L.J. Guggenberg and R.E. Rundle, J. Am. Chem. Soc., 90(1968)5375.

194 J. Kress, J. Organometal. Chem., 111(1976)1.

195 J. Kress and A. Novak, J. Chim. Phys., 4(1977)506.

196 S.P. Randall, F.T. Greene and J.L. Margrave, J. Phys. Chem., 63(1959)758.

197 E. Weiss, J. Organometal. Chem., 4(1965)101.

198 A.P. Akisin and V.P. Spiridonov, Kristallografia, 2(1957)475.

199 J. Kress and A. Novak, J. Organometal. Chem., 121(1976)7.

200 J. Kress and A. Novak, J. Mol. Struct., 23(1974)215.

201 H. Schibillu and M.T. Lebihan, Acta Cryst., 23(1967)232.

202 B. Silvi and C. Sourisseau, Spectrochim. Acta, 31 A(1975)565.
    B. Silvi and C. Sourisseau, J. Chim. Phys., 1(1976)101.

203 E.J. Lanpher, J. Am. Chem. Soc., 79(1957)5578.
    E.J. Lanpher, L.M. Redman and A.A. Morton, J. Org. Chem., 23(1958)1370.
204 D. Seyferth and M.A. Weiner, J. Org. Chem., 26(1961)4797.
205 P. West, J.I. Purmort and S.V. Mc Kinley, J. Am. Chem. Soc. 90(1968)797.
206 B. Gross, Thèse, Paris, CNRS n° AO 1285 (1967).
207 A.Y. Meyer and M. Chrinovitzky, J. Mol. Struct., 12(1972)157.
208 J. Kress, C. Sourisseau and A. Novak, "Metal Ligands Interactions in Organic
    Chemistry and Biochemistry", B. Pullman and N. Goldblum Eds., part 2,
    Reidel Dordrecht, Holland, (1977), p. 299.
209 A.A. Morton and M.E.T. Holden, J. Am. Chem. Soc., 69(1947)1675.
210 P.L. Goggin and I.A. Woodward, Trans Farad. Soc., 62(1966)1423.
211 H.P. Fritz and R. Schneider, Chem. Ber. 93(1960)1171.
212 R. Zerger and G. Stucky, J. Organometal. Chem., 80(1974)7.
213 K.A. Allan, B.G. Gowenlock and W.E. Lindsell, J. Organometal. Chem. 55(1973)229.
214 W.T. Ford, J. Organometal. Chem., 32(1971)27.
215 N. Sheppard, Trans Faraday Soc., 51(1955)1465.
216 J. Kress, Thèse de Doctorat, Université Paris VI, CNRS n° AO 9349.
217 R.G. Vranka and E.L. Anna, J. Am. Chem. Soc., 89(1967)3121.
218 W.B. Maxey and A.I. Popov, J. Am. Chem. Soc., 91(1969)20.
219 J.P. Mathieu and D. Massignon, Compte Rend, 212(1941)1084.
220 N. Jonathan, J. Mol. Spectrosc., 7(1961)105.
221 H. Feuer, C. Savides and C.N.R. Rao, Spectrochim. Acta, 19(1963)431.
    F. Fabian and M. Legrand, Bull. Soc. Chim. France, (1956), 1461.
222 J. Yardwood and W.J. Orville-Thomas, J. Chem. Soc., (1963), 5991.
223 C.M. Drew, J.R. Mc Nesby and A.S. Gordon, J. Am. Chem. Soc., 77(1955)2622.
224 M.J. Brookes and N. Jonathan, J. Chem. Soc. (A), (1968), 1529.
225 E.R. Lippincott, T.E. Kenney, I.R. Nanncy and C.K. Weiffenbach, J. Chem. Soc.,
    B(1967)32.
226 C. Krüger, J. Organometal. Chem. 9(1967)125.
227 G.A. Gornowiej and R. West, J. Am. Chem. Soc., 93(1971)1714.
228 R. Das and C.A. Wilkie, J. Am. Chem. Soc. 94(1972)4555.
229 I.N. Juchnovski and I.G. Binev, J. Organometal. Chem., 99(1975)1.
230 I.G. Binev, R.I. Todorova-Moncheva and I.N. Juchnovski, C.R. Acad. Bulgare
    Sciences, 29(1976)1301.
231 I.N. Juchnovski, J.S. Dimitrova, I.G. Binev and J. Kanchi, Tetrahedron 34(1978)?
232 I.N. Juchnovski, V.D. Radomirska, I.G. Binev and E.A. Grekova, J. Organometal.
    Chem., 128(1977)139.
233 D.A. Long, R.A.G. Carrington and R.B. Gravenor, Nature (London), 196(1962)371.
234 E. Mayer, D.J. Gardinev and R.E. Hester, J. Mol. Struct., 20(1974)127.
235 F.A. Miller and W.K. Baer, Spectrochim. Acta, 19(1963)73.
236 Tseng Kuang Chih, Acta Chim. Sinica, 32(1966)107.
237 P. Anderson, B. Klewe and E. Thom., Acta Chem. Scand., 21(1967)1530.
238 G. Albagnac, B. Bran, B. Calas and L. Giral, Bull. Soc. Chim. France., 7,8
    (1974)1469.
239 I.N. Jukhnovskii, Tcoret i Eksperim Khimiya 3(1967)410.
240 I.N. Juchnovski, I.G. Binev and T.M. Kolev, Tetrahedron Lett., 18(1976)1519.
    I.N. Juchnovski and I.G. Binev, Tetrahedron 33(1977)2993.
241 I.N. Juchnovski and I.G. Binev, Bull. Soc. Chim. Belg., 86(1977)793.
242 H.D. Zook, T.J. Russo, E.F. Ferrand and D.S. Stotz, J. Org. Chem., 33(1968)2222
243 H.O. House and B.M. Trost, J. Org. Chem. 30(1965)2502.
244 Y. Maroni-Barnaud, J. Bertrand, F. Ghozland, L. Gorrichon-Guignon and Y. Koudsi
    C.R. Acad. Sci. Paris, Serie C 280,(1975)221.
245 R. Meyer, L. Gorrichon and P. Maroni, J. Organometal. Chem., 129(1977)C.7
246 L. Lochmann, R.L. De and J. Trekoval, J. Organometal. Chem., 156(1978)307.
247 P. Schmidt, L. Lochmann and B. Schneider, J. Mol. Struct., 9(1971)403.

248 V.M. Defalma and E.M. Arnett, J. Am. Chem. Soc., 100(1978)3514.
    V.M. Defalma and E.M. Arnett, J. Am. Chem. Soc., 98(1976)7447.
249 P. Markov, C. Ivanoff and Arnaudov, Chem. Ber. 97-11(1964)2987.
    B. Jordanov, C. Ivanoff, M. Arnaudov and P. Markov, Chem. Ber. 99-5(1966)1518.
250 F.A. Cotton and R.A. Schunn, J. Am. Chem. Soc., 85(1963)2394.
251 F.A. Cotton, R. Hügel and R. Eiss, Inorg. Chem., 7(1968)18.
252 M. Kirilov and G. Petrov, Monatsh. Für Chemie, 193(1972)1651.
253 P.J. Taylor, Spectrochim. Acta, 34 A(1978)115.
254 T. Bottin-Strzalko, J. Corset, F. Froment and J. Seyden-Penne, to be published.
255 H.G. Gutowsky, J. Chem. Phys., 17(1949)128.
256 M. Raban, E.A. Noe and G. Yamamoto, J. Am. Chem. Soc., 99(1977)6527.
    M. Raban and D. Haritos, J. Chem. Soc. Chem. Comm., (1978)925.
257 S. Wolfe, A. Rauk and I.G. Csizmadia, J. Am. Chem. Soc., 91(1969)1567.
    S. Wolfe, A. Rauk and I.G. Csizmadia, J. Am. Chem. Soc., 89(1967)5710.
    S. Wolfe, A. Rauk, L.M. Tel and I.G. Csizmadia, Can. J. Chem., 47(1969)113.
    S. Wolfe, A. Rauk, L.M. Tel and I.G. Csizmadia, Chem. Comm., (1970), 96.
    A. Rauk, E. Buncel, R.Y. Moir, and S. Wolfe, J. Am. Chem. Soc., 87, 5498, (1965)
258 J.M. Lehn and G. Wipff, J. Am. Chem. Soc. 98(1976)7498.
    J.M. Lehn, G. Wipff, and J. Demuynck, Helv. Chim. Acta 60(1977)1239.
259 G. Chassaing and A. Marquet, Tetrahedron 34(1978)1399
260 I.Y. Kachkurova, Dokl. Akad. Nauk. S.S.S.R, 163(1965)1198.
261 P.C. Li, J.P. Devlin and H.A. Pohl, J. Phys. Chem., 76(1972)1026.
262 I.V. Aleksandrov, Ya.S. Bobovich, Y.G. Maslov and A.N. Sidorov, Zh. Exper.
    Theoret. Fiz. 17(1973)306 ; J.E.T.P. Lett., 17(1973)219.
263 C. Takahashi and S. Maeda, Chem. Phys. Lett., 24(1974)584.
264 C. Takahashi and S. Maeda, Chem. Phys. Lett., 28(1974)22.
265 M. Szwarc "Carbanions Living Polymers and Electron Transfer Processes", Inter-
    science, New York, 1968.

CHAPTER 5

ELECTRON-TRANSFER REACTIONS OF CARBANIONS AND RELATED SPECIES

ROBERT D. GUTHRIE

Department of Chemistry, University of Kentucky, Lexington, Kentucky

CONTENTS

I. INTRODUCTION

The evolution of mechanistic understanding of organic chemistry has relied heavily on the concept of carbocations, carbanions and carbon-centered radicals as intermediates in reactions. Even when these species are not present as kinetically discrete intermediates, a predictive capability is often generated when compounds are viewed as incipient carbanions or incipient carbocations. This point of view becomes unavoidable with the realization that charged intermediates are never truly free in solution and that there is a gradual transition from covalency through ion pairing to solvation which can be controlled within limits by the chemist.

This chapter will deal with the conversion of carbanion-like intermediates to radical-like intermediates. The reactions have electron-transfer-like character and are formally oxidations approximated by eq. 1.

$$C: \quad + \quad A^n \quad \longrightarrow \quad C\cdot \quad + \quad A^{n-1} \qquad [1]$$

Because these reactions connect the entire manifold of carbanion chemistry to that of radical chemistry, it might have been expected that the interface would be too large for coverage in this short chapter. The fact that the subject is still manageable is partly because investigations in this area have only recently become popular. Another reason is that carbanions frequently react with electron deficient molecules by processes which do not appear to involve one-electron transfer. Whether the number of examples of eq. 1 remains small during the next ten years depends partially on the development of techniques for their detection but also, probably more critically, on whether alterations in solution environment can be used to favor eq. 1 in competition with nucleophilic processes. We will discuss this problem further at appropriate points in the chapter.

The chapter will be organized according to acceptor type, that is, around the nature of A in eq. 1. We will work from the structurally simple to the more complex, starting with molecular oxygen and proceeding to biologically significant acceptors. We will try to cover the major synthetic and mechanistic aspects.

In order to save space, we will make frequent use of a nomenclature system that we have developed as a shorthand method for representing mechanistic sequences. Although this system has been completely discussed in the literature,[1] a brief review seems appropriate here. The principle is extremely simple and can be learned in a few minutes. The symbol A (association) indicates bond making (regardless of bond strength) and D (dissociation) indicates bond breaking. A "+" sign between terms indicates that the processes are not concerted. Thus an S_N1 reaction is a D + A process and an S_N2 is AD (or DA). Nucleophilicity or electrophilicity (toward carbon or another atom which is obviously playing a role normally played by carbon) is indicated by the subscript "E" for electrophilic and no subscript (an economy from our original proposal) for nucleophilic. A dot, ".", following a term indicates a homolytic process. Thus the process of eq. 1 is AD., as written, or A + D. if an intermediate complex is involved. (It is not usually known which is correct and we will use the former out of ignorance.) A more elaborate and unambiguous version of the system will also be used, in which the subscripts represent the atoms involved in bond making or bond breaking. The $\underline{first}$ subscripted atom in a given term is understood as carrying the electron pair in a heterolytic process. Thus $A_{OC}D_{IC}$ is an S_N2 reaction in which I: is displaced by O: . If it is desired to incorporate more structure in the subscripts, a comma is used to separate structural units, but the first atom in each unit is always the one involved in bond making or breaking. For example, $A_{OH^-,CH_2}D_{I,CH_2}$ indicates displacement of I: from ICH_2- by OH^-. Homolytic processes are indicated by a dot between the subscripted terms.

II. $\underline{\text{MOLECULAR OXYGEN}}$

A. $\underline{\text{Products}}$

Most simple, in terms of product distribution, is the reaction of tertiary carbon acids with base and molecular oxygen, O_2.[2,3] The earliest detectable product is usually the

$$R_3CH \ + \ O_2 \ \xrightarrow{\text{base}} \ R_3COOH \tag{2}$$

hydroperoxide as shown in eq. 2. If dimethyl sulfoxide (DMSO) is used as solvent, the hydroperoxide is reduced according to

$$R_3COOH \ + \ CH_3\overset{\overset{\displaystyle O}{\|}}{S}CH_3 \ \longrightarrow \ R_3COH \ + \ CH_3\underset{\underset{\displaystyle O}{\|}}{\overset{\overset{\displaystyle O}{\|}}{S}}CH_3 \tag{3}$$

eq. 3. A sampling of carbon functionalization by these reactions is given in Table 1.

When secondary carbon acids are used in this reaction, mechanistic logic suggests that the initially generated hydroperoxide will undergo base-catalyzed elimination as shown

$$B: \quad + \quad HCR_2OOH \quad \xrightarrow{\quad A_{BH}D_{CH}D_{OO} \quad} \quad R_2C=O \quad + \quad OH^- \qquad [4]$$

TABLE 1
AUTOXIDATION OF TERTIARY CARBON ACIDS

R_3CH	Solvent (%)	Base	Product(%)	Ref.
Diphenyl -naphthylmethane	DMSO(80) t-BuOH(20)	t-BuOK	$R_3COH(95)$	3
Triphenylmethane	" "	" "	$R_3COH(95)$	3
" "	DMF(80) t-BuOH(20)	" "	$R_3COOH(87)$	3
" "	t-BuOH 18-crown-6	" "	$R_3COOH(80)$	4
tris-(4-Nitro -phenyl)methane	EtOH	NaOH	$R_3COOH(50\%)$	5
9-Phenylfluorene	DMSO(80) t-BuOH(20)	t-BuOK	$R_3COH(73)$	3
9-Methyfluorene	" "	" "	$R_3COH(79)$	3
9-Methylfluorene	t-BuOH	" "	$R_3COOH(70)$	3
9-Alkylfluorenes	pyridine	R_4NOH	$R_3COOH(72-85)$	2
1,1,4,4-Tetraphenyl -butane	THF	as dianion	$(CH_2CR_2OOH)_2$ (50)	6

in eq. 4. This is clearly the case when a relatively acidic substrate such as fluorene is used.[2,7-9] With less acidic substrates, such as diphenylmethane, the hydroperoxide is sufficiently long-lived to oxidize DMSO by eq. 3, giving benzhydrol in 85% yield.[7] If hexamethylphosphoric triamide

(HMPA) is substituted for DMSO, the reaction proceeds via eq. 4, provided that a proton source is available to form the hydroperoxide from its anion.[7] 9,10-Dihydroanthracene is oxidized by base and O_2 to a mixture of anthraquinone and anthracene[10-12] but there is some disagreement about the intermediates involved.[11]

The utility of base-catalyzed autoxidation of hydrocarbons is obviously limited by the acidity of potential substrates. If, however, the definition of "carbanion" is extended to lithium and magnesium derivatives, simple alkyl and aryl "carbanions" can be oxidized.[13-17] In the case of aryl Grignard reagents, the reaction probably proceeds via the hydroperoxide but this intermediate is not stable. The reaction is nonetheless useful as a step in the preparation of phenols from the corresponding halides.[18] Phenyllithium, as its tetramethylethylenediamine (TMEDA) complex, is converted by O_2 to a mixture of phenoxide and biphenyl with the relative amounts depending on reaction conditions.[19] With aliphatic Grignard reagents, Walling and Buckler[20] have developed the reaction as a synthesis of alkyl hydroperoxides with yields ranging from 30 to 90%.

The reaction of carbanions with O_2 will also occur when the negative charge is partially distributed to an atom of a more electronegative element. The reaction with enolate ions is one of the earliest cases[21] and many more recent examples can be found in a 1970 review.[22] The initial steps are not qualitatively different from those described above. In cases where the most acidic α-hydrogen in a ketone is tertiary, the hydroperoxide is often isolable and this is occasionally true for hindered secondary cases.[23-27] In addition to the products already discussed, an α,β-unsaturated carbonyl compound may be generated.[28] The mechanism for its formation may involve elimination of hydrogen peroxide or it may arise via a precursor of the hydroperoxide as discussed later.

For tertiary α-ketohydroperoxides (1), prolonged treatment with base will produce cleavage of the carbon-carbon bond as shown in eq. 5. The traditional mechanism[21,23-27] for this reaction invokes a dioxetan intermediate (2). This mechanism is less compelling now that

the stable form of the initial intermediate has been shown to
be ($\underline{1}$) rather than ($\underline{2}$).[26,29,30] Although the dioxetan
mechanism has persisted[31] and recently chemiluminescence
studies have been interpreted in its support,[32] we suggest

$$
\begin{array}{ccc}
\overset{O}{\underset{}{\overset{\|}{\text{R-C}}}}\overset{R''}{\underset{}{\overset{|}{\text{-C-R}'}}} & \xrightarrow{A_{OH^-},C=O} & \overset{O^-}{\underset{}{\overset{}{\text{R-C}}}}\overset{R''}{\underset{}{\overset{|}{\text{-C-R}'}}} \quad [5] \\
\overset{}{\underset{O}{\overset{O}{\diagdown}}} \qquad (\underline{1}) & & \overset{O}{\underset{}{}}\quad\overset{O}{\underset{}{}} \\
\overset{}{\underset{H}{\overset{|}{O}}} & & \text{H} \quad O \\
& & \qquad\quad\text{H}
\end{array}
$$

$A_{BH}D_{OH} + A_{O^-},C=O + A_{OH}D_{BH}$

$\xrightarrow{D_{OH}D_{CC}D_{OO}}$

$$
\begin{array}{ccc}
\overset{H}{\underset{}{\overset{}{O}}}\overset{R''}{\underset{}{}} & & \\
\overset{}{\underset{}{\overset{|}{\text{R-C}}}}\overset{|}{\underset{}{\text{-C-R}'}} & \underset{\xleftarrow{}}{\xrightarrow{A_{OH^-},H + D_{OH}D_{OO}}} & R-\overset{O}{\overset{\|}{C}}-O^- + R'R''C=O + H_2O \\
\overset{}{\underset{O}{\overset{|}{}}}\overset{}{\underset{O}{\overset{|}{}}} & & \\
(\underline{2}) & &
\end{array}
$$

that the upper path in eq. 5 avoids the high energy dioxetan,
while arriving at the same products. There is some precedent
for this suggestion in the observation that acetone enolate
will attack the carbonyl of α-hydroperoxybutyrophenone at a
rate competitive with cleavage.[33]

When the α-ketohydroperoxide is secondary, the
elimination of eq. 4 gives an α-diketone which can itself
serve as an electron acceptor,[10,34,35] reacting with either
the original enolate or the enolate of the α-diketone. In
addition to these electron transfer processes which will be
discussed later in the chapter, the diketone can undergo the
benzilic acid rearrangement,[36] $A_{OH^-},C=O + (D_{R,CO}-A_{R,C=O})$.
(Note that the parentheses indicate an intramolecular process.)
Although α-diketones have not been invoked as intermediates in
any of the bond-cleavage processes, it is interesting to note
that superoxide ion, which could well be present under the
reaction conditions for ketone autoxidation, is found to

cleave α-diketones to the corresponding carboxylic acids.[37]

Carbon acids activated by cyano,[38-40] carboalkoxy,[41,42] nitro,[43-45] and even carboxylate groups,[46] react with base and O_2 in qualitatively similar ways.[47] For cyano compounds with two α-hydrogens, the reaction proceeds in analogy with eq. 4, followed by $A_{OH^-,C=O} + D_{C\equiv N,C}$. For cases with only one α-hydrogen, the reaction follows eq. 5 with $A_{OH^-,C=O}$ replaced by $A_{OH^-,C=N}$ leading to formation of cyanate ion. With nitroalkanes, there is a formal similarity to the nitrile systems in that the nitro group is removed and replaced by a carbonyl group. The mechanism seems likely to be more complex, although a hydroperoxide is believed to be involved.[44] A similar outcome can be effected with carboxylic acids, although an additional step is required as shown in eq. 6.[46]

$$R_2C=C\overset{OLi}{\underset{OLi}{\big\backslash}} \quad \xrightarrow{O_2} \quad R_2\overset{\overset{\displaystyle OLi}{|}}{\underset{\underset{\displaystyle O}{\|}}{C}}-C-OLi \quad \xrightarrow[Me_2NCH(OMe)_2]{H^+} \quad R_2C=O \quad [6]$$

α,β-Unsaturated ketones will participate in this reaction through removal of a γ-hydrogen.[48,49] In some early work by Treibs,[50-54] it appeared that base and O_2 would effect oxidation of the double bond in such compounds without functionalization of the γ-carbon. Treibs, however, showed that oxidation at the double bond to give the same products could be carried out using hydrogen peroxide and base. He suggested that hydrogen peroxide was produced in the autoxidation. It seems possible that the difference between Treibs' experiments and those of later workers[48,49] may have been the presence of substrate at very high concentrations which favored bimolecular reactions between neutral substrate and peroxidic species generated in the normal reaction.

B. Mechanism

As may be seen from the preceding examples, the

hydroperoxide is the pivotal intermediate in the reaction of carbanions with O_2. Three different mechanisms have been proposed for its formation which we will term the electron-transfer chain mechanism, the electron-transfer non-chain mechanism and the direct mechanism. The first two involve an electron-transfer process with the consequent generation of radicals, eq. 7, while the latter, which is forbidden for

$$R^- \quad + \quad O_2 \quad \longrightarrow \quad R\cdot \quad + \quad O_2^{\cdot -} \qquad [7]$$

ground-state O_2 by the rules of spin conservation, does not

$$R^- \quad + \quad O_2 \quad \longrightarrow \quad ROO^- \qquad [8]$$

invoke electron transfer, eq. 8.

It is clear that radicals are formed in many of the reactions discussed above because of the observation of dimers $(R-R)$.[8,12,19,55-58] Although in some cases these could result from carbanion-radical combination $(A_{C^-},\cdot_C)$ as well as from the more conventional radical coupling $(A_{C,C})$, their presence is an unmistakable sign of free radical involvement. Another process which could involve radical intermediates is the occasional dehydrogenation observed when the carbon next to the one carrying the negative charge bears an acidic hydrogen.[19,59-61] In the most incontrovertable case, the radical which forms by eq. 7 is sufficiently stable for direct identification.[62]

The radical formed in eq. 7 would be expected to react with molecular oxygen by eq. 9 (providing that it escapes from superoxide ion). If this is followed by eq. 10, a kinetic

$$R\cdot \quad + \quad O_2 \quad \longrightarrow \quad ROO\cdot \qquad [9]$$

$$ROO\cdot \quad + \quad R^- \quad \longrightarrow \quad ROO^- \quad + \quad R\cdot \qquad [10]$$

chain sequence may be established. The most convincing evidence for a chain process is observed for the carbanion from 2-nitropropane, $(\underline{3})$.[43,44] This carbanion does not undergo a direct reaction with O_2[63] as demonstrated by the fact that solutions in which the carbon acid has largely been converted to carbanion show a marked induction period for reaction with this reagent. Russell has provided evidence for the initiation process of eq. 11. The reaction shows

$$Me_2C=NO_2^- + Me_2CHNO_2 \longrightarrow Me_2\dot{C}NO_2 + Me_2CHNO_2^{\bar{\cdot}} \quad [11]$$

autocatalysis which points to the generation of secondary acceptors as the reaction proceeds. One of these may be the peroxyl radical reacting as shown in eq. 10.

A similar mechanistic sequence is now accepted for the reaction of Grignard reagents with molecular oxygen. Although Walling's initial experiments seemed to point to a direct mechanism for the formation of magnesium hydroperoxide,[20] experiments by Garst suggested that a radical intermediate is involved.[64] Walling and Cioffari then showed 5-hexenylmagnesium bromide, (4), gives some cyclized product when treated with molecular oxygen. The proportion of cyclization products decreases with increasing O_2 concentration,[65] which suggested the partitioning shown in eq. 12.

$$CH_2=CHCH_2CH_2CH_2CH_2MgBr \xrightarrow{O_2}$$
$$(\underline{4})$$

[12]

Although the electron-transfer chain mechanism seems almost unavoidable when the reaction of eq. 9 occurs in the presence of high concentrations of carbanion (or Grignard reagent), it would seem a less obvious choice when the carbanion is present at low, steady state concentrations.

Russell has argued for the occurrence of short kinetic chains in the reaction of fluorene with O_2 catalyzed by potassium t-butoxide in t-butyl alcohol.[66] However, this mechanism relies critically on the reaction of eq. 10 for chain propagation and it seems remarkable that peroxyl radical (ROO·) would survive in sufficient concentration to compete with the primary acceptor. The major piece of evidence for a chain mechanism is the fact that initiation by nitrobenzene produces a rate for the O_2 reaction which is 21 times greater than the rate of the direct reaction with nitrobenzene in the absence of O_2. This has been interpreted as indicating a kinetic chain length of 21, i.e., that 21 product molecules are formed for each initiation step.[66] An alternative view of this phenomenon is that the electron transfer to nitrobenzene is reversible with only one of 21 electron transfer events leading to products. This reversibility would be eliminated by the presence of O_2 (through its rapid reaction with the nitrobenzene radical anion),[67] thereby explaining the observed rate difference. We have used this latter interpretation in explaining the effect of O_2 on the reaction of 9-methoxyfluorene with nitrobenzene in methanol-methoxide.[68] Additional details will appear later in this chapter. In cases like these where the carbanion concentration remains low and particularly where deprotonation of the carbon acid is a slow, rate-determining process, it seems likely that the electron-transfer step is followed either by recombination with superoxide, eq. 13, or possibly by the sequence of eqs. 9 and 14. In either case, a kinetic

$$R\cdot \quad + \quad O_2^{\bar{\cdot}} \quad \longrightarrow \quad ROO^- \qquad\qquad [13]$$

$$R\text{-}OO\cdot \quad + \quad O_2^{\bar{\cdot}} \quad \longrightarrow \quad ROO^- \quad + \quad O_2 \qquad [14]$$

chain is not involved.

A mechanism involving direct reaction between O_2 and carbanion to give hydroperoxide ion has been resisted by most workers because O_2 is a triplet in its ground state. Reaction with a singlet carbanion would be expected to produce

an excited state of the product, based on the usual spin
conservation rules. Some interesting recent experiments by
Nishinaga and co-workers appear to violate this principle,
however.[69] Their important discovery is that the
hydroperoxide, (5), reacts with base to give O_2 and (6) which
appear to be in their ground states. As eq. 15 is simply the
reverse of eq. 8, microscopic reversibility requires that spin
conservation be disregarded as an objection to the forward

(5)   (6)   R=t-Bu

process.

Nishinaga suggests[69] that this result, along with other
experiments which militate against the chain process in this
system, provides evidence for a one-step, direct reaction
between triplet O_2 and singlet phenolate to give
hydroperoxide. We would challenge this assertion because we
feel that these experiments are not capable of ruling out the
sequence of eq. 16, provided that the equilibrium lies to the

(6)   (7)   (5⁻)

R=t-Bu   plus other products

left. It is clear that the equilibrium between (5⁻) and (6)
lies on the side of (6) because it is the product when (5)
reacts with t-BuOK in dimethylformamide (DMF). Moreover,
Nishinaga has shown that (7) will react with
O_2⁻ to give (6).[69] Compound (5) can be produced from (6) using
ethanol-water solvent,[70] but this is apparently made possible
by a solvent effect favoring (5⁻) in ethanol-water and (6) in
DMF. Compound (6) does undergo autoxidation in DMF and other

aprotic, polar solvents,[71] but (5[-]) is a relatively high
energy intermediate on the path to the eventual products.

Nishinaga has pointed to literature analogies for the
direct reaction of O_2 with diamagnetic metal
complexes[72] and with strained acetylenes.[73] While we do not
wish to discount this possibility for the reaction of
phenolates with O_2, we do not feel it has been proven. At
least in the autoxidation of some carbanions there is
definitive evidence for the intermediacy of radicals.

C. Trapping Experiments

Molecular oxygen has not been as useful in intercepting
carbanion intermediates of organic reactions as it has been in
trapping radicals. The usual fate of carbanions is
protonation which, if exothermic, is a fast, often diffusion-
limited reaction. Reaction with O_2 does not compete with
protonation as well as might be expected from its reduction
potential, possibly because of the spin restrictions discussed
in the previous section. The cases in which carbanions have
been found to react with O_2 faster than they undergo
protonation[3,4,7] represent cases which, in our opinion,
involve relatively low protonation rates. Although
Russell[3] initially concluded that protonation of
triphenylmethide ion by t-BuOH in 80% DMSO - 20% t-BuOH was
nearly diffusion limited, this estimate was based on data of
Ritchie and Uschold which they later revised.[74,75] It seems
likely to us[76] that the protonation rates are well below the
diffusion limit for systems which exhibit efficient trapping
by O_2.

In several systems[4,10,68] it has been found that
nitrobenzene is a better carbanion trap than O_2. Although
this comparison is somewhat unfair because the concentrations
of O_2 employed are necessarily rather low, the reduction
potential of O_2 is -0.8 V vs. SCE in aprotic polar solvents[77]
whereas that of nitrobenzene is -1.13 V under the same
conditions.[78] It seems likely that the difference will be
greater in protic solvents and should counterbalance
concentration effects. A case in point is that of
9-methoxyfluorene in methanol-methoxide[68] in which direct

reaction with O_2 is immeasurably slow under conditions where nitrobenzene is effective. The fact that O_2 will trap nitrobenzenide but not carbanion when it is used in conjunction with nitrobenzene suggests strongly that the relative inefficiency of the oxygen reaction is a kinetic and not an equilibrium phenomenon.

A case in which a carbanion reaction is diverted from its normal course by O_2 has been studied by McGrath.[79] When α-haloketones in the 8,13-epoxylabdan-2-one series (8), are subjected to the conditions of the Favorskii rearrangement in the presence of O_2, the normal ring-contracted-ester product (9) is partially supplanted by ring-contracted alkene (10),

[17]

eq. 17. The trapping reaction appears to involve the α'-enolate but is sensitive to the nature of the halogen or other leaving group.

The efficiency of the trapping of carbanions by O_2 is highly sensitive to the nature of the medium in which the reaction is carried out. We will discuss this phenomenon in detail in section V.

III. TRANSITION METAL COMPLEXES

In considering possible reagents for carrying out one-electron oxidation of carbanions, an obvious choice would seem to be a transition metal complex. There are relatively few examples of success with this approach, however, for two main reasons. One is that the complex must be stable to the

conditions required to generate carbanions (normally strongly
alkaline) and second that it be soluble in the reaction medium
(usually an organic solvent). These difficulties are easily
demonstrated using complexes of iron as examples.

It is perhaps worth pointing out to those of marginal
familiarity with inorganic chemistry that the nature of the
complexing agent is frequently more important in determining
the characteristics of a transition metal complex than is the
metal itself. As illustration, consider the examples of Table

TABLE 2 (ref. 80)

REDUCTION POTENTIALS OF SELECTED IRON COMPLEXES

Complex	E^o in V vs. SCE
$Fe(CN)_6$	-0.36
Ferrocene	-0.56
Fe(aq)	-0.71
Fe(dipyr)$_3$	-1.096
Fe(o-phen)$_3$	-1.14

2.[80] The relevant characteristic is the reduction potential
and for the five possibilities listed, the upper three show
promising values (compare nitrobenzene, a known oxidizer of
carbanions, E^o = -1.13 V vs. SCE in DMF).[78] It is clear,
however, from the well known tendency of Fe(III) salts to form
insoluble hydroxides in alkaline medium that only the most
tightly coordinated complexes will be useful. Even
ferricinium salts (fourth entry in Table 2) react with
OH$^-$ to form $(C_5H_5)_2FeOH$[81] which undergoes subsequent
decomposition. Of the five entries in Table 2 all are thus
eliminated except for ferricyanide (hexacyanoferrate).
Ferricyanide ion is stable to alkali because the ligands are
very tightly bound to the iron atom.[82] Unfortunately the

common salts of this triply charged ion are insoluble in organic solvents.

A. Ferricyanide

Although these considerations have limited the use of transition metal complexes as one-electron oxidants in organic solvents, a few alkali-stable complexes such as ferricyanide[83] are regularly used in aqueous solutions. Relatively hydrophilic carbanions such as enolates,[84-90] phenolates,[91,92] nitrobenzyl anions[93,94] and nitroalkanides[88] have been oxidized by ferricyanide. Representative examples are given in eqs. 18-21.

The existing evidence suggests strongly that these reactions (eqs. 18-21) are initiated by anion formation followed by one-electron transfer. In the case of phenolates,[91,92] the anion is preformed and the electron transfer is probably rate determining. For ketones and aldehydes, the proton removal is probably rate determining in a few cases involving highly substituted radicals. For example, the oxidation of isobutyraldehyde is zero order in ferricyanide, whereas for n-butyraldehyde, the dependence of ferricyanide changes from first order to zero order as the aldehyde concentration is increased.[88] Various speculative schemes have been suggested for the mechanistic steps following radical formation.[85,87,88] However an obvious but unsuggested possibility is the sequence of eq. 22 (shown for

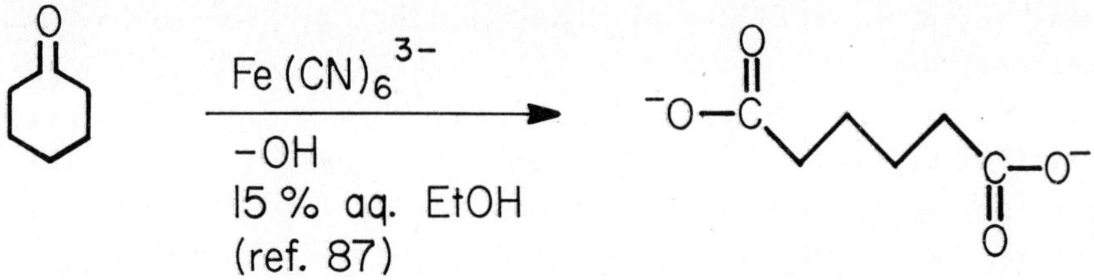

$$Fe(CN)_6^{3-}$$
$-OH$
15 % aq. EtOH
(ref. 87)

[18]

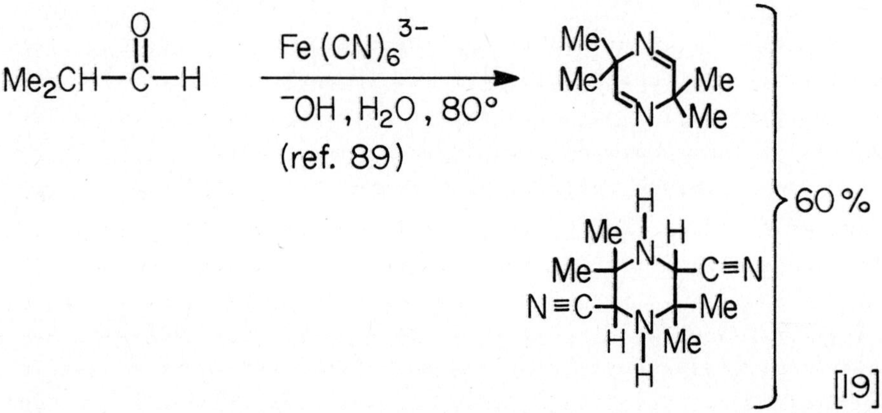

$$Me_2CH-C-H$$

$$Fe(CN)_6^{3-}$$
$^-OH, H_2O, 80°$
(ref. 89)

60 %

[19]

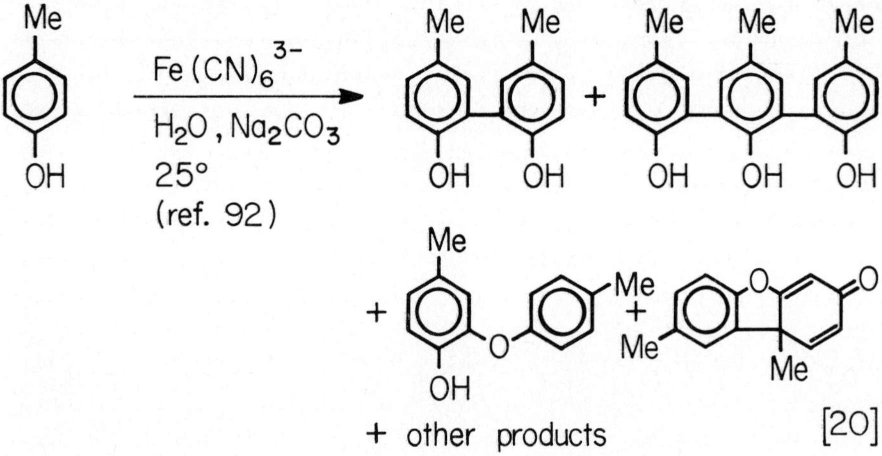

$$Fe(CN)_6^{3-}$$
H_2O, Na_2CO_3
25°
(ref. 92)

+ other products

[20]

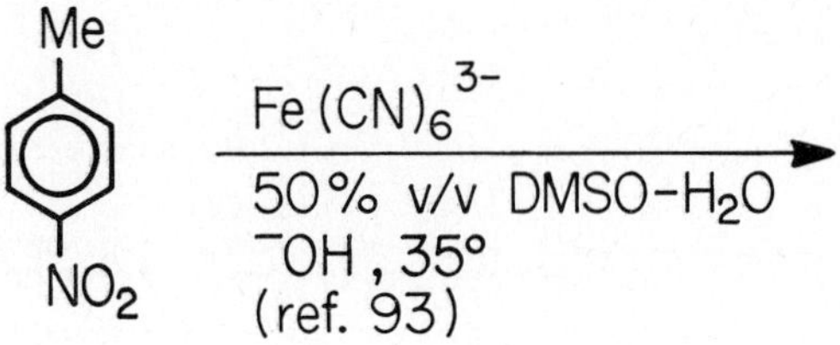

$$Fe(CN)_6^{3-}$$
50% v/v DMSO-H_2O
$^-OH, 35°$
(ref. 93)

[21]

the enolate case). This would be a good start toward the products of eqs. 18 and 21. It would also help to explain the production of oxalic acid from acetone and methyl ethyl ketone.[85] The $A_{OH^-}, \cdot C-C=O$ process is modeled after the product-forming step in the $S_{RN}1$[95,96] mechanism originally proposed by Russell[97] and Kornblum[98] with the only difference being that the radical is produced oxidatively rather than reductively.

The products of eq. 19 require a more involved mechanism because it has been shown that α-hydroxyisobutyraldehyde does not give these products under the reaction conditions.[89] Moreover, an aminoketone can be isolated from the reaction of phenyl isopropyl ketone with ferricyanide.[90] By analogy to the suggestion of eq. 22, an $A_N, \cdot C-C=O$ process could be invoked. The nucleophilic nitrogen could be provided by ferricyanide ion itself, as originally suggested,[90] or by some other species generated through reaction of ferri- or ferrocyanide with hydroxide at 80°.

The yields in these reactions have rarely been reported and are probably rather poor. In addition to the possibilities for competing base-catalyzed reactions, the mechanism of eq. 22 would suggest the possibility that the carbanion itself could serve as nucleophile, $A_{C^-}, \cdot C-C=O$, a process which could explain the apparent coupling products in eq. 20.

Although the reduction potential of ferricyanide suggests that it should be a better oxidant than most of the reagents discussed in this chapter, it nevertheless has its limits. The ylid-type "carbanions" formed from quaternary pyridinium salts do not react with ferricyanide[99] despite the appearance created by the formation of pyridones in the presence of base and ferricyanide. The actual route is that shown in eq. 23.[100,101] The mechanism by which (12) is converted to (13) has not been established with certainty. Recently a closely related system was suggested to proceed from an intermediate analogous to (12) to an alkoxide, $A_{BH}D_{OH}$, followed by hydride transfer from this intermediate to ferricyanide, $A_{HFe}D_{HC}$, to produce $HFe(CN)_6^{4-}$.[102] If such a process were to prove possible, it would necessitate reexamination of a large number

$$\text{(11)} \quad \xrightarrow{\text{OH}^-} \quad \text{(12)} \quad \xrightarrow[\text{Fe(CN)}_6{}^{3-}]{\text{OH}^-} \quad \text{(13)} \qquad [23]$$

$$\text{(11)} \;\Big\updownarrow\; \text{OH}^-$$

$$\xrightarrow{\text{Fe(CN)}_6{}^{3-}} \quad \text{no reaction}$$

of mechanistic conclusions based on the assumption that ferricyanide always functions as a one-electron acceptor. A more expected pathway would be simple one-electron transfer from (12), $A_N Fe D_N \cdot Fe$, followed by proton removal, $A_{BH} D_{CH}$, and a second electron transfer. This alternative does not explain all of the experimental data,[102] however. These challenging questions notwithstanding, electron transfer mechanisms are clearly operative for the reactions of the majority of carbanions with ferricyanide.

These reactions are not entirely restricted to aqueous systems because we have successfully employed a two-phase system in two unpublished cases. Unfortunately, mechanistic studies or trapping experiments are difficult under these conditions. The design of one-electron-accepting transition metal complexes for use in organic solvents containing strong bases would be a worthy research enterprise.

B. Other Complexes

With the exception of the ferricyanide reaction there are very few extensively studied examples of carbanion oxidation by transition metal complexes. There are a number of cases in which the carbanion forms a complex with copper (II) salts and these complexes, in turn, transfer one electron to a secondary acceptor such as O_2.[103-105] The copper seems to serve a purely passive role in this process, facilitating in some way the electron-transfer to the actual acceptor.

In a very similar type of reaction alkyllithium compounds and other organometallics react with complexed copper (I) salts to form copper (I) "ate" complexes[106-109] as shown in

$$4RLi \ + \ 1/2[ICuPBu_3]_4 \quad \xrightarrow[-78]{THF} \quad R_4Cu_2Li_2 \qquad [24]$$

$$R_4Cu_2Li_2 \quad \xrightarrow{O_2 \text{ or } PhNO_2} \quad R-R \qquad [25]$$

eq. 24. An oxidant such O_2 or nitrobenzene can then be used to convert the complex to the dimer of the alkyl group originally bound to lithium, eq. 25. The reaction of eq. 25 apparently does not proceed via the radicals, R· , as demonstrated by the fact that only partial epimerization occurs when stereoisomers of RHgBr are used to prepare the initial "ate" complex[106] and various other tests.[109] Dimer formation is best viewed as a rearrangement of R_4Cu_2Li. Alkyllithiums have also been shown to react with $TiCl_4$. The generation of alkyl radicals has been demonstrated by ESR.[110]

In other recent reports, copper t-butoxide has been seen to effect coupling between 1,3-dinitrobenzene and aryl iodides,[111] and organoaluminates are oxidized by lead tetraacetate.[112] These processes could conceivably involve electron transfer steps. Sargeson[113] has also reported a case in which a cobalt complex is used to both activate a carbon acid and oxidize the resultant carbanion.

It is clear from the meticulous studies of Kochi[114,115] that organometallics can rarely be expected to react with transition metal oxidants to simply generate the corresponding radicals. An exception occurs when tetraalkyllead compounds react with hexachloroiridate (IV) as

$$R_4Pb \ + \ IrCl_6^{2-} \quad \longrightarrow \quad R_4Pb^{\ddagger} \ + \ IrCl_6^{3-} \qquad [26]$$

$$R_4Pb^{\ddagger} \quad \xrightarrow{fast} \quad R\cdot \ + \ R_3Pb^+ \qquad [27]$$

shown in eqs. 26 and 27.[114,115] To demonstrate the care that must be exercised in interpreting such reactions, however, consider the apparently analogous case of eqs. 28 and 29. Again alkyl radicals are produced from tetraalkyllead, the reagent undergoes reduction, but no electron transfer reaction

$$R_4Pb + CuX_2 \longrightarrow R_3PbX + RCuX \qquad [28]$$

$$RCuX \xrightarrow{\text{fast}} R\cdot + CuX \qquad [29]$$

is involved. Substituent effects suggest that eq. 28 is best regarded as an electrophilic substitution. In still another variation, carbanionoids proceed to form dimers under the influence of transition metal compounds without forming radical intermediates.[114,115]

These reactions are often synthetically useful[116,117] but, as can be seen, their mechanisms are difficult to generalize. For purposes of predicting reaction outcome, the possibility of simple ligation to form a stable complex[118-121] or nucleophilic attack on the ligand[122,123] must also be kept in mind.

IV. ORGANIC ACCEPTORS

Most unsaturated functional groups and carbon-halogen bonds can, in the proper molecular environment, be observed to participate in electron transfer reactions with carbanions. Whether or not a particular acceptor-carbanion pair is suitable, is potentially predictable[124,125] from the reduction potential of the acceptor and the oxidation potential of the donor. The excellent compilation of Mann and Barnes[126] is a good place to start looking for the former and, even when data for the carbanion are not available, allows relative judgments for the acceptors. Unfortunately, carbanions are usually oxidized irreversibily in electrochemical systems and thermodynamically meaningful data are much more difficult to obtain. A start in this area has been taken by Federlin[127] who has established a scale of half-wave potentials for a number of carbanions in DMSO. The $E_{1/2}$ values determined are in the same order as the pK_a values of the corresponding hydrocarbons.

The use of electrochemical information to predict the occurrence of electron transfer is subject to a few additional hazards. Even if the calculated energetics for electron transfer suggest success, some other chemical reaction may be faster. Moreover, the circumstances of electrochemical experiments are restricted by the requirement for a soluble electrolyte which excludes many systems of interest to the organic chemist. As will be seen later, ion pairing and solvation can completely regulate the rates and equilibria of electron transfer reactions. Oxidation-reduction potential data obtained in a polar solvent may be useless for predicting reactions in tetrahydrofuran (THF), dimethoxyethane (DME), t-butyl alcohol and other favorite solvents of the carbanion chemist.

For the reasons discussed above, it is not possible to engage in much useful prognostication regarding the likelihood of individual reactions. We will therefore confine ourselves to summarizing the cases where carbanions have been claimed to react with organic acceptors and leave generalizations and predictions to the imagination of the reader. Table 3 is a listing of representative examples. Where these are discussed in the text, an asterisk marks the spot.

A. Ketones

1. Reaction with Alkyl Magnesium Halides

The careful studies of Ashby[128-133] demonstrate that a delicate balance exists between the mechanistic alternatives of nucleophilic addition and one-electron reduction in the reactions of Grignard reagents with ketones. Although these investigations have been complicated by the effect of trace amounts of transition metal impurities in the commercial grades of magnesium used to prepare Grignard reagents,[130,131] it has been shown that, even in the absence of such catalysts, t-butylmagnesium halides will reduce diarylketones by a one-electron process. The reaction produces benzpinacols as well as 1,2-, 1,4- and 1,6-addition products.*[134] At the other extreme, methylmagnesium bromide reacts with diarylketones by an apparent polar-addition

TABLE 3

ELECTRON TRANSFER FROM CARBANIONS TO ORGANIC ACCEPTORS

Acceptor	Donor (Solvent)	Product %	Ref.

$Ph_2C=O^a$ $t-BuMgX$ (ether) → products:

$Ph_2C-Bu-t$ with OH (44)

benzophenone–$Bu-t$ (50)

Ph_2C-CPh_2 with HO OH (6) — Ref. 134

Ph–C(=O)–tolyl (Me)   MeMgBr, 0.5 mole % $FeCl_3$ (ether) → products:

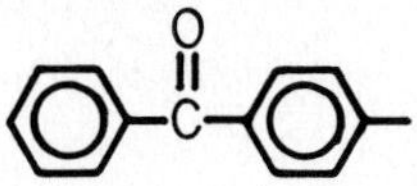

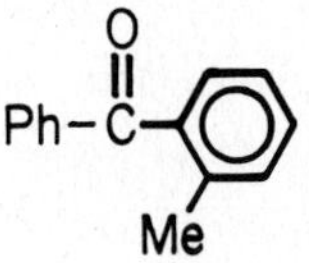

$Ph-C(OH)-tol-o$ with Me (29)

$o-tol-C(HO)-C(OH)-tol-o$ with Ph Ph (71)

(no $FeCl_3$, no pinacol) — Ref. 132

$Ph_2C=O$ (alkenyl MgCl) → products:

$Ph_2C(OH)$ with alkenyl chain (38)

$Ph-C(=O)$–benzene–cyclopentyl (46)

$Ph-C(=O)$–benzene–alkenyl (16) — Ref. 129

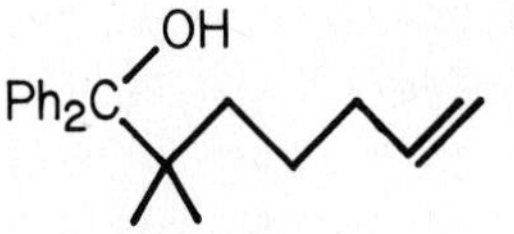

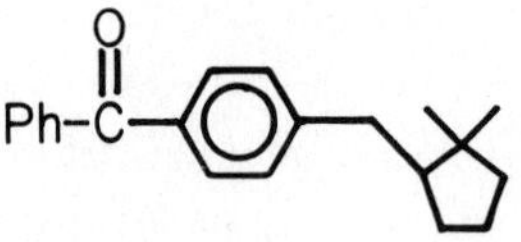

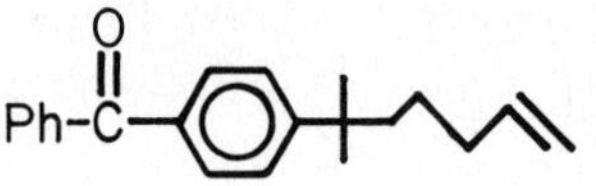

Acceptor	Donor (Solvent)	Product (%)	Ref.
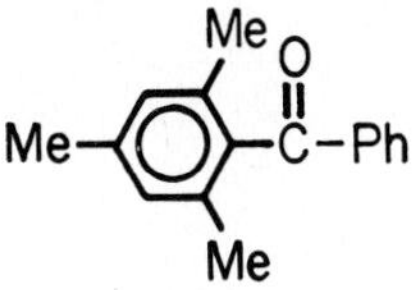	PhMgBr (THF)	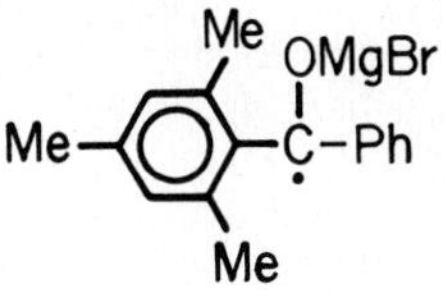 (30)	142
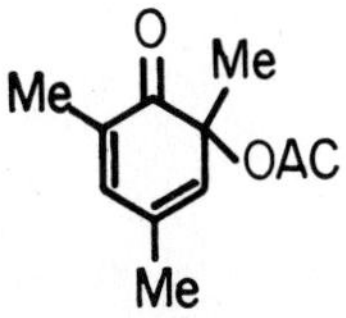	$PhCH_2MgCl$ (ether)	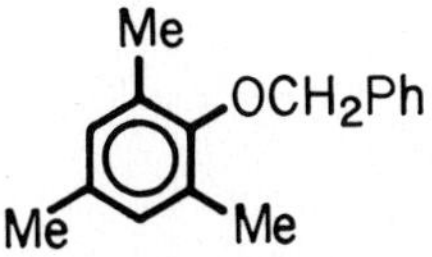 (91)	136–139
$PhCH{=}CH{-}C(O){-}Ph$	Ph_3CLi	$Ph_3C{-}CH(Ph){-}CH_2C(O)Ph$ (80)	143
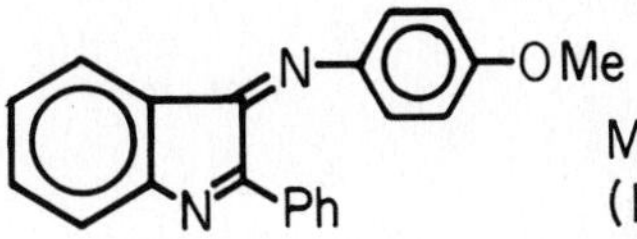	MeLi (benzene–THF)	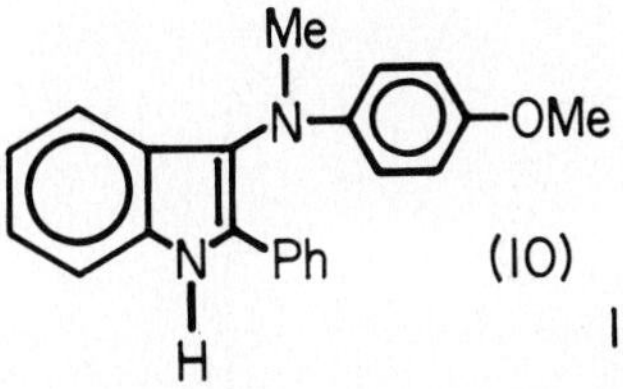 (10)	145
$Me_2C{=}CH{-}C(O){-}Me$	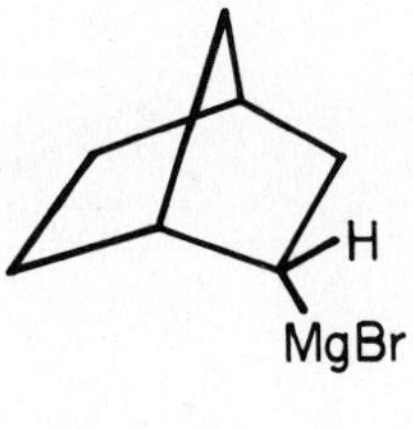 + R_3PCuI + Me_3CLi (ether)	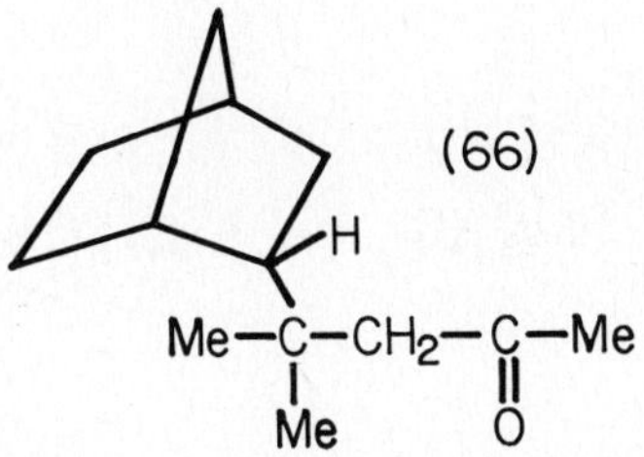 (66) (no exo)	150

Acceptor	Donor (Solvent)	Product (%)	Ref.

t-Bu, H : C=C : t-Bu, C–Bu-t with =O   Me₄CuLi₂ (ether)   t-Bu, H / H product C–Bu-t =O (69)

t-Bu–C(H)(Me)–CH₂–C(=O)–Bu-t (23)   124

Ph–C(Me)(Me)–Cl   Me,Me C=C=C H,Li (ether)   Ph–C(Me)(Me)–C(Me)(Me)–C≡C–H (27)

Ph–C(Me)(Me)–C(Me)(Me)–Ph (15)

Me,Me C=C=C(H)–C(Me)(Me)(Ph) (15)   174

ArNO₂   fluorene-OMe (MeOH)   fluorenylidene=N(Ar)→O (25)

MeO,OMe bifluorenyl (50)   199

Acceptor	Donor (Solvent)	Product (%)	Ref.

Acceptor	Donor (Solvent)	Product (%)	Ref.
PhNO$_2$	9-Methylfluorenyl anion, Me (MeOH)	(73)	199
ArNO$_2$	9-Hydroxyfluorenyl, OH (MeOH)	(99) fluorenone, O	199
ArNO$_2$	9-Aminofluorenyl, NH$_2$ (MeOH)	(97) fluorenone imine, N–H	199
PhNO$_2$	Ph$_2$C=C=N$^-$ (MeOH)	N≡C, Ph$_2$C–C$_6$H$_4$–N=CPh$_2$, ↓O (96)	200
PhNO$_2$	Ph$_3$CK (t–BuOH)	Ph$_3$COH (48)	
		Ph$_3$C–C$_6$H$_4$–N=N(→O)–Ar (41)	
		Ph$_3$C–C$_6$H$_4$–CHPh$_2$ (trace)	205

Acceptor	Donor (Solvent)	Product (%)	Ref.
$O_2N-\!\!\bigcirc\!\!-CH_2Cl$	$O_2N-\!\!\bigcirc\!\!-\overset{-}{C}H-Cl$ (H$_2$O–dioxane)	$(O_2N-\!\!\bigcirc\!\!-CH{=}\!)_2$ (28 cis, 24 trans)	
		$O_2N-\!\!\bigcirc\!\!-CH-CH-\!\!\bigcirc\!\!-NO_2$ with bridging O (25 cis, 19 trans)	
		$O_2N-\!\!\bigcirc\!\!-CH_2OH$ (3)	
		$O_2N-\!\!\bigcirc\!\!-\overset{O}{\overset{\|}{C}}-H$ (trace)	
		$(O_2N-\!\!\bigcirc\!\!-C{\equiv}\!)_2$ (trace)	
		$O_2N-\!\!\bigcirc\!\!-CH_3$ (trace)	223
$O_2N-\!\!\bigcirc\!\!-Me$	$O_2N-\!\!\bigcirc\!\!-\overset{-}{C}H_2$	$(O_2N-\!\!\bigcirc\!\!-CH_2{+}\!)_2$ (55)	203
$O_2N-\overset{Me}{\underset{Me}{\overset{\|}{\underset{\|}{C}}}}-Cl$	$Et\overset{-}{C}(CO_2Et)_2$ (EtOH)	$Me_2C-\overset{NO_2}{\underset{Et}{\overset{\|}{\underset{\|}{C}}}}(CO_2Et)_2$ (68)	231, 234
$O_2N-\overset{Me}{\underset{Me}{\overset{\|}{\underset{\|}{C}}}}-\overset{O}{\underset{O}{\overset{\|}{\underset{\|}{S}}}}-\!\!\bigcirc\!\!-Me$	cyclohexanone $\overset{+}{N}$-oxide, O^- (DMSO)	$O_2N-\overset{Me}{\underset{Me}{\overset{\|}{\underset{\|}{C}}}}-$ (cyclohexane with NO$_2$) (83)	233

Acceptor	Donor(Solvent)	Product (%)	Ref.

2,4,6-tri-tert-butylnitrosobenzene, t-BuMgCl[b] (Et₂O) → N(H)(t-Bu) product (43); NH₂ product (38); 258

Me_2N–C₆H₄–$N=O$, COT[=c] (ether) → $(Me_2N$–C₆H₄–N)₂ (56)

$(CF_3)_2C(F)$–$N=O$, $(CF_3)_3C$– (DMF) → $(CF_3)_2C=N$–$O(CF_3)_3$ (37); 260

$(N\equiv C)_2C=C(C\equiv N)_2$, t-BuMgBr[d] (THF) → $Me_2C=CH_2$ (5); Me_3CH (5); t-Bu–C(C≡N)–CH(C≡N)₂ (46)

$(N\equiv C)_2C=C(C\equiv N)_2$, Et_4Pb[e] (MeCN) → Et_3Pb–C(C≡N)(N≡C)–C(C≡N)–Et ; 263

t-Bu–O–O–Bu-t, EtLi (toluene) → EtH (40); CH₂=CH₂ (10); Et–Et (13); t-BuOEt (33); t-BuOLi (100) 264

Acceptor	Donor (Solvent)	Product (%)	Ref.

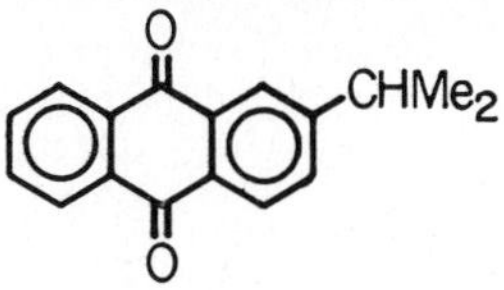

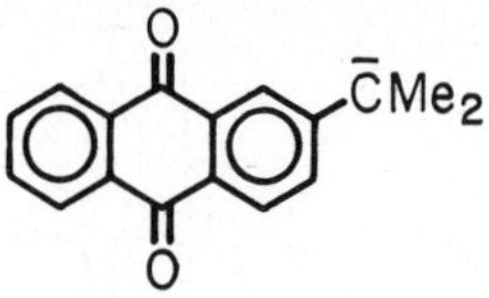

Anthraquinone with CHMe₂ / $\bar{C}Me_2$ substituent.

(t-BuOH, DME, H₂O)

(56)

(35)

270

Ph–C(=O)–C(=O)–Ph | COT⁼ᶜ (Et₂O) | Ph–C(O⁻)=C(O⁻)–Ph | 272

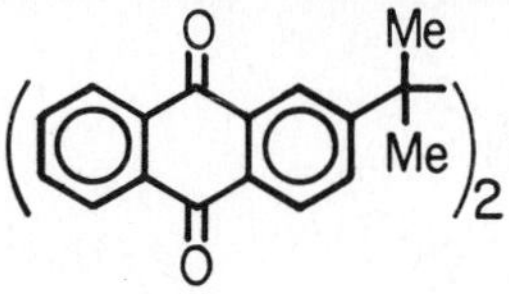

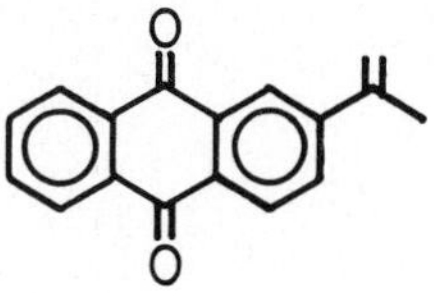

Tropone-OMe | + MeO⁻ (MeOH–DMSO) | O⁻ radical, f | 273

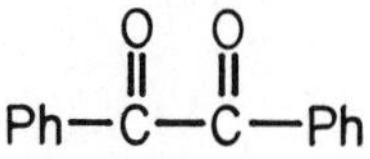

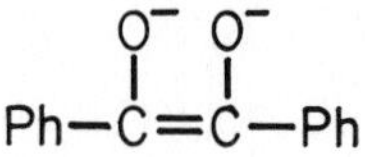

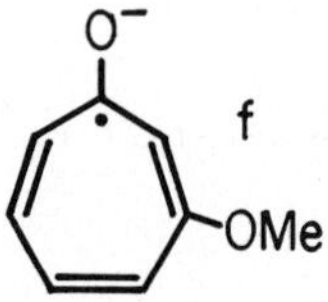

$(C_6Cl_5)_3C\cdot$ | Me–S(=O)–Me + HO⁻ (ether – DMSO) | $(C_6Cl_5)_3CH$ (94) | 275

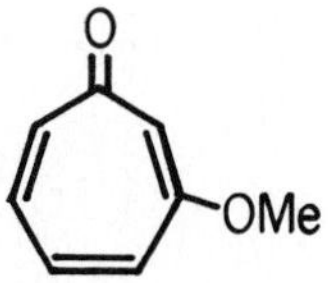

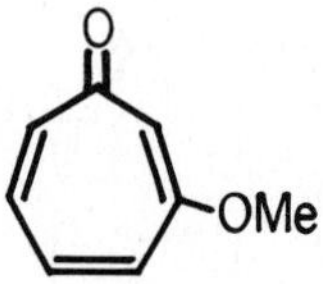

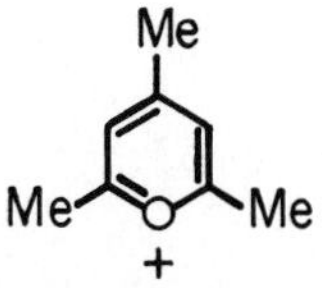

Trimethylpyrylium cation | COT⁼ᶜ (THF) | coupled pyran dimer | 277

Tropylium cation | COT⁼ᶜ (THF) | bitropyl | 276

Trimethylcyclopropenyl cation | trimethylcyclopropenyl (MeCN) | coupled cyclopropene dimer, g | 278, 279

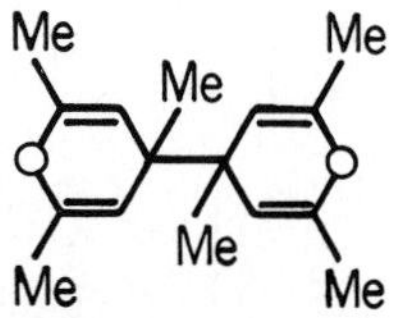

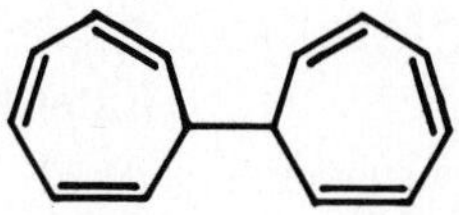

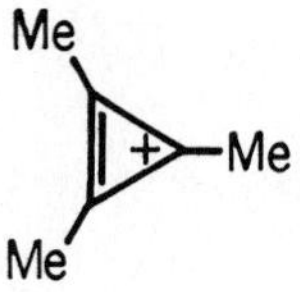

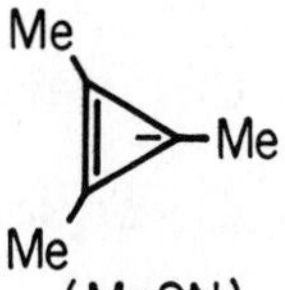

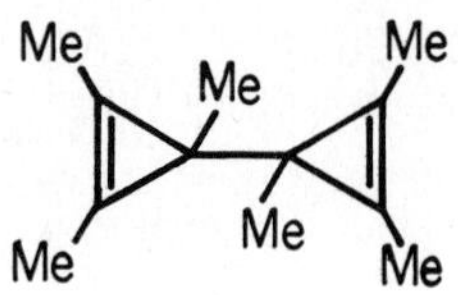

Acceptor	Donor (Solvent)	Product (%)	Ref.
(structure: bicyclic deuterated enone with Me, Me, H-D)	LiCuMe$_2$ (Et$_2$O)	(structure: cyclohexenone with Me, Me, Me, H, D, cyclopropyl) (52)	i 151
Ph–C≡N	COT$^{=c}$ (Et$_2$O)	(structure: triazine, Ph, Ph, Ph) (27)	259
Ph–C(=O)–Cl	t–BuMgCl (DME)	Ph–C(=O)–Bu–t (24) CH$_2$=CH$_2$ (26) t–BuH (20) (t–Bu)$_2$ (4) (Ph–C(=O))$_2$ (3)^h	280
t–BuN(–O–)C–Ph, H	(structure: hexenyl–MgBr) (Et$_2$O)	(structure: dispiro cyclopentane) (43)	281
CCl$_4$	Ph–S(=O)(=O)–C–Ph, Me (t–BuOH–CCl$_4$)	Ph–S(=O)(=O)–C(Cl)–Ph, Me (100)	180
CCl$_4$	Ph–C–C≡N, NR$_2$ (CCl$_4$–phase transfer)	Ph–C(CCl$_3$)–C≡N, NR$_2$ (40)	184

Notes to Accompany Table 3

a. See ref. 134 for substituted derivatives.

b. Ring attack with 1° and 2° Grignard reagents is believed to be due to $A_{Nu,Ar}$.

c. Cyclooctatetraene dianion.

d. 1° and 2° Grignard reagents may give $A_{Nu,C=C}$.

e. An analogous reaction occurs with R_4Sn and R_2Hg.

f. Other products were not identified.

g. The electron-transfer, coupling route AD. + A., has been disputed, ref. 278.

h. Other minor products have been identified.

i. Absolute configuration is unknown.

mechanism, $A_{CMg,C=O}$, to give exclusively 1,2-addition. Even this case, however, can be forced into the electron-transfer route by the presence of transition metal impurities, particularly ferric chloride.* If the reduction potential of the ketone is made less negative (e.g., acetone), even t-butyl Grignard reagents give results which can be interpreted without invoking electron transfer.

In an interesting series of experiments,[128] Ashby has shown that inclusion of p-dinitrobenzene in the reaction mixture of t-butylmagnesium chloride and 2-methylbenzophenone, completely eliminates pinacol formation without affecting the ratio of 1,2- to 1,6-addition products. This clearly shows that a different intermediate is involved in pinacol formation as compared to addition. By comparing the rate of this reaction to that of t-butylmagnesium chloride with acetone, it can be concluded that the 2-methylbenzophenone reaction involves no component of polar addition. Moreover, the excellent Hammett correlation for this reaction,[134] independent of product distribution, provides no support for mechanistic duality prior to the rate-determining step. Based on these considerations, Ashby has proposed the sequence of eq. 30.[128] In the absence of transition metal compounds $A_{R,C=O}D(R.C=O)$ is rate determining. The product determining process is a competition between two decomposition modes of

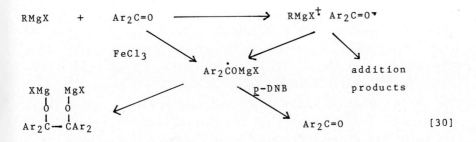

$$[30]$$

the initially formed ion pair. Although the exact sequence of bond breaking has not been specified, an A_{OMg} term must occur either before, after, or in synchrony with the $A_{R,C=O}D(R.C=O)$ step. At some stage $D_{R.Mg}$ must occur to form the magnesium ketyl. An interesting question is whether the radical pair generated by this process is on the path to addition products (via $A_{R.C}$) or whether the initially formed ion pair gives addition products directly. It seems likely that the 1,2- and 1,6 products originate from different intermediates because only the 1,6-adduct showed rearrangement in the alkyl group when 2-methylhept-6-en-2-ylmagnesium chloride was allowed to react with benzophenone.*

One feature of this reaction that we find especially remarkable is the apparent preference for Grignard reagents to undergo one-electron transfer to ketones, even when provided the alternative of an acceptor with a much more positive reduction potential. Although Ashby[128] has shown that p-dinitrobenzene (p-DNB) also reacts with the Grignard reagent, the two reactions occur with comparable rates despite the large discrepancy in reduction potential relative to diaryl ketones.[135]

Neither reaction has a rate even close to the diffusion limit[134] so the preference for reaction with the ketone must reflect an energetically favorable interaction between magnesium and the carbonyl oxygen that is not possible or is less favorable with the oxygens of the nitro compound. Whatever the reason, the danger of predictions made from electrochemical data is manifest.

Reactions of o-quinol acetates with secondary and tertiary alkylmagnesium halides are believed to proceed via electron transfer*[136-139] and other cases have appeared where a relationship between product distribution and the electron-transfer component of a Grignard reaction is suggested.[140,141] Even phenylmagnesium bromide is believed to give electron transfer when it reacts with phenyl mesityl ketone.*[142]

As with most reactions where an electron-transfer variant has been observed, the mechanism of the apparently polar counterpart cannot be clearly differentiated. If the proper characteristics are selected for the intermediates of eq. 30, it can be defensibly argued that all reactions of Grignard reagents with ketones proceed by an electron-transfer mechanism. In the absence of trappable intermediates, the methods of the reaction mechanician are simply inadequate for making the distinction. It is clear that methylmagnesium bromide is much more sensitive to steric influences in its

reactions   with   diaryl   ketones   than   t-butyl   Grignard
is,[134] but such suggestive results are not definitive.

2.   Reaction with Other Carbanionoids

There is evidence in a number of cases that organolithium
compounds, particularly highly-substituted ones,   undergo one-
electron   transfer   to α,β-unsaturated   ketones*[143,144]   and
related   compounds.*[145]   As   might   be   expected   from   the
observation that transition metal compounds   catalyze the one-
electron   reduction   of   ketones   by   Grignard
reagents,[128-123] the   same type of   catalysis can   be observed
for   alkyllithium   compounds.   n-Butyllithium   will   reduce
fluorenone   to its   pinacol   plus   9-hydroxyfluorene,   in   the
presence of   an iron-sulfur   cluster type   compound.   Octane,
butane and butenes were also formed.[146]

A   synthetically important   variation   of this   reaction,
developed   by   House   and   described   in   a   recent
review,[124]   employs   lithium   cuprates, $R_4Cu_2Li_2$,   as   donor
species   and   leads   to β-alkylation   in α,β-unsaturated
ketones.[124,147] The   reagent also   adds to   diaryl ketones.[148]
The reactivity of the acceptor ketone varies directly with its
reduction   potential,   although this   relationship does   not
extend to   non-ketonic acceptors.   This correlation   plus the
fact that the   enones will undergo cis-trans   isomerization in
the   presence of   such   reagents,*[124,149]   suggested that   the
mechanism involves electron transfer to form the radical anion
of the enone.   The subsequent transfer of   alkyl groups does
not   involve   alkyl   radicals because   the   transfer   takes place
with   retention   of   configuration*[150] in   the   alkyl   moiety.
Recently,   Casey   and   Cesa   have   demonstrated   absence   of
racemization   at   the   site   of   substitution   when   a
γ-cyclopropyl-α,β-unsaturated ketone undergoes ring opening in
its reaction with lithium dimethylcuprate.*[151] This result has
led Casey and Cesa to question   the correctness of the radical
anion mechanism for the normal conjugate addition reactions of
cuprates with α,β-unsaturated ketones.   It   is clear that the
next few years will see considerable research activity in this
area.   One possibility that will have   to be considered as an

explanation for the stereospecificity of the cyclopropane ring opening is a concerted $A_{Me.C}D_{Me.Cu}D_{C.C}$ process.

The mechanistic arguments involved in the cuprate reaction are very analogous to those for the Grignard case. The one-electron-oxidized state of the lithium organocuprate could play a similar role to that of the alkylmagnesium halide radical cation of eq. 30. The stereochemical integrity of the more covalent alkyl copper species allows more convincing experiments to be used to test for radical intermediates than are possible in the Grignard case.

B. Alkyl Halides

A revealing approach to the reactions of carbanions and carbanionoid species with alkyl halides may be taken by considering their substitution stereochemistry. Table 4 lists representative examples.

It will be noted that, for the most part, benzyl and allyl carbanionoid species react with alkyl halides with inversion of configuration. Cases where small, non-zero percent racemizations are reported may well represent complete inversion, because such experiments are entirely dependent on accurate knowledge of the maximum rotations for starting materials and products. These cases which show inversion presumably proceed by $A_{C-,C}D_{XC}$ (S_N2) mechanisms. It is interesting to consider that the solvents for the reactions in Table 4 are very nonpolar and an inversion process must be strongly opposed by the necessity to generate separated cations and anions. Although this phenomenon could be explained away by arguments invoking ion aggregation, it still seems that any other mechanism for the substitution would adopt an electrostatically preferable stereochemistry.

The simple metalloalkanes (with the possible exception of the second entry) obviously proceed by a different mechanism from the other entries in Table 4. The sequence of eq. 30 has been suggested by Ward, Lawler and Cooper to explain the observation of chemically induced dynamic nuclear polarization (CIDNP) in such reactions.[162] It is especially significant that compounds which show CIDNP during their reactions are

TABLE 4

STEREOCHEMISTRY OF THE SUBSTITUTION REACTION BETWEEN CARBANIONS AND ALKYL HALIDES

RM	R′X	Solvent	T (°C)	% Yield of R-R′	% Rac.[a]	Ref.
EtNa	2-Oct-Br	pentane	-10	25	97	152
EtNa	2-Oct-Cl	pentane	-10	6.4	20	153
EtLi	2-Oct-Br	ether or THF	0		100	154
n-BuLi	2-Bu-Br	dodecane	65	37	98	155
BenzylNa	2-Bu-Br	pet. ether	20	69	0[b]	156
AllylNa	1-PhEt-Cl	octane	-45		13	157
AllylNa	2-Oct-Br	pet. ether	0	83	13-21	158
AllylLi	2-Oct-Br	ether THF	0	87-95	0	154, 159
AllylLi	2-Oct-OTs	ether	20	60	7	160
AllylLi	2-Oct-I	ether	20	65	10	160
AllylLi	2-Oct-Cl	ether		59	8	159
AllylLi	1-PhEt-Cl	ether		34-39	62-71	159
BenzylLi	2-Oct-Br	ether		58	0	159
BenzhydrylLi[d]	1-PhEt-Cl	ether-hexane	reflux	48	0	159
AllylMgBr	2-Oct-Br	ether	reflux	78	13-21	158
BenzylMgBr	2-But-Br	ether	reflux	17	91	158
PyrrylMgBr	2-But-Br			44[c]	0[c]	160

a. Absence of racemization should be interpreted as inversion.
b. Originally reported as 25% but corrected for an improved maximum rotation for starting material determined later.[161] c. Both the 2-isomer (31%) and the 3-isomer (13%) were recovered and both showed 100% inversion.
d. Diphenylmethyl.

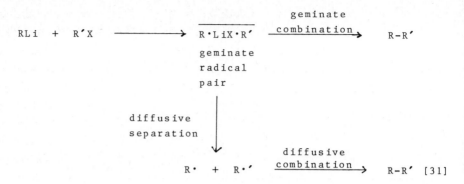

generally in the same structural category as those which have been shown to give racemic substitution products.

The observation of CIDNP by NMR is an extremely powerful tool for analyzing reactions of this type. It demands that at least part of the products which exhibit the CIDNP phenomenon arise by radical processes. Although there are experimental problems to measuring CIDNP in the coupling products formed by eq. 31, the disproportionation and halide-exchange products which are formed concurrently from the intermediate radicals do display characteristic enhanced absorption, and emission. In the case of ethyllithium with either allyl or benzyl chloride CIDNP was observed for the substitution products themselves.[162] CIDNP can also be observed for the halogen-metal exchange reaction of isopropyl Grignard reagent with $\underline{n}$-butyl bromide, but the reaction must be catalyzed by ferrous chloride.[163] Ferric chloride will catalyze the reaction of Grignard reagents with propargyl chloride, but the reaction is not believed to involve electron transfer.[164]

The fact that benzhydryllithium reacts with 1-phenylethyl chloride with complete inversion of configuration (Table 4) might tempt one to conclude that as the carbanionic site becomes more delocalized, the mechanism will remain in the $A_{C-}, C^{D}{}_{XC}$ category. A damaging argument against this generalization is presented by Zieger[165,166] who has observed the results of eq. 32. An $A_{C-}, C^{D}{}_{XC}$ (S_N2) process would surely show some discrimination for displacement of the halide at the least substituted carbon, whereas an electron-transfer process for the rate-determining step followed by geminate

$$\text{Ph}_2\text{CHLi} \quad + \quad \text{Ph}_2\text{CHCl} \quad \longrightarrow \quad \text{Ph}_2\text{CHCHPh}_2 \quad\quad\quad [32]$$

$$\text{and} \quad\quad\quad\quad\quad\quad \text{and}$$

$$\text{PhCH}_2\text{Cl} \quad\quad\quad\quad \text{PhCH}_2\text{CHPh}_2$$

$$\text{(equimolar)} \quad\quad\quad \text{(equimolar)}$$

$$\text{(no PhCH}_2\text{CH}_2\text{Ph)}$$

recombination would better explain the lack of selectivity.
The absence of cross-coupling product argues against product
formation by diffusive recombination. It also probably rules
out an $A_{C^-, \cdot C}$ step enroute to these products.

It was also found that when an experiment parallel to
that of eq. 32 was carried out, replacing chloride with
fluoride, the least congested substitution product was
favored.[165] The authors interpret this as evidence for an
$A_{C^-, C}D_{XC}$ process for the fluorides, although it should be
noted that the selectivity is only 2:1 despite the much slower
rate of this reaction.

Of additional importance to these arguments is the
formation of (14) from the reaction of triphenylmethyllithium
with triphenylmethyl chloride.[166] This product would be
expected if triphenylmethyl radicals were present.[167,168] It

(14)

should be recognized, however, that the fact that this product
is a known coupling product of triphenylmethyl radicals does
not rule out its production by a different mechanism under
Zieger's conditions. In fact, Zieger supports an
$A_{C^-, C(para)}D_{FC}$ mechanism when triphenylmethyl fluoride is the
substrate.

The resolution of the questions raised above is also
pertinent to the reaction of halides with radical ions.
Garst[169] has proposed that the dimeric products which arise in
this reaction result from the process of eq. 33 wherein the

234

$$RX + C_{10}H_8^{\cdot -} \longrightarrow R\cdot \xrightarrow{\;C_{10}H_8^{-}\;} R^- \xrightarrow{\;RX\;} R-R \quad [33]$$

initially formed radical is reduced faster than it dimerizes.
The eventual products result from reaction of carbanion and
halide.   The evidence for the first part of this sequence is
excellent[169] and has recently been supported by an elegant
trapping experiment[170] in which the bibenzyl, which is
normally formed from the reaction of benzyl halides with
lithium or sodium naphthalenide in 70-90% yields, is nearly
completely diverted to toluene by the presence of t-butyl
alcohol.   A similar result was obtained with benzhydryl
chloride and the use of t-butyl alcohol-O-d gave deuterated
diphenylmethane. In the studies reported by Garst,[169,171-173]
an electron-transfer, geminate-recombination scheme has been
assumed for the last step and is undoubtedly correct where
haloalkanes are used.

A recent case*[174] in which the electron-transfer,
geminate-recombination sequence has been demonstrated by CIDNP
is the reaction of 3,3-dimethylallenyllithium with benzyl
bromide. The product distribution, which favors alkylation at
the tertiary end of the allenyl anion even when cumyl chloride
is used, argues against an appreciable
$A_{C^-}, _CD_{XC}$ component.

Using stereochemistry and CIDNP as the most definitive
indicators of mechanism, we summarize present understanding of
this reaction as follows.   Aliphatic carbanions react with
aliphatic halides by an electron-transfer process.   Some
benzylic and allylic type carbanions react with aliphatic
halides by an $A_{C^-}, _CD_{XC}$ type process (S_N2), but the mechanism
of the reaction of benzylic and allylic carbanions with
benzyl- and allyl-type halides is less certain.   Evidence is
available for both mechanisms in individual cases.   Probably
the most definitive approach would be a stereochemical study
in a variety of systems from the latter category.

Halides are a unique class of electron acceptors in that
the one-electron reduction process is never
reversible.[175,176] It is possible that the bond-breaking
process in which halide is lost from the intended radical

anion occurs in concert with electron transfer from the donor, $A_{C^-}, Cl^D_{C}.Cl^R_{D}Cl.R$. This hypothesis seems particularly justified in the case of benzyl halides, the half-wave reduction potentials for which are nearly one volt more positive than those of the corresponding aliphatic halides.[177] The half-wave potentials for benzyl halides are also well above those for aromatic rings,[162] giving substance to the calculations of Fukui[178] which indicate that the electron is placed in the lowest unoccupied orbital. At least in benzyl halides it seems likely that the resultant state would be unstable relative to bond dissociation. With haloalkanes, it is possible that the radical anion has a finite, albeit short, lifetime. This suggestion has been put forward by Garst[179] based on the observation of a halogen-dependent product ratio in the reaction of haloalkanes with disodium tetraphenylethylene. Garst has suggested that the haloalkane radical anion is sufficiently long-lived to allow it to diffuse from its inceptive solvent cage. The phenomenon is invoked to explain the effect on product distribution through

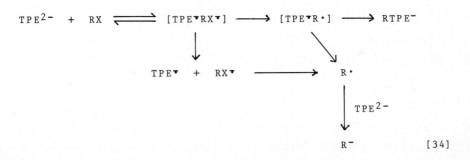

the logic of eq. 34. This provocative suggestion deserves further examination particularly in view of the fact that it predicts an order of lifetimes for $RX^{\bullet}$ of $X = I > Br > Cl$. Contrary to expectation, this is the same order as that for ease of reduction, judged by half-wave potentials.[177]

A synthetically useful variation in this class of reactions involving carbon tetrachloride and other perhalomethanes as electron acceptors was originally reported by Meyers*[180] and by Makosza.[181] The reaction normally begins with the simple attachment of a chlorine atom to the carbanionic center but a great variety of subsequent paths have been observed.[182,183] Recently, a different reaction outcome has been demonstrated for carbanions derived from phenyl(dialkylamino)acetonitrile (see Table 3).*[184] The mechanism of these reactions is believed[180,182,183] to involve electron transfer from the carbanion to CCl_4, $A_{C^-}, _{Cl}C^D_{C.Cl}C$, followed by generation of $Cl\cdot$ and radical recombination, $D_{Cl.CCl} + A_{C.Cl}$.

C. Aromatic Hydrocarbons as Acceptors

As would be anticipated from the reduction potentials of aromatic compounds which lack a charge-stabilizing functional group,[185] only the most reducing carbanions would be expected to react. What would appear to be simply a dibasic version of a diphenylmethyl carbanion, (15), reacts with anthracene, pyrene, tetracene or perylene in the unfavorable equilibrium process of eq. 35.[186] The rate constant, k_{-1}, is believed to

$$A + \underset{(15)}{\overset{Na^+ \quad Na^+}{Ph_2\bar{C}CH_2CH_2\bar{C}Ph_2}} \underset{\underset{THF}{k_{-1}}}{\overset{k_1}{\rightleftharpoons}} \underset{(16)}{\overset{Na^+}{Ph_2\bar{C}CH_2CH_2\dot{C}Ph_2}} + A^{\bullet}Na^+ \qquad [35]$$

A = anthracene, pyrene, tetracene or perylene

be diffusion limited and a net reaction would not be observed were it not for a rate-determining $D_{CH.CH}$ process, generating diphenylethylene and its radical anion.

When the negative charges in (15) are moved to adjacent carbons by removing the two insulating CH_2 groups, electron-transfer equilibria become much more favorable.[187] The disproportionation equilibrium constant for eq. 36 is subject

$$2 Ph_2\dot{C}\bar{C}Ph_2 \rightleftharpoons Ph_2\bar{C}\bar{C}Ph_2 + Ph_2C=CPh_2 \qquad [36]$$

to enormous effects of changes in solvent and counterion, varying from 2×10^{-4} in HMPA,[188] where only free ions are present, to over 10^4 for cesium ion pairs in THF.[189] Recently a value of over 10^6 was determined for the Ba^{2+} salt in DME.[190] The disproportionation is also affected by strain when the 1,2-diphenylethylene unit is incorporated in a ring[191] or when _cis_ and _trans_ configurations can be distinguished in the radical ions.[192-194] Other radical anion-dianion disproportionation systems, such as cyclooctatetraene, also show ion-pairing effects.[195-197]

D. Nitro Compounds

A comprehensive survey of the reaction of carbanions with aromatic nitro compounds was carried out by Russell, Janzen and Strom in 1964.[198] Using _t_-butoxide as base in a solvent of 80% DMSO - 20% _t_-butyl alcohol, a variety of carbon acids were found to react with nitrobenzene. The conversion of nitrobenzene to nitrobenzenide was monitored by ESR. The more acidic carbon acids provided higher concentrations of carbanions, but these carbanions were generally more difficult to oxidize, thus allowing comparison of a wide spectrum of carbon acids under comparable conditions. (Note that this relationship requires that radical stabilities vary less with structure than do carbanion stabilities. This does not hold true for all structural modifications.)

Although these studies showed considerable generality for the electron-transfer reaction, the eventual fate of the carbon radical produced was known for relatively few cases. More recently, thorough product studies have been made by our own group[199] and that of Makosza.[200,201] These evidence remarkable variety. We have proposed a mechanistic scheme to explain and, within limits, predict these products as a function of carbanion structure, solvent, and substituents on the nitro compound.

The first step, $A_{C^-, O_2N} D_{C \cdot O_2N}$, generates the radical anion of the nitro compound and the radical from the carbanion. Obviously, two radicals can couple, $A_{C \cdot C}$, and this is a common result.*[199,202] In cases where the radical has the general structure C-C=X, where X is an atom or group capable of stabilizing negative charge, an $A_{C^-, C}$ process may also give rise to dimer.*[203,204]

238

In cases where the nitro radical ion is not destroyed by protonation and its consequential processes, the radical and radical ion may undergo coupling, $A_{C.O}$, to give intermediate (17). We have suggested that it is this intermediate which

$$\underset{(17)}{Ar-\overset{\overset{O^-}{|}}{N}-O-R} \xrightarrow{\quad D_{ON} \quad} ArN=O \quad + \quad RO^- \qquad [37]$$

gives rise, by the D_{ON} process of eq. 37, to alcohols. Triphenylcarbinol is the major product of the reaction of triphenylmethane with nitrobenzene in $\underline{t}$-butoxide - $\underline{t}$-butyl alcohol.*4,205 We also found that, in DMSO, 9-methylfluorenide ion reacts with nitrobenzene to give 31% of 9-hydroxy-9-methylfluorene along with dimer. It is not clear why, in the latter case, products from reaction of the radical with nitrosobenzene were not observed. Perhaps nitrosobenzene is consumed by some rapid reaction with the excess base present. A recent example of oxygen transfer involves reaction of N-($\underline{p}$-nitrobenzyl)pyridinium chloride with hydroxide.206 The product is $\underline{p}$-azoxybenzaldehyde ($\underline{p},\underline{p}'$-diformylazoxybenzene). The reaction is unaffected by O_2, suggesting a direct oxygen transfer from $PhNO_2$ or an electron-transfer, oxygen-transfer sequence occurring within a solvent cage: ($A_{C,ArNO_2}D_{C.ArNO_2} + A_{C.O} + D_{ON}$).

If the acidity of the proton source is increased by changing the solvent to methanol, the new products are best explained by the coupling of radicals with nitroso compounds or their radical anions. We have argued that coupling at nitrogen, $A_{C.N}$, eq. 38, must be faster than coupling at the $\underline{para}$ position (of Ar), because when a leaving group (X =

$$\underset{X}{\overset{|}{\underset{|}{-C}}}\cdot \quad + \quad Ar\overset{\overset{O^-}{\diagup}}{N}\cdot \quad \underset{\longleftarrow}{\overset{\longrightarrow}{\quad}} \quad \underset{X}{\overset{|}{\underset{|}{-C}}}\overset{\overset{O^-}{|}}{\underset{|}{N}}-Ar \qquad [38]$$

OCH_3) is attached to the carbanionic carbon, the product is a nitrone in which no ring substitution has occurred, eq. 39. An apparent exception to this generalization observed by

$$-\underset{\underset{X}{|}}{\overset{\overset{O^-}{|}}{C}}-N-Ar \quad \xrightarrow{\text{D}_{XC}} \quad \overset{\overset{O}{\uparrow}}{C}=N-Ar \qquad [39]$$

Makosza is shown in eq. 40.[200] It seems likely that this

$$Ph_2CHC{\equiv}N \quad + \quad \text{(2-Cl-nitrobenzene)} \quad \xrightarrow[\text{MeOH}]{\text{NaOMe}} \quad Ph_2C\text{—(Cl-aryl)—}N{=}CPh_2 \qquad [40]$$

process occurs, as suggested by Makosza, via the Meisenheimer adduct, (18). We prefer the $A_{O^-}, A^D_{O \cdot A} + A_{BH}D_{CH}$ mechanism of eq. 41 (A = acceptor, B = base) to the hydride transfer proposed by Makosza for formation of the final product. The

$$R-\text{(ring)}-N^+\overset{O^-}{\underset{O^-}{}} \quad \xrightarrow[\text{(2)} -H^+]{\text{(1)} -e^-} \quad R-\text{(ring)}-NO_2^{\cdot -} \qquad [41]$$

$$(\underline{18}) \qquad\qquad\qquad (\underline{19})$$

sequence of eq. 41 was first proposed by Russell and coworkers[198] to explain the formation of nitrobenzenide ion from nitrobenzene and t-butoxide in DMSO - t-butyl alcohol. Radical anion (19) would explain a number of products observed in Makosza's study and, in particular, would account for the observation of substituted nitro compounds.

In our study of 9-substituted fluorenes, carbanions which lacked a leaving group at the 9-position did give para-substitution with aromatic nitro compounds, but always in lower oxidation state products.* We reasoned that nitroxyl radical (20) could couple with fluorenyl radical, $A_{C \cdot C(para)}$, as shown in eq. 42. The reasonableness of

$$R\cdot \quad + \quad \text{(ring)}-\overset{\overset{\cdot O}{|}}{N}-R \quad \longrightarrow \quad \overset{R}{\underset{H}{}}\text{(ring)}-\overset{\overset{O}{\uparrow}}{N}-R \qquad [42]$$

$$(\underline{20}) \qquad\qquad\qquad (\underline{21})$$

intermediate (20) is affirmed by the isolation of its coupling product (22) in the system of eq. 43.   Intermediate (21) can,

$$\text{[43]}$$

(22)

of course, lose a proton and an electron to lead to products analogous to (22) in which the N-phenyl ring is substituted. This is observed when nitrobenzene is substituted for 3,5-dichloronitrobenzene in the reaction of eq. 43

The other major product type obtained from carbanions and aromatic nitro compounds is azoxybenzene and its ring-substituted derivatives.*4,199,201,200,205 These are believed to arise from nitrosobenzene radical anions by the mechanism suggested by Russell,207 $A_{N.N}$ + A_{OH} + D_{ON} . No azoxy compounds are obtained with 9-methoxyfluorene as substrate, because the sequence of eqs. 38 and 39 removes the requisite radical anion.

One additional outcome which must be kept in mind if the carbanionic carbon carries an -OH or an -NH- group is dehydrogenation. In such cases, the radical produced by electron transfer may, as we have suggested for 9-aminofluoren-9-yl radical,*199 transfer another electron, followed by a proton, to give an imine, $A_{C.A}D_{AC}$ + $A_{BH}D_{NH}$ (A = acceptor, B = base), or, as in the case 9-hydroxyfluoren-9-yl radical, transfer of a proton followed by an electron, $A_{BH}D_{OH}$ + $A_{C.A}D_{AC}$, to give a ketone. An example which demonstrates the ease of oxidation of α-amino radicals has been reported recently.208

The predictive ground rules naturally change in cases where the radical anion of an aromatic nitro compound can undergo some fast unimolecular transformation. The best known example of this is the reaction of nitro-substituted-benzyl halides with 2-nitro-2-propyl anion. The mechanism was diagnosed by Kornblum[98] and Russell.[97] This reaction is initiated by electron transfer from the 2-nitro-2-propyl anion and the halomethyl radical anion rapidly loses halide,

$$\overset{\cdot\text{O}}{\underset{^{-}\text{O}}{}}\text{N}-\langle\rangle-\text{CH}_2-\text{X} \longrightarrow \overset{\cdot\text{O}}{\underset{^{-}\text{O}}{}}\text{N}^+=\langle\rangle=\text{CH}_2 + \text{X}^- \qquad [44]$$

D_{XC}, as shown in eq. 44. The rate constant for this reaction is 10^4 sec^{-1} for chloride and 6×10^8 sec^{-1} for bromide,[209] which is sufficiently fast to compete with reactions at the nitro group. The product of eq. 43 then combines with unreacted nitropropyl anion in an

$$\overset{\cdot\text{O}}{\underset{^{-}\text{O}}{}}\text{N}^+=\langle\rangle=\text{CH}_2 + \underset{\text{CH}_3}{\overset{\text{CH}_3}{}}\text{C}=\text{N}^+\underset{\text{O}_-}{\overset{\text{O}^-}{}} \longrightarrow \overset{\cdot\text{O}}{\underset{^{-}\text{O}}{}}\text{N}-\langle\rangle-\text{CH}_2-\underset{\text{CH}_3}{\overset{\text{CH}_3}{\text{C}}}-\text{NO}_2 \quad [45]$$

$A_{C^-},\cdot_C$ process as shown in eq. 45. The resultant radical ion can then transfer an electron to starting nitrobenzyl halide, thus completing the propagation sequence of a kinetic chain reaction. This mechanism explains the preference for C-alkylation with ring-nitrated benzyl halides and also the observation of "entrainment" products in which added nucleophiles can substitute for the carbanion in eq. 45, A_{NuC}.[210]

If the Kornblum - Russell sequence is termed as AD. + D + A process, there is also the possibility of an AD. + D + A. reaction in which the bond-forming step is homolytic rather than nucleophilic. This is a non-chain sequence and should give cross-coupling products when recombination is not confined to a solvent cage. An example is shown in eq. 46.[211,212] Product (23) seems to arise in large part from cage recombination as judged from the fact that its formation is not averted in the presence of free radical traps. If this mechanism is correct, the D_{XC} process of eq. 44 must occur before the carbanion-derived radical can diffuse from the cage. This would require a rate constant much greater than the value of 10^4 sec^{-1} measured in acetonitrile.[209] Perhaps

$$\text{Ph}_2\bar{\text{C}}\text{-C}\equiv\text{N} \; + \; \text{ClCH}_2\text{-}\langle\bigcirc\rangle\text{-NO}_2 \; \xrightarrow{\text{THF}} \; \text{Ph}_2\underset{\overset{|}{\text{C}\equiv\text{N}}}{\text{C}}\text{-CH}_2\text{-}\langle\bigcirc\rangle\text{-NO}_2 \qquad [46]$$

$$(\underline{23}) \quad (50 - 70\%)$$

$$\text{Ph}_2\underset{\overset{\|}{\text{C}}}{\overset{|}{\text{C}}}\text{---}\underset{\overset{\|}{\text{N}}}{\overset{|}{\text{CPh}_2}} \qquad\qquad (\text{O}_2\text{N-}\langle\bigcirc\rangle\text{-CH}_2)_2$$

$$(10 - 20\%) \qquad\qquad (7 - 14\%)$$

counterions present in the less polar solvent increase the rate of D_{XC}.

An interesting reaction that may fall in the AD. + D + A category occurs when 4-nitrobenzyl chloride, fluoride or dimethylsulfonium derivatives are treated with methoxide, hydroxide or another strong base.*[213-221] The products are cis and trans-4,4-dinitrostilbene, 4,4-dinitrobibenzyl, bis-(4-nitrophenylacetylene, 4-nitrotoluene, 4-nitrobenzyl alcohol and cis and trans-4,4-dinitrostilbene oxide. The reaction was originally explained using a carbene mechanism, $A_{BH}D_{CH} + D_{XC}$,[214] but this has gradually evolved[215-221] to what is presently proposed as an AD. + D + A sequence.[222,223]

There remains some confusion over the origin of 4-nitrobenzaldehyde which is the logical precursor of the stilbene oxides.[222,223] The fact that the stilbene oxides are also formed when 4-nitrobenzyl bromide, iodide, and tosylate are treated with sodium hydroxide, the other products being mainly 4-nitrobenzyl alcohol and very little of the stilbene or bibenzyl,[223] suggests to us that 4-nitrobenzyl alcohol is oxidized by one of the nitro compounds present in the reaction mixture. Oxidation of primary alcohols by aromatic nitro compounds is a well documented phenomenon.[224-227]

Perhaps the most elegant demonstration of the AD. + D part of the nitrobenzyl halide reaction has been provided by Julia[228,229] who used an intramolecular cyclization to trap the intermediate nitrobenzyl radical as shown in eq. 47. The product distribution was similar to that observed when the anticipated nitrobenzyl radical was generated by thermolysis of a perester.

$$O_2N{-}\langle ring \rangle{-}\underset{CH_2}{\overset{Cl}{CH}}{-}CH{=}CH_2 \xrightarrow[\substack{toluene \\ aq.\ NaOH \\ (two\ phase)}]{80} O_2N{-}\langle ring \rangle{-}CH_2{-}CH{=}CH_2 \;+\; O_2N{-}\langle ring \rangle{-}\langle cyclopentyl \rangle$$

$$O_2N{-}\langle ring \rangle{-}\langle cyclohexyl \rangle \;+\; \text{other} \qquad [47]$$
products

An apparently related reaction occurs when 4-nitrotoluene is treated with t-butoxide in DMSO – t-butyl alcohol.*203,204,230 The major product of this reaction is 4,4′-dinitrobibenzyl which clearly arises from the 4-nitrobenzyl carbanion via an electron-transfer process. An A_{C^-},$\cdot_C$ step seems logical. However no significant entrainment of 2-nitro-2-propyl anion can be observed.

The AD. + D + A sequence is not limited to aromatic nitro compounds. α-Halonitroalkanes are believed to undergo substitution by this mechanism.*231-234 The reaction can also be employed for ring synthesis.235 It has also recently been used with the difficultly oxidizable acetylenide type ions when present as lithium derivatives.236 Under certain conditions, the reaction can be used to attach isopropylidene groups at the α-carbon of enolates.237 Polynitroalkanes have also been shown to react with carbanions.98,238,239

In concluding this section, we would remind those who might consider using nitro compounds as carbanion traps that they also undergo non-electron-transfer processess when treated with bases and nucleophiles. Even unsubstituted nitrobenzene will react with strong base to form 2-nitrophenyl anions, $A_{BH}D_{CH}$.240 With additional electronegative substituents present, this process becomes quite facile.241-243 Examples of nucleophilic addition to aromatic nitro compounds, A_{NuAr}, are too numerous to discuss in this chapter.244-254 Most examples involve polynitroaromatics which form stable, spectroscopically observable Meisenheimer or Janovsky complexes. However, it seems likely that low concentrations of such adducts, which are themselves carbanions of a sort, could be present and possibly serve as one-electron donors198,255 when mononitroaromatics are treated with nucleophiles.256,257

It is interesting to note that as more than one nitro group is attached to an aromatic ring, the tendency toward adduct formation, $A_{C^-,Ar}$, increases at the expense of electron transfer, $A_{C^-,Ar}D_{C.Ar}$. This possibly results from a destablization of the aromatic system caused by excessive electron withdrawal. There is perhaps less energetic benefit to be derived from maintaining such a system, even with an extra electron, than there is to be gained by carbon-carbon bond formation. We suspect that an analogous balance exists for most of the reactions discussed in this chapter.

E. Other Functional Groups

Many organic electron acceptors with more positive reduction potentials than those discussed so far, undergo electron transfer with carbanions or carbanionoid species but have not been generally used because of instability under the strongly basic conditions normally required for carbanion generation. The occasional cases which have been reported are shown in Table 3. They include both aromatic[*258,259] and aliphatic[*260] nitroso compounds, tetracyanoethylene[*261-263] and dialkylperoxides.[*264] Quinones undergo reactions with bases and nucleophiles which in some cases involve A_{NuQ}[265-267] possibly followed by electron transfer,[268] $A_{QNu^-}, A^D_{ANu.Q}$, and in other cases proceed by side chain proton removal, $A_{BH}D_{CH}$,[269] which can also be followed by a sequence of electron transfer, $A_{C^-,Q}D_{C.Q}$,[*270] and dimerization through either $A_{C.C}$ or $A_{C^-,\cdot C}$. The reaction of 2-methylanthraquinone[*270] is strongly reminiscent of the reactions of nitrotoluenes.[203,204] α-Diketones, like quinones, can serve as one-electron acceptors.[*271,272] Russell has shown that the carbanions from α-hydroxyketones transfer one electron to the corresponding diketones to give semiquinone radical ions.[271] The A + AD. sequence is probably involved in the reaction of 2-methoxytropone with methoxide.[*273] Triphenylmethyl radicals, in which the benzene rings carry strongly electron withdrawing substituents, may undergo one-electron reduction by carbanions.[*274,275]

With strongly reducing carbanions such as cyclooctatetraene dianion, $COT^=$, stable carbocations such as tropylium ions*[276] and even oxonium ions*[277] can be reduced. Reduction of cyclopropenium ion by cyclopropenide ion has also been debated.*[278,279]

Simple carboxylic acid derivatives are rarely seen as carbanion oxidants because of their relatively low reduction potentials and their susceptibility to nucleophilic attack. COT⁼ will reduce benzonitrile, however, to give the product shown in Table 3.*[259] Benzoyl chloride has been suggested as a one-electron acceptor in its reaction with t-butylmagnesium chloride on the basis of CIDNP studies.*[280] Grignard reagents and alkyllithiums have been shown to undergo electron transfer in the presence of oxaziridines.*[281] An interesting new class of acceptors is the alkylmercury halides.[282] Here the organometallic compound serves as acceptor rather than donor.

V. ION-PAIRING EFFECTS

A certain forecast from the many studies of cation and solvent effects on electron exchange in radical ion systems[283] is that ion pairing and solvation will cause profound variations in both the kinetics and equilibria of eq. 1. This area of carbanion electron transfer has been relatively neglected because there is no counterpart to the convenient technique of ESR exchange broadening and narrowing which has proven so revealing in the radical ion systems. Also, the products in eq. 1 are usually being destroyed,[284] making equilibrium measurements inaccurate and kinetic determinations complex. The rewards for overcoming these problems are likely to be substantial, however. We have already mentioned that the disproportionation constant for eq. 35 varies by ten powers of ten as solvent and counterion are changed. Is it possible that such easily variable parameters can be used to create new reactions? Panek has shown that alkyllithium compounds and Grignard reagents in THF can be made to quantitatively produce biphenyl radical anion from biphenyl by adding no more than 1.9 M HMPA.[285]

An early example of solvent dependence was discovered by Garst and co-workers who showed that decreasing solvent polarity increases the rate of reaction of carbanion (24) with air to give Koelsch's radical, (25).[62] There is little question about the mechanistic details of this reaction because product (25) is directly observed. The solvent effect is exactly that anticipated for a reaction which is <u>localizing</u>

$$(24) + O_2 \longrightarrow (25) + O_2^{\cdot -} \qquad [48]$$

charge. Just as adding aprotic polar solvents increases the rate of reaction between localized alkoxide anions and the carbon acid precursors of delocalized carbanions,[286,287] the use of DMSO instead of 2-methyltetrahydrofuran in the reaction of eq. 48 has the opposite effect by a factor of five powers of ten in rate constant. The presence of a counterion in the solvation sphere of (24) should reduce the energy required to concentrate charge in the superoxide ion.

In the face of this precedent, we were surprised to find that the reaction of triphenylmethane with potassium <u>t</u>-butoxide and O_2 in <u>t</u>-butyl alcohol was made more efficient by the addition of crown ether.[4] Moreover, while Russell had demonstrated an ionization-limited reaction between triphenylmethane and O_2 catalyzed by <u>t</u>-butoxide in 80% DMSO - 20% <u>t</u>-butyl alcohol, we could show that in <u>t</u>-butyl alcohol with no DMSO or crown ether present, less than 1% of the triphenylmethide ions formed could be trapped by O_2 in an O_2 saturated solution. Thus it appeared that in one case, carbanion (22), ion pairing conditions increased the rate of the O_2 reaction and in another, triphenylmethide ion, the reaction was slowed.

To resolve this apparent contradiction, we suggested that the difference could be attributed to the fact that the triphenylmethide case involves a competition between protonation and electron transfer as written in eq. 49. In contrast to the situation in eq. 48, the efficiency of this reaction could be promoted in two ways, increasing k_e or decreasing k_h. Because for reaction in <u>t</u>-butyl alcohol,

$$Ph_3CH \xrightleftharpoons[k_h]{k_H} Ph_3C^- \xrightarrow{k_e[O_2]} \quad products \qquad [49]$$

the k_h reaction involved charge localization and, in fact, a more severe charge localization than the k_e reaction, it seemed possible that DMSO or crown ether would reduce k_h more than k_e. Adding substance to this theory are the results of Bockrath and Dorfman[288,289] showing that, even for the highly reactive benzyl carbanion, protonation by alcohols in THF is faster for the ion pair with sodium than for the free ion or the ion pair with tetrabutylammonium. This accelerating effect on carbanion protonation by alkali metal ions is believed to be due to the incursion of an S_EC or S_E2 (coord) type mechanism,[290,291] A_{OM} + $A_{CH}D_{CM}D_{OH}$, in which coordination of the alcohol oxygen to the metal ion increases the protonation rate. Whether the predicted reduced protonation rate for triphenylmethide when its counterion is complexed or solvated is sufficient to explain the large difference in the efficiency with which it is trapped by O_2 is a question that must be answered by future research.

Another discrepancy in this pattern of analysis is work of Bethell[292] which showed a substantially lower rate for the autoxidation of sodium 9-cyanofluoradenide in t-butyl alcohol with 1.0 M DMSO than in t-butyl alcohol alone. Because this carbanion is not significantly protonated in these solvents, the argument used for the triphenylmethide case is not applicable. One possibility is that 9-cyanofluorenide should be viewed as a localized ion relative to superoxide. The alternative is to invoke some special power of alkali metal ions for catalyzing the reduction of O_2.

We have also investigated the effects of ion pairing on the reaction between carbanions and aromatic nitro compounds. Very early, we found that the efficiency of electron transfer from triphenylmethide to nitrobenzene ($k_e[PhNO_2]/k_h$ - see eq. 48)[205] is reduced by increasing solvent polarity and other factors which are understood to decrease the tightness of ion pairing.[293]

    We initially interpreted this on the basis that
protonation would be slowed by ion pairing. In view of the
findings of Bockrath and Dorfman[288,289] however, it now seems
likely that the opposite is true. As pointed out earlier, the
less efficient reaction of triphenylmethide in the presence of
contact potassium ions can be explained if potassium ions
catalyze protonation. Why then does electron transfer to
nitrobenzene compete less efficiently with protonation when
the cation is solvated or complexed?

    In the first place, it is apparent that the reaction
between potassium triphenylmethide contact ion pair and
nitrobenzene is very fast. At only 0.2 $\underline{M}$, nitrobenzene traps
ten times as many of these pairs as does $\underline{t}$-butyl alcohol when
$\underline{t}$-butyl alcohol is the solvent ($\sim$10 $\underline{M}$). Could potassium ions
catalyze the electron transfer process? Catalysis of electron
transfer by ion pairing is not observed for electron exchange
between hydrocarbon radical ions. In all cases
studied,[294] the rate of electron transfer is free ion > loose
ion pair > tight ion pair. The reverse order has been noted,
however, for the exchange of alkali metal ketyls, at least as
regards the loose and tight ion pairs.[295] The argument here is
that when the energy of the transition state for electron
transfer is lowered by involvement of the counterion
coordination shell, strong solvation will slow the
process.[296]

    Applied to the triphenylmethide - nitrobenzene case, this
principle suggests that in order to compete effectively with
$\underline{t}$-butyl alcohol for the carbanion, nitrobenzene may also use
the coordination sites of potassium. This helps to
rationalize the efficiency with which nitrobenzene competes,
but it does not explain the differential effect of cation
solvation favoring protonation. Both protonation and electron
transfer should be slowed by tying up the cation, so why
should there be a greater effect on electron transfer?

    We believe that the answer may be found in the fact that
the electron transfer reaction becomes reversible when HMPA or
crown ether occupy the cation. Evidence for this phenomenon
is provided by the observation that triphenylmethyl bromide is
reduced to triphenylmethane-$\underline{d}$ by nitrobenzenide in HMPA - $\underline{t}$-

butyl alcohol-0-d. The explanation for this apparent equilibrium shift is not at all obvious. Considering the two equilibria in eq. 50, our results indicate that the overall

$$R'O^- + RH \xrightleftharpoons[k_h]{k_H} ROH + R^- \xrightleftharpoons[k_{-e}]{k_e} R\cdot + PhNO_2^{\cdot -} \qquad [50]$$

equilibrium constant, $k_H k_e / k_{-e} k_h$, decreases with cation coordination. This is entirely unexpected for a process which moves charge from localized alkoxide to delocalized nitrobenzenide. We suspect that aggregation of potassium nitrobenzenide in t-butyl alcohol may effectively remove it from the reaction mixture. Perhaps if some means were available to destroy the nitrobenzenide formed in the HMPA solutions, electron transfer would compete as effectively as in t-butyl alcohol alone.

We have also examined the efficiency of electron transfer relative to protonation in the polar protic solvent, methanol.[68] It was not clear that a cation dependence should be expected in this more highly-solvating medium, but it was discovered that the fraction of 9-methoxyfluorenide ions converted to free-radical-derived products by nitrobenzene varies with counterion in the order $K^+ > Na^+ > Me_4N^+ \overset{\sim}{} Li^+$. When the nitrobenzene reaction is run in an O_2 atmosphere, the order is $Me_4N^+ > K^+ > Li^+$ with rate increases in all but the lithium case which is unaffected. This oxygen effect is independent of O_2 concentration and is interpreted as a destruction of nitrobenzenide which eliminates the reversibility present in the anaerobic reaction. It is interesting that oxygen does not compete with nitrobenzene for the carbanion under these conditions but its effect on the nitrobenzene reaction allows us to show that k_e/k_h is larger for the larger cations -- at least in the case of 9-methoxyfluorenide ion.

In order to evaluate the possibility that ion pairing would provide an explanation for these results, we switched our attention to the methanol-stable fluoradenide ion, (26). By examining changes in the spectrum of this carbanion as a

250

function of counterion, we were able to show that carbanions
do indeed ion pair with tetraalkylammonium ions, a variety of
complexed potassium ions and even uncomplexed cesium
ions.[297] The broad, featureless absorption band observed for
(26) in the presence of lithium, sodium and potassium ions has
been assigned to hydrogen-bonded free ions by Hogen-

(26)

Esch.[298]

    Electron transfer from (26) to nitrobenzene can be
studied and offers the advantage that carbanion protonation
rate variations have no effect on the observed kinetics. The
electron transfer is reversible, followed by a rate
determining bimolecular destruction of nitrobenzenide ion. By
following the concentration of nitrobenzenide using ESR, it
can be shown that the electron-transfer equilibrium lies much
farther to the side of carbanion when the counterion is
tetramethylammonium ion than when it is potassium ion, even
though nitrobenzenide also appears to form ion pairs with
tetramethylammonium ions. It is our present hypothesis that
solvation of potassium ions by methanol prevents the formation
of tight ion pairs and requires stabilization of the anions to
occur by hydrogen bonding. This is less effective for the
highly delocalized (26) than for nitrobenzenide causing a
shift in equilibrium to the radical ion side.

    It is not certain that this analysis will be applicable
to other carbanions and the results discussed earlier suggest
that 9-methoxyfluorenide may respond differently. Moreover,
there appears to be a pronounced counterion effect on the rate
constants for the electron transfer step in the
9-methoxyfluorene system. Unfortunately only effects on the
equilibrium constant can be measured for (26).

Clearly the contrast between the large number of carbanion - electron-transfer systems mentioned in this chapter and the small number for which ion pairing and solvation effects have been investigated points to a research area for the future. The complex kinetic schemes which are characteristic of these systems make complete understanding a distant goal. However, the existing examples in which reactions have been turned on, turned off, or redirected by solvent and counterion changes suggest great practical rewards.

VI. BIOORGANIC EXAMPLES

Probably for the same reasons that carbanions are never truly "free" in solution, enzymatic systems have evolved low energy intermediates to permit proton removal from carbon, $A_{BH}D_{CH}$. The best known of these are enamine systems (27)[299] and (28)[300] which carry only partial negative charge. Coordination of enolate-type oxygen to Lewis acid metal complexes can also avoid isolation of negative charges[301] and the simple expedient of synchronous protonation at a conjugated atom, $A_{BH}D_{CC=O}, H^A O=CCH, H*B*^D B*H*$, or synchronous carbon-carbon bond formation, $A_{BH}D_{CH}A_{C,C=O}A_{OH*}$,

(27)

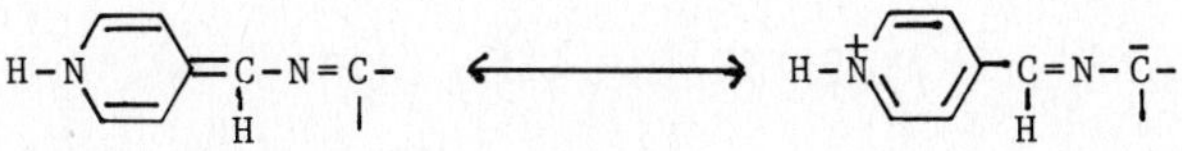

(28)

can avoid a carbanionoid species entirely.[302,303] There is at least one coenzyme which forms carbon-metal bonds (Vitamin B_{12})[304,305] and the possibilities for effective carbanion oxidation within this complex have been discussed.[306]

Although it might seem unlikely that the carbanionoid intermediates of enzyme chemistry could be trapped in the manner possible for their solution counterparts, a suggestive example was recently provided by Christen and Gasser.[307] They found that the carbanion-like intermediate of transaldolase could be oxidized by ferricyanide as shown in

$$
\begin{array}{c}
\underset{|}{CH_2OH} \\
\underset{|}{C=O} \\
\underset{|}{HOCH} \\
\underset{|}{HCOH} \\
\underset{|}{HCOH} \\
CH_2OPO_3^=
\end{array}
\quad\xrightarrow[\textstyle 2Fe(CN)_6^{3-}]{\textstyle Transaldolase}\quad
\begin{array}{c}
\underset{|}{CH_2OH} \\
\underset{|}{C=O} \\
H-C=O \\
+ \\
H-C=O \\
\underset{|}{H-C-OH} \\
CH_2OPO_3^=
\end{array}
\qquad [51]
$$

eq. 51. It should be noted, however, that considerable license is taken in considering the enamine intermediate in this reaction as a carbanion, because the dihydroxyacetone unit does not undergo transaldolase-catalyzed hydrogen isotope exchange. The intermediate which is oxidized in this experiment is probably very long-lived. Trapping experiments for other enzymes with enamine intermediates have also been reported.[308-310]

A number of good oxidants are present in biological systems. The respiratory chain, through which substrates are indirectly oxidized by O_2, consists of a series of reversible oxidation-reduction couples.[311] The oxidized forms of the electron carriers include iron complexes (iron-sulfur clusters and porphyrin complexes), a copper containing species (mediating electron transfer to oxygen), quinones, pyridinium salts (NAD^+ and $NADP^+$) and isoalloxazines (FMN and FAD). Several of the substrates for the respiratory chain are potential enolate forming species and, as might be expected, one electron oxidation has been considered as a mechanistic entry to the chain. The initial oxidant for such compounds is known to be a substituted isoalloxazine or flavin ring system (29) which is reduced to its dihydro derivative (30).

Although the involvement of carbanions in the enzymatic reaction is questionable, it has been shown by Bruice that carbanions can be oxidized by flavins in model studies.[312,313] Flavin-promoted oxidations which have been clearly proven to occur via carbanion intermediates are shown in

$$(\underline{29}) \rightleftharpoons (\underline{30}) \qquad [52]$$

$$[53]$$

$$[54]$$

$$Y = Aryl, \ Alkyl, \ H$$

$$X = Aryl, \ Alkyl, \ H, \ NH_2, \ OEt$$

$$HOCH_2C\equiv N \longrightarrow H-\overset{O}{\overset{\|}{C}}-C\equiv N \qquad [55]$$

$$R-\underset{H}{\overset{NO_2}{\underset{|}{\overset{|}{C}}}}-R \longrightarrow R-\overset{O}{\overset{\|}{C}}-R \ + \ NO_2^- \qquad [56]$$

$$R = H, \ alkyl$$

$$Ph-\underset{}{\bigcirc}-\overset{O-H}{\underset{C\equiv N}{\overset{|}{\underset{|}{C}}}}^- \longrightarrow Ph-\underset{}{\bigcirc}-\overset{O}{\overset{\|}{C}}-OH \qquad [57]$$

eqs. 53-57.[312,313] For none of these cases has the question of whether the carbanion reacts by nucleophilic attack or electron transfer been settled experimentally. In the case of eq. 53, it has been shown that the log of the rate constant did not correlate well with $E_{1/2}$ for a series of variously substituted flavin catalysts. Although this fact militates against a direct electron transfer process, a sequence of complex formation,[314] followed by nonsynchronous electron transfer $A_{C^-,Fl} + D_{C.Fl}$, is possible. Bruice supports this alternative based on a relationship between the trapping efficiency of the flavin and its equilibrium constant for complex formation with tryptophan or β-resorcylic acid. For eq. 54, an electron-transfer mechanism is favored based on free energy calculations.[315]

Very recently, Bruice has provided the incontrovertible example of carbanion – flavin electron transfer shown in eq. 58.[316] Dimer (31) is a definitive indicator of radical involvement and is the same product as that obtained when this carbanion reacts with nitrobenzene (see sect. IV D). Adduct (32) could conceivably arise by a different mechanism, but the

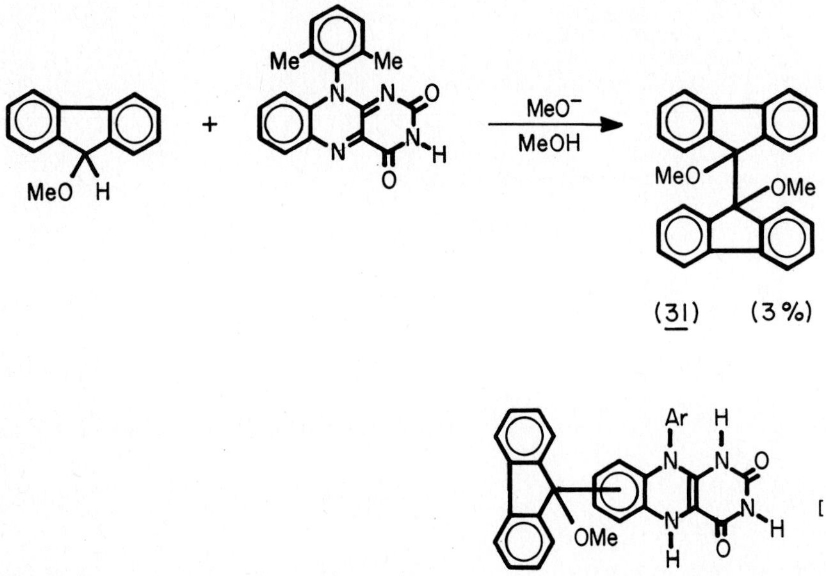

(31)   (3%)

[58]

(32)   (97%)

fact that both (32) and (31) are completely supplanted by fluorenone when the reaction is run under O_2 rules out simple nucleophilic addition. It is known that O_2 will not trap the carbanion in the absence of an electron acceptor and thus it

seems   highly   probable[317]   that O_2 is   intercepting   the
9-methoxyfluorenyl radical.

A fair evaluation of the situation would seem to be the
following.   Flavins can serve as one-electron oxidants for
nonnucleophilic, low-oxidation-potential carbanions.   It is
not yet proven whether the enolate-type substrates typical of
biological systems will fall in this category.   Even if it is
possible to   show an electron-transfer route for the enolate
plus flavin reaction,   it will be more difficult to conclude
that this is the lowest energy path when the reaction occurs
in an enzyme cavity.

REFERENCES

1 R.D. Guthrie, J. Org. Chem., 40(1975)402.

2 Y. Sprinzak, J. Am. Chem. Soc., 80(1958)5449.

3 G.A. Russell and A.G. Bemis, ibid., 88(1966)5491.

4 R.D. Guthrie, G.R. Weisman and L.G. Burdon, J. Am. Chem. Soc., 96(1974)6955.

5 M.F. Hawthorn and G.S. Hammond, ibid., 77(1955)2549.

6 R. Reeb, Y. Vinchon, G. Riess, J-M. Catala and J. Brossas, Bull. Soc. Chem. Fr., (1975)2717.

7 G.A. Russell, A.G. Bemis, E.J. Geels, E.G. Janzen and A.J. Moye, Adv. Chem. Ser., 75(1968)174.

8 G.A. Russell, E.G. Janzen, H.D. Becker and F.J. Smentowski, J. Am. Chem. Soc., 84(1962)2652.

9 K. Kinoshita, D. Okada and S. Hashimoto, Nippon Kagaku Zasshi. 80(1959)206, Chem. Abstr. 55(1958)4449.

10 G.A. Russell, E.G. Janzen, A.G. Bemis, E.J. Geels, A.J. Moye, S. Mak and E.T. Strom, Adv. Chem. Ser., Am. Chem. Soc., 51(1965)112.

11 J.O. Hawthorn, K.A. Schowalter, A.W. Simon M.H. Wilt and M.S. Morgan, Adv. Chem. Ser., Am. Chem. Soc., 75(1968)203.

12 D.R.H. Barton and D.W. Jones, J. Chem. Soc., (1965)3563.

13 F. Bodroux, Compt. Rend., 136(1903)158.

14 F. Bodroux, Bull. Soc. Chim. Fr., 31(1904)33.

15 L. Bouveault, ibid., 29(1903)1051.

16 H. Wuyts, Bull. Soc. Chim. Belg., 36(1927)222.

17 C.W. Porter and C. Steel, J. Am. Chem. Soc., 42(1920)2650.

18 M.S. Kharasch and O. Reinmuth, Grignard Reactions of Nonmetalic Substances Prentice-Hall, Inc., New York, N.Y., 1954, pp. 1264 - 1274.

19 H. Yasuda, M. Walczak, W. Rhine and G. Stucky, J. Organomet. Chem., 90(1975)123.

20 C. Walling and S.A. Buckler, J. Am. Chem. Soc., 77(1955)6032.

21 E.P. Kohler, Am. Chem. J., 36(1096)177, 529 ibid., 37(1907)339.

22 G. Sosnovsky and E.H. Zaret, in D. Swern (Editor), Organic Peroxides, Wiley-Interscience, New York, N.Y. 1970, Chap. VIII, p. 517.

23 E.P. Kohler, M. Tishler and H. Potter, J. Am. Chem. Soc., 57(1935)2517.

24 E.P. Kohler and R.P. Thompson, ibid., 59(1937)887.

25 R.C. Fuson, R.E. Foster, W.J. Shenk, Jr. and E.W. Maynert, ibid., 72(1950)1637.

26 R.C. Fuson and H.L. Jackson, ibid., 72(1950)1637.

27 R.C. Fuson and T.L. Tan, ibid., 70(1948)602.

28 E.E. van Tamelen, J. Am. Chem. Soc., 78(1958)4405.

29 J. Rigaudy, C.R. Hebd. Seances Acad. Sci., 226(1948)1911.

30 C. Du Fraisse A. Etienne and J. Rigaudy, Bull. Soc. Chim. Fr., 15(1948)804.

31 T.J. Wallace, H. Pobiner and A. Schriesheim, J. Org. Chem., 30(1965)3768.

32 T. Kamiya and T. Sugimoto, Chem. Lett., (1976)33.

33 J.E. Baldwin, D.H.R. Barton, D.J. Foulkner and J.F. Templeton, J. Chem. Soc., (1962)4743.

34 G.A. Russell and E.R. Talaty, Science, 148(1965)1217.

35 G.A. Russell, Am. Chem. Soc., Div. Petrol. Chem., Preprints, 10(1965)A7.

36 See p. 139 in Ref. 10.

37 J. San. Filippo, Jr., C.I. Chern and J.S. Valentine, J. Org. Chem., 41(1976)1077.

38 H.G. Aurich, Tetrahedron Lett., (1964)657.

39 N. Rabjohn and C.A. Harbert, J. Org. Chem., 35(1970)3240.

40 Y. Masuyama and M. Okawara, Chem. Lett., (1977)1439.

41 H.H. Wasserman and B.H. Lipshutz, Tetrahedron Lett., (1975)1731.

42 D.A. Mayers and J. Kagan, J. Org. Chem., 39 (1974)3147.

43 G.A. Russell, J. Am. Chem. Soc., 76(1954)1595.

44 Ref. 10, p. 146 and p. 130.

45 See ref. 97.

46 H.H. Wasserman and B.H. Lipshutz, Tetrahedron Lett., (1975) 4611.

47 G.A. Russell, A.J. Moye and K.L. Nagpal, J. Am. Chem. Soc., 84(1962)4145.

48 R. Howe and F.J. McQuillin, J. Chem. Soc., (1958)1513.

49 H.C. Volger and W. Brackman, Rec. Trav. Chim. Pays-Bas, 84(1965)579.

50 W. Treibs, Ber. Dtsch. Chem. Ges., 63(1930)2423.

51 W. Treibs, *ibid*., 64(1931)2545, 2178.

52 W. Treibs, *ibid*., 65(1932)153, 1314.

53 W. Treibs, *ibid*., 66(1933)1483.

54 Ref. 22, pp. 533-535.

55 P.L. Pauson and B.J. Williams, J. Chem. Soc., (1961)4158.

56 K. Ziegler and B. Schnell, Justus Liebigs Ann. Chem., 437(1924)227.

57 C.B. Wooster, Chem. Rev., 11(1932)1.

58 G.A. Russell and G. Kaupp, J. Am. Chem. Soc., 91(1969)3851.

59 H. Hock and F. Ernst, Ber. Dtsch. Chem. Ges., 92(1959) 2732.

60 G.A. Russell and A.G. Bemis, Chem. Ind. (London), (1965)1262.

61 A.A. Aansheidt, J. Russ. Phys. Chem. Soc., 58(1926)249.

62 J.G. Pacifici, J.G. Garst and E.G. Janzen, J. Am. Chem. Soc., 87(1965)3014.

63 This statement is only true if oxygen is present in its ground state, triplet form. Nitronate salts will react with singlet oxygen - J.R. Williams, L.R. Unger and R.H. Moore, J. Org. Chem., 43(1978)1271.

64 R.C. Lamb, P.W. Ayers, M.K. Toney and J.F. Garst, J. Am. Chem. Soc., 88(1966)4261.

65 C. Walling and A. Cioffari, *ibid*., 92(1970)6609.

66 Ref. 10, p. 114-123.

67 C.L. Greenstock and I. Dunlop, Int. J. Radiat. Biol., 23(1973)197.

68 R.D. Guthrie, G.W. Pendygraft and A.T. Young, J. Am. Chem. Soc., 98(1976)5877.

69 A. Nishinaga, T. Shimizu and T. Matsuura, Chem. Lett., (1977)547.

70 H.R. Gersmann and A.F. Bickel, J. Chem. Soc., (1959)2711.

71 A. Nishinaga, T. Itahara and T. Matsuura, Chem. Lett., (1974)667.

72 J.S. Valentine, Chem. Rev., 73(1973)235.

73 N.J. Turro, V. Ramamurty and K. Liu, J. Am. Chem. Soc., 98(1976)6759.

74 C.D. Ritchie and R.E. Uschold, J. Am. Chem. Soc., 89(1967) 2960.

75 C.D. Ritchie and R.E. Uschold, _ibid_., 90(1968)3515.

76 R.D. Guthrie, Intra-Sci. Chem. Rept., 7(1973)27.

77 M.E. Peover and B.S. White, Electrochim. Acta., 11(1966)1061.

78 J.M. Frisch, T.P. Layoff and R.N. Adams, J. Am. Chem. Soc., 87(1965)1724.

79 M.J.A. McGrath, Tetrahedron, 32(1976)377.

80 E.G. Perevalora and T.V. Nikitina, in E.I. Becker and M. Tsutsui (Editors), Organometallic Reactions, John Wiley and Sons, New York, N.Y. 1972, V. 4, p. 358.

81 A.A. Pendin, M.S. Zakharevskii and P.K. Leonteskaya, Kinet. Katal., 7(1966)1074.

82 W.M. Lattimer, The Oxidation States of the Elements and their Potentials in Aqueous Solution, Prentice-Hall, New York, N.Y., 1938, p. 212.

83 I.R. Wilson, Rev. Pure Appl. Chem., 16(1966)103.

84 P.S. Radhakrishnamurti and S. Devi, Indian J. Chem., 10(1972)496.

85 V.N. Singh, M.P. Singh and B.B.L. Saxena, _ibid_., 8(1970)529.

86 P.A. Nadar, A. Shanmugasundaram and R. Murugesan, _ibid_., 14A(1976)146.

87 P.S. Radhakrishnamurti and S. Devi, _ibid_., 11(1973)768.

88 P.T. Speakman and W.A. Waters, J. Chem. Soc., (1955)40.

89 J.B. Conant and J.G. Aston, J. Am. Chem. Soc., 50(1928)2783.

90 J.B. Conant, J.G. Aston and C.O. Tongberg, _ibid_., 52(1930)407.

91 R.C. Eckert, H. Chang and W.P. Tucker, J. Org. Chem., 39(1974)718.

92 C.L. Chen and W.J. Connors, _ibid_., 39(1974)3877.

93 P.S. Radhakrishnamurti and S.N. Maphapatra, Indian J. Chem., 14A(1976)613.

94 P.S. Radhadrishnamurti and S.N. Mahaptra, _ibid_., 13(1975)1029.

95 J.K. Kim and J.F. Bunnett, J. Am. Chem. Soc., 92(1970)7463, 7464.

96 J.F. Bunnett, Acc. Chem. Res., 11(1978)413.

97 G.A. Russell and W.C. Danen, J. Am. Chem. Soc.,

88(1966)5663.

98 N. Kornblum, R.E. Michel and R.C. Kerber, J. Am. Chem. Soc., 88(1966)5662.

99 R.A. Abramovitch and A.R. Vinutha, J. Chem. Soc. B., (1971)131.

100 T. Fujii, M. Ohba, S. Yoshigugi and M. Kirisawa, Chem. Pharm. Bull., 25(1977)2877 and references therein.

101 E.I. Tomilenko, Zh. Vses. Khim. O-va, 21(1976)462, Chem. Abstr., 85(1976)159094k.

102 J.W. Bunting, P.A. Lee-Young and D.J. Norris, J. Org. Chem., 43(1978)1132.

103 D.L. Allara, J. Org. Chem., 37(1972)2448.

104 M.S. Kharasch and G. Sosnovski, Tetrahedron, 3(1958)97.

105 H.C. Volger and W. Brackman, Rec. Trav. Chim. Pays-Bas, 84(1965)1017, 1203.

106 D.E. Bergbreiter and G.M. Whitesides, J. Am. Chem. Soc., 96(1974)4937.

107 W.H. Mandeville and G.M. Whitesides, J. Org. Chem., 39(1974)400.

108 G.M. Whitesides, W.F. Fischer, Jr., J. San Filippo, Jr., R.W. Bashe and H.O. House; J. Am. Chem. Soc., 91(1969)4871.

109 G.M. Whitesides, J. San Filippo, Jr., C.P. Casey and E.J. Panek, ibid., 89(1976)5302.

110 G.A. Russell and D.W. Lamson, J. Organometal. Chem, 156(1978)17.

111 J. Cornforth, A.F. Sierakowski and T.W. Wallace, J. Chem. Soc., Chem. Commun., (179)294.

112 F. Sato, Y. Mori and M. Sato, Tetrahedron Letters, (1979)1405.

113 I.I. Creaser and A.M. Sargeson, J. Chem. Soc., Chem. Commun., (1975)324.

114 J.K. Kochi, Acc. Chem. Res., 7(351)1974.

115 J.Y. Chen, H.C. Gardner and J.K. Kochi, J. Am. Chem. Soc., 98(1976)6150.

116 K.G. Hampton and J.J. Christie, J. Org. Chem., 40(1975)3887.

117 C.A. Maranoff, B.E. Maryanoff, R. Tang and K. Mislow, J. Am. Chem. Soc., 95(1973)5839.

118 E.O. Fischer and H. Werner, Metal Pi-Complexes, Elsevier, Amsterdam (1966).

119 J.S. Thayer in F.G.A. Sonte and R. West (Editors), Advances in Organometallic Chemistry, Academic Press, New York, N.Y., V. 13, p. 1.

120 Y.A. Zolotov, Extraction of Chelate Compounds, Ann Arbor-Humphrey, London, 1970, Chap. I, p. 1.

121 N.A. Bailey, B.M. Higson and E.D. McKenzie, J. Chem. Soc., Dalton Trans., (1975)1105.

122 M.F. Semmelhack, Y. Thebtaranonth and L. Keller, J. Am. Chem. Soc., 99(1977)959; and references therein.

123 M.F. Semmelhack, G. R. Clark, R. Farina and M. Saeman, J. Am. Chem. Soc., 101(1979)217.

124 See H.O. House, Acc. Chem. Res., 9(1976)59.

125 F.M. Martens, J.W. Verhoeven, R.A. Gase, U.K. Pandit and Th.J. DeBoer, Tetrahedron, 34(1978)443.

126 C.K. Mann and K.K. Barnes, Electrochemical Reductions in Non-Aqueous Systems, Marcel Dekker, New York, N.Y. (1970)p. 226.

127 J.M. Kern and P. Federlin, Tetrahedron Lett., 1977(837).

128 E.C. Ashby and T.L. Wiesemann, J. Am. Chem. Soc., 100 (1978)189.

129 E.C. Ashby, J.S. Bowers, Jr., ibid., 99 (1977)8504.

130 E.C. Ashby, J.D. Buhler, I.G. Lopp, T.L. Wiesemann, J.S. Bowers, Jr. and J.T. Laemmle, ibid., 98(1976) 6561.

131 I.G. Lopp, J.D. Butler and E.C. Ashby, ibid., 97(1975)4966, 1964.

132 E.C. Ashby, J.T. Laemmle and H.M. Newman, Acc. Chem. Res., 7(1974)272.

133 E.C. Ashby and T.L. Weisemann, J. Am. Chem. Soc., 100(1978)3101.

134 T. Holm and I. Crossland, Acta. Chem. Scand., 25(1971)59.

135 Ref. 126 pp. 358 and 184.

136 B. Miller, J. Org. Chem., 42(1977)1402.

137 B. Miller, ibid., 42(1977)1408.

138 B. Miller, J. Am. Chem. Soc., 95(1973)8458.

139 B. Miller, E. Matjeca and J.G. Haggerty, Tetrahedron Lett., (1977)323.

140 C. Berti, L. Greci and L. Marchetti, Chem. Ind. (Milan),

59(1977)384.

141 C. Berti, L. Greci and L. Marchetti, J. Chem. Soc., Perkin Trans. 2, (1979)233.

142 M. Okubo, Bull. Chem. Soc. Jpn., 48(1975)1327.

143 H.O. House and P.D. Weeks, J. Am. Chem. Soc., 97(1975)2785.

144 R.A. Lee and W. Reusch, Tetrahedron Lett., (1973)969.

145 C. Berti, L. Greci and L. Marchetti, J. Chem. Soc., Perkin 2, (1977)1032.

146 H. Inoue, N. Fujimoto and E. Imoto, J. Chem. Soc., Chem. Commun., (1977)412.

147 H.O. House and J.M. Wilkens, J. Org. Chem., 41(1976)4031.

148 H.O. House and C.Y. Chu, J. Org. Chem., 41(1976)3083.

149 H.O. House and P.D. Weeks, J. Am. Chem. Soc., 97(1975)2770.

150 G.M. Whitesides and P.W. Kendall, J. Org. Chem., 37(1972)3718.

151 C.P. Casey and M.C. Cesa, J. Am. Chem. Soc., 101(1979)4236.

152 N.G. Brink, J.F. Lane, and E.S. Wallis, J. Am. Chem. Soc., 65(1943)943.

153 S.E. Ulrich, F.H. Gentes, J.F. Lane and E.S. Wallis, J. Am. Chem. Soc., 72(1950)5127.

154 J. Sauer and W. Braig, Tetrahedron Lett., (1969)4275.

155 H.D. Zook and R.N. Goldy, J. Am. Chem. Soc., 75(1953)3975.

156 R.L. Letsinger, J. Am. Chem. Soc., 70(1948)406.

157 R.L. Burwell, Jr., A.D. Shields and H. Hart, J. Am. Chem. Soc., 76(1954)908.

158 R.L. Letsinger and J.G. Traynham, J. Am. Chem. Soc., 72(1950)849.

159 L.H. Sommer and W.D. Korte, J. Org. Chem., 35(1970)22.

160 W.D. Korte, L. Kinner and W.C. Kaska, Tetrahedron Lett., (1970)603.

161 P.S. Skell, R.G. Allen and G.K. Helmkamp, J. Am. Chem. Soc., 82(1960)410.

162 H.R. Ward, R.G. Lawler and R.A. Cooper, in A.R. Lepley and G.L. Closs (Editors), Chemically Induced Dynamic Nuclear Polarization, Wiley-Interscience, New York, N.Y., 1973, pp. 281-322.

163 R.G. Lawler and P. Livant, J. Am. Chem. Soc., 98(1976)3710.

164 D.J. Pasto, S-K. Chow, A. Waterhouse, R. Shults and G.F. Hennion, J. Org. Chem., 43(1978)1385.

165 H.E. Zieger, I. Angres and L. Maresca, J. Am. Chem. Soc., 95(1973)8201.

166 H.E. Zeiger, I. Angres and D. Mathisen, ibid., 98(1976)2580.

167 G. Lankamp, W.T. Nauta and C. McLean, Tetrahedron Lett. (1968)249.

168 R.D. Guthrie and G.R. Weisman, J. Chem. Soc., Chem. Commun., (1969)1316.

169 J.F. Garst, Acc. Chem. Res., 4(1971)400.

170 Y-J. Lee and W.D. Clossen, Tetrahedron Lett., (1974)1395.

171 J.F. Garst and J.T. Barbas, J. Am. Chem. Soc., 96(1974)3239.

172 J.F. Garst and J.T. Barbas, ibid., 96(1974)3247.

173 J.F. Garst and C.D. Smith, ibid., 98(1976) 1520.

174 X. Creary, J. Am. Chem. Soc., 99(1977)7632.

175 A. Streitwieser, Jr., and C. Perrin, J. Am. Chem. Soc., 86(1964)4938.

176 A. J. Bard and A. Merz, J. Am. Chem. Soc., 101(1979)2959.

177 Ref. 126, p. 226.

178 K. Fukui, K. Morokuma, H. Kato and T. Yonezawa, Bull. Chem. Soc. Jpn., 36(1963)217.

179 J.F. Garst, R.D. Roberts and J.A. Pacifici, J. Am. Chem. Soc., 99(1977)3528.

180 C.Y. Meyers, A.M. Malte and W.S. Matthews, J. Am. Chem. Soc., 91(1969)7510.

181 M. Makosza, B. Serafin and I. Gajos, Rocz. Chem., 43(1969)671.

182 C.Y. Meyers, W.S. Matthews, L.L. Ho, V.M. Kolb and T.E. Parady, Catalysis in Organic Synthesis - 1977, G.V. Smith, ed.; Academic Press, New York, N. Y., 1978, p 197.

183 (a) C.Y. Meyers and V.M. Kolb, J. Org. Chem., 43(1978)1985. (b) R.T. Arnold and S.T. Kulenovic, J. Org. Chem., 43(1978)3687.

184 A. Jonczyk, A. Kwast and M. Makosza, J. Org. Chem., 44(1979)1192.

185 Ref. 126, p. 31.

186 S. Lillie, S. Slomkowski, G. Levin and M. Swarc, J. Am. Chem. Soc., 99(1977)4608.

187 G. Levin, T.A. Ward and M. Swarc, J. Am. Chem. Soc., 96(1974)270.

188 M. Szwarc and J. Jagur-Grodzinski in M. Szwarc, (Editor), Ions and Ion Pairs in Organic Reactions Wiley-Interscience, New York, N.Y., V. 2, p. 98.

189 J.F. Garst and E.R. Zabolotny, J. Am. Chem. Soc., 87(1965) 495, and references therein.

190 B. DeGroof, G. Levin and M. Szwarc, J. Am. Chem. Soc., 99(1977)474.

191 F. Jachimowitz, G. Levin and M. Szwarc, J. Am. Chem. Soc., 99(1977)5977.

192 H.C. Wang, G. Levin and M. Szwarc, J. Am. Chem. Soc., 99(1977)2642.

193 T.A. Ward, G. Levin and M. Szwarc, ibid., 97(1975)258.

194 H. Levanon and P. Netta, J. Chem. Phys. Lett., 48(1977)345.

195 F.F. Smentowski and G.R. Stevenson, J. Phys. Chem., 73(1969)340.

196 G.R. Stevenson and J.G. Conception, ibid., 76(1972)2176.

197 G.R. Stevenson, E. Williams, Jr. and G. Caldwell, J. Am. Chem. Soc., 101(1979)520.

198 G.A. Russell, E.G. Janzen and E.T. Strom, J. Am. Chem. Soc., 86(1964)1807.

199 R.D. Guthrie, D.P. Wesley, G.W. Pendygraft and A.T. Young, J. Am. Chem. Soc., 98(1976)5870.

200 M. Makosza, M. Jagusztyn-Grochowska, M. Ludwikow and M. Jawdosiuk, Tetrahedron, 30(1974)3723.

201 M. Makosza and M. Jawdosiuk, J. Chem. Soc., Chem. Commun., (1970)648.

202 W.H. Barschers and T.L. Loh, Tetrahedron Lett, (1971)3483.

203 A possible example is: G.A. Russell and E.G. Janzen, J. Am. Chem. Soc., 89(1967)300, although the authors have found objections to this interpretation.

204 G.A. Russell and A.J. Moye, Chem. Soc., Div. Petrol. Chem., 5(1960) C25.

205 R.D. Guthrie, J. Am. Chem. Soc., 91(1969)6201.

206 G.A. Russell and J.M. Pecoraro, J. Am. Chem. Soc., 101(1979)3331.

207 G.A. Russell and E.J. Geels, J. Am. Chem. Soc., 87(1965)122.

208 J.M. Burns, D.L. Wharry and T.H. Koch, J. Am. Chem. Soc., 101(1979)2750.

209 D.E. Bartak and M.D. Hawley, J. Am. Chem. Soc., 94(1972)640.

210 For a recent review see: N. Kornblum, Angew. Chem., Int. Ed. Engl., 14(1975)734.

211 R. Seux, G. Morel and A. Foucaud, Tetrahedron, 31(1975) 1335.

212 A similar system was reported by S.H. Goh, Malays. J. Sci., 1(1972)141.

213 E. Tommila and M. Savolainen, Acta. Chem. Scand., 20(1966)946.

214 E. Bergmann and J. Hervey, Ber. Dtsch. Chem. Ges., 62(1929)893.

215 S.B. Hanna, Y. Iskander and Y. Riad, J. Chem. Soc., 217(1961).

216 S.B. Hanna, Y. Iskander and A. Salama, _ibid_., 221(1961).

217 C.G. Swain and E.R. Thornton, J. Am. Chem. Soc., 83(1961)4033.

218 I. Rothberg and E.R. Thornton, _ibid_., 86(1964)3296, 3302.

219 D.M. Doeleib and Y. Iskander, J. Chem. Soc., J. Chem. Soc. B., 1159(1967).

220 G.L. Closs and S.H. Goh, J. Chem. Soc., Perkin Trans. 1 (1972)2103.

221 G.L. Closs and S.H. Goh, J. Chem. Soc., Perkin Trans. 2, (1972)1473.

222 F.M. Fouad and P.G. Farrell, J. Org. Chem., 40(1975)3881.

223 S.D. Hanna and P.H. Ruehle, _ibid_., 40(1975)3882.

224 I.R. Bellabono, A. Gamba, G. Sala and M. Tampieri, J. Am. Chem. Soc., 94(1972)5781.

225 I.R. Bellabono, P. Govoni and F. Zavattarelli, J. Chem. Soc., Perkin 2,(1974)981.

226 I.R. Bellabono and P. Beltrame, Gazz, Chim. Ital., 105(1975)275.

227 V. Ogata and J. Mibae, J. Org. Chem., 27(1962)2048.

228 M. Barreau and M. Julia, Tetrahedron Lett., (1973)1537.

229 M. Julia, Pure Appl. Chem., 40(1974)553.

230 For a recent example, see: S.R. Robinson, B.C. Webb and C.H.J. Wells, Chem. Ind. (London) (1975)519.

231 N. Ono, H. Eto, R. Tamura and J. Hayami, Chem. Lett., (1976)757.

232 N Ono, R. Tamura, J. Hayami and A. Kaji, ibid., (1977)189.

233 N. Kornblum, S.D. Boyd and N. Ono, J. Am. Chem. Soc., 96(1974)1580, and references therein.

234 E.E. van Tamelen and G. Van Zyl, J. Am. Chem. Soc., 71(1949)835.

235 G. A. Russell, M. Makosza and J. Hershberger, J. Org. Chem., 44(1979)1195.

236 G.A. Russell, M. Jawdosiuk and M. Makosza, J. Am. Chem. Soc., 101(1979)2355.

237 G.A. Russell, M. Jawdosiuk and F. Ros, J. Am. Chem. Soc., 101(1979)3378.

238 V.K. Schchedrova, A.G. Bazanov, V.F. Selivanov, I.V. Tselinskii and B.V. Gidaspov, J. Org. Chem. USSR. (Eng.), 14(1979)2062.

239 S. W. Jewett and T.C. Bruice, Biochemistry, 11(1972)5662.

240 R.D. Guthrie and D.P. Wesley, J. Am. Chem. Soc., 92(1970)4057.

241 E. Buncel and E.A. Symons, J. Org. Chem., 38(1973)1201.

242 R.A. Foster and C.A. Fyfe, J. Chem. Soc. B, Phys. Org., (1966)53.

243 M.R. Crampton and V. Gold, ibid., 498(1966).

244 Some recent examples are: I. Kolb, U. Makosza and U. Sseiba, Coll. Czech. Chem. Commun., 41(1976)1914.

245 M. Makosza and M. Ludwikow, Rocz. Chem., 51(1977)829.

246 M. Makosza, J.M. Jagusztyn-Grochowska and M. Jawdosiuk, ibid., 50(1976)1841; M. Makosza and J.M. Jagusztyn-Grochowska, ibid., 50(1976)1859.

247 K. Kohashi, T. Kabeya and Y. Ohkura, Chem. Pharm. Bull., 25(1977)50.

248 K. Kohashi, Y. Tsuruta, M. Yamaguchi and Y. Ohkura, ibid., 25(1977)1103.

249 C.A. Fyfe, C.D. Malkiewich, S.W. Damji and A.R. Norris, J. Am. Chem. Soc., 98(1976)6983.

250 R. Foster and C.A. Fyfe, Rev. Pure Appl. Chem., 16(1966)61.

251 E. Buncel, A.R. Norris and K.E. Russell, Q. Rev., Chem. Soc., 22(1968)123.

252 M.R. Crampton, Adv. Phys. Org. Chem., 7(1969)211.

253 P. Buck, Angew. Chem., Int. Ed. Engl. 8(1969)120.

254 M.J. Strauss, Chem. Rev., 70(1970)667.

255 H.M. Relles, D.S. Johnson and J.S. Manello, J. Am. Chem. Soc., 99(1977)6677.

256 L.S. Levitt and B.W. Levitt, Chem. Ind. (London), (1975) 520.

257 R. Wohl, Ber. Dtsch. Chem. Ges, 32(1899)3486.

258 R. Okazaki, Y. Inagaki and N. Inamoto, J. Chem. Soc., Chem. Commun., (1974)414.

259 T.A. Antkowiak and H. Shechter, J. Am. Chem. Soc., 94(1972)5361.

260 B.L. Dyatkin, L.G. Martynova (Zhuravkova), B.I. Martynov and S.R. Sterlin, Tetrahedron. Lett., (1974)273.

261 H.C. Gardner and J.K. Kochi, J. Am. Chem. Soc., 98(1976)558.

262 H.C. Gardner and J.K. Kochi, *ibid*., 97(1975)5026.

263 J.K. Kochi, *ibid*., 98(2460)1976.

264 W.A. Nugent, F. Bertini and J.K. Kochi, J. Am. Chem. Soc., 96(1974)4945.

265 C.A. Bishop and L.K. J. Tong, Tetrahedron Lett., (1964)3043.

266 Van Damme and R. De Neve, Farm. Tijdschr. Belg., 50(1973)327, Chem. Abstr., 80(1974)59760c.

267 F.M. Dean, K.B. Hindley and L.E. Houghton, J. Chem. Soc. C, (1971)1171.

268 T.C. Hollocher and M.M. Weber, Nature, 195(1962)247.

269 P. Karrer, Helv. Chim. Acta., 22(1939)1146.

270 D.G. Davis, P. Hodge and P. Yates, J. Chem. Soc., Perkin Trans. 1, (1973)850.

271 Ref. 10, p. 140.

272 T.S. Cantrell and H. Shechter, J. Am. Chem. Soc., 89(1967)5877.

273 C. Festa, L. Nucci, F. Pietra and A.M. Moresco, L. Pardi and S. Santucci, J. Chem. Soc., Perkin Trans. 2,

(1976)180.

274 M.T. Jones and S.I. Weissman, J. Am. Chem. Soc., 84(1962)4269.

275 M. Ballester, J. Riera, J. Cataner, C. Badia and J.M. Monso, ibid., 93(1971)2215.

276 M.L. Kaplan and R.W. Murray, J. Org. Chem., 31(1966)962.

277 K. Conrow and P.C. Radlick, J. Org. Chem., 26(1961)2260.

278 M.R. Wasielewski, Abstr. of 174th Natl. Meet. of Amer. Chem. Soc., Aug., 1977, paper 92.

279 M.R. Wasielewski and R. Breslow, J. Am. Chem. Soc., 98(1976)4222.

280 V.I. Savin, Zh. Org. Khim, 12(1976)1857, 1818-Eng. trans.

281 F.A. Davis, P.A. Mancinelli, K. Balasubramanian and U.K. Nadir, J. Am. Chem. Soc., 101(1979)1044.

282 G.A. Russell, J. Hershberger and K. Owens, J. Am. Chem. Soc., 101(1979)1312.

283 Ref. 188, p. 1.

284 See Ref 274 for an exception.

285 E.J. Panek, J. Am. Chem. Soc., 95(1973)8460.

286 D.J. Cram, Fundamentals of Carbanion Chemistry, Academic Press, New York, N.Y., 1965 p. 32.

287 E. Buncel, Carbanions, Elsevier, New York, N.Y., 1975, Ch. 1.

288 B. Bockrath and L. Dorfman, J. Am. Chem. Soc., 97(1975)3307.

289 B. Bockrath and L.M. Dorfman, ibid., 96(1974)5708 L.M. Dorfman, R.T. Sujdak and B. Bockrath, Acc. Chem. Res., 9(1976)352.

290 J. March, Advanced Organic Chemistry, Second Ed., McGraw-Hill, New York, N.Y. p. 531.

291 Ref. 287, Ch. 7.

292 D. Bethell, C.S. Fairclough, R.J.E. Talbot and R.G. Wilkinson, J. Chem. Soc., Perkin 2, (1976)55.

293 R.D. Guthrie, J. Am. Chem. Soc., 92(1970)7219.

294 Ref. 188, p. 72.

295 N. Hirota and S.I. Weissman, J. Am. Chem. Soc., 86(1964)2537.

296 See discussion in Ref. 188, p. 68.

297 R.D. Guthrie and N.S. Cho, J. Am. Chem. Soc.,

97(1975)2280.

298 T.E. Hogen-Esch, J. Am. Chem. Soc., 95(1973)1939.

299 E. Zeffren and P.L. Hall, The Study of Enzyme Mechanisms, Wiley-Interscience, New York, N.Y., 1973, p. 244.

300 J.N. Lowe and L.L. Ingraham, An Introduction to Biochemical Reaction Mechanisms, Prentice-Hall, Englewood Cliffs, N.J., 1974, p. 37.

301 Ref. 299, p. 247.

302 J.R. Knowles and W.J. Albery, Acc. Chem. Res., 10(1977)105 and references therein.

303 K.R. Hanson and I.A. Rose, Acc. Chem. Res., 8(1975)1 and references therein.

304 Ref. 300, p. 125.

305 J.N. Lowe and L.L. Ingraham, J. Am. Chem. Soc., 93(1971)3801.

306 R.H. Abeles and D. Dolphin, Acc. Chem. Res., 9(1976)114.

307 P. Christen and A. Gasser, J. Biol. Chem., 251(1976)4220.

308 S.V. Shylyapnikov and M.Y. Karpeisky, Eur. J. Biochem., 11(1969)424.

309 H. Holzer and R.M.M. Crawford, Nature, 188(1960)410.

310 E. Grazi, Biochem. J., 151(1975)167.

311 D.E. Metzler, Biochemistry, Academic Press, New York, N.Y., 1977, p. 588.

312 T.C. Bruice in E.T. Kaiser and F.J. Kezdy (Editors), Progress in Bioorganic Chemistry, Wiley-Interscience, V. 4, 1976, pp. 33-40.

313 S. Shinkai, T. Yamashita and O. Manabe, J. Chem. Soc., Chem. Commun., (1979)301.

314 T.W. Chan and T.C. Bruice, Biochemistry, 17(1978)4784.

315 R.F. Williams and T.C. Bruice, J. Am. Chem. Soc., 98(1976)7752.

316 M. Novak and T.C. Bruice, J. Am. Chem. Soc., 99(1977)8079.

317 It is possible that O_2 intercepts a carbanion-flavin complex. It would be interesting to know whether the trapping efficiency of eq. 58 correlates with $E_{1/2}$ for the series of flavins studied in the reaction of eq. 53.

CHAPTER 6

THE NUCLEAR MAGNETIC RESONANCE OF CARBANIONS

Daniel H. O'Brien

Department of Chemistry, Texas A&M University, College Station, Texas 77843

CONTENTS

I. INTRODUCTION

    Proton and carbon-13 magnetic resonance has been used extensively to character-
ize the structure of carbanions in homogeneous solutions.[1] Several structural
features of carbanions are well suited for study with magnetic resonance through
the interpretation of the proton and carbon-13 chemical shifts, proton-proton

couplings, and the relative areas of proton resonances. Magnetic resonance is
used to show the presence of carbanions in solution most often by qualitatively
comparing chemical shifts of the precursor to those of the carbanion. Hydrogens
attached to electron rich carbons experience upfield chemical shift changes compared to the precursor due to an increase in electron density. The upfield chemical shift changes due to electron density in proton NMR may be complicated by
the anisotropy of the carbanion's π-system and additional upfield or compensating
downfield shift changes may be observed in going from precursor to carbanion ("ring
current" effects).[2,3] Shift changes due to ring current effects have been widely
used as a criterion for aromaticity in carbanions. Similarly, upfield carbon-13
chemical shift changes occur in going from precursor to carbanion but the changes
are much larger and less sensitive to effects other than changes in electron density.
For delocalized carbanions, proton shifts, corrected for ring current effects, and
carbon-13 shifts have been used as empirical guides to differences in electron density within carbanions.

Carbanion stereochemistry has been studied mainly through analysis of vicinal
proton-proton couplings. If isomerization is rapid on the NMR time scale, conformer
populations can be estimated from the size of the averaged vicinal coupling compared
to the cis and trans vicinal couplings in model compounds where only one conformer
is present. If isomerization is slow on the NMR time scale or if it can be slowed
at lower temperatures, isomer concentrations and equilibrium constants can be measured directly by proton integration. Proton NMR has also been used to determine
rotational barriers to isomerization. Other aspects of carbanion structure have been
studied with magnetic resonance. These include estimating the equilibrium between
contact ions and solvent separated ions as a function of carbanion structure, cation,
solvent, and temperature and directly observing the reaction of one carbanion to
give another.

Proton NMR has been used more than carbon-13 to study carbanions because it became routinely available in the early 1960's. More recently, Fourier transform car-
bon-13 magnetic resonance has yielded complementary and additional information about
the structure of carbanions in solution. Since the carbon-13 shift "ruler" is approximately fifteen to twenty times larger than for proton chemical shifts and carbon-
13 "sees" carbons directly rather than the more indirect observation of the hydrogens
attached to the carbanion's carbon framework, it is expected that carbon-13 study
of carbanion solutions will greatly increase in the future. However, even with the
greatly enhanced sensitivity of Fourier transform NMR, carbon-13 is still concentration limited and proton-decoupled carbon-13 spectra are not amenable to integration. Although as yet little used to study carbanion solutions, proton Fourier
transform NMR will be useful in the future, particularly to investigate dilute
solutions.

In this chapter, the NMR data and discussion are organized according to carb-

anion structure and to the size of the π-electron system. The NMR of all-carbon,
delocalized carbanions dissolved in donor solvents such as THF and liquid ammonia
will be emphasized. It is felt that comparing such systems offers the best oppor-
tunity to show how proton and carbon-13 chemical shifts and couplings vary as a
function of carbanion structure, cation, solvent, and temperature. Carbanions
with heteroatoms such as enolates will be discussed only where their structures
can be compared to similar all-carbon systems. More information on the NMR of enolates can be obtained from a recent review.[4] The NMR of alkyllithiums dissolved in
non-polar hydrocarbon solvents and the lithium-7 NMR of organolithium reagents
will not be treated.

II. ALLYL CARBANIONS

A. Alkylallyl Carbanions

Early applications of proton NMR to the study of organometallics were to allyl
Grignard,[5] allyllithium,[6] and methyl substituted allyl Grignards.[7-9] The chemical
shifts and couplings found in these studies and in later investigations of alkyl
substituted allyl carbanions [10-18] established the basis for the interpretation
of the proton NMR of carbanions with larger π-systems. Table 1 presents a summary
of the proton chemical shifts and couplings for allyl and alkylallyl carbanions.[19]
Proton chemical shifts alternate: upfield, downfield, upfield. This indicates high
electron density at the terminal carbons of the three carbon allyl system. It will
be seen that this pattern of shift alternation is characteristic of the chemical
shifts for larger π-systems. Alkyl substitution at carbon-3 causes an upfield shift
change at carbon-1 of about one ppm due to an increase in electron density at the
primary carbon. In donor solvents (Et_2O, Me_2O, and THF), proton chemical shifts
show little change with the different cations, lithium or magnesium.

Analysis of the proton-proton vicinal couplings, J_{12} and J_{23}, for allyllithiums
gives important stereochemical information. For allyllithium, the four terminal
protons are magnetically equivalent at 37° and give rise to an AB_4 [20] doublet and
quintet pattern with an averaged vicinal coupling of 12 Hz.[10] Lowering the temperature slows the rotation about the carbon-carbon bonds and below about -60° in
d_8-THF an AA'BB'C spectrum is obtained with a larger _trans_ coupling of 15.2 Hz
and a smaller _cis_ coupling of 8.6 Hz. These vicinal couplings establish the size
to be expected for _cis_ and _trans_ vicinal couplings in carbanions and have been
used to determine stereochemistry of other allyl and larger carbanions.

Bond rotation is rapid on the proton NMR time scale for allyl and alkylallyl
Grignards and only averaged spectra are obtained even down to -100°.[14] The steady
increase in J_{23} as the size of the alkyl group increases shows the increase in the
population of the E conformer over the Z conformer with increasing steric hindrance (Table 1: No. 9-12; 1Z ⇄ 1E).[21] The low temperature spectrum of 3,3-dimethyl-
allylmagnesium chloride in diethyl ether is particularly revealing.[8,9] Below about

-10°, the terminal methyls become nonequivalent and analysis of the variable temperature spectra gives a rotational barrier of 7.0 kcal/mol compared to a value of

TABLE 1

Proton Chemical Shifts and Couplings for Alkylallyl Carbanions [19]

No.	R_3	H_1	H_2	H_3	J_{12}	J_{23}	Z:E	Solv.	Ref.
Li^+:									
1	H	2.24(Z) 1.78(E)	6.38		15.2(Z) 8.6(E)			Et_2O,THF -60°	6,10
2	Z-CH_3	1.2	6.0	2.9	10.2	10.2	85:15	TMEDA	11
3	Z-CH_3	1.17	6.21		10.2			Me_2O	12,13
4	Z-$(CD_3)_3CCH_2$ E-$(CD_3)_3CCH_2$	0.80 0.77	6.11 6.06	4.49 4.64	10.0 9.4	10.0(E) 14.5(Z)	33:67	$PhCH_3$	15,16
5	Z-$(CD_3)_3CCH_2$ E-$(CD_3)_3CCH_2$	0.98 1.15	5.99 5.87	3.16 3.52	9.6 10.0	9.0(E) 13.8(Z)	57:43	THF -35°	17
6	2-CH_3	1.95						TMEDA-Hex	18
Mg^{++}:									
7	H	2.50	6.38		12.0			Et_2O	5,8
8	1,3-di-CH_3	2.82	6.20		11.0			Et_2O	14
9	CH_3	0.76	5.93	4.52	9.6	11.7	60:40	Et_2O	7,8,14
10	CH_3CH_2	0.79	5.94	4.56	9.5	12.4	45:55	Et_2O	14
11	$(CH_3)_2CH$	0.78	5.91	4.54	9.4	13.6	30:70	Et_2O	14
12	$(CH_3)_3C$	0.71	5.95	4.73	9.1	15.1	3:97	Et_2O	14
13	3,3-di-CH_3	0.57	5.58					Et_2O	8,9

10.5 kcal/mol for allyllithium.

The observation of discrete conformers at low temperatures for allyllithiums
and for other delocalized organolithiums and rapidly equilibrating conformers
for allyl Grignards has led to two contrasting interpretations of the proton NMR
data concerning the exact nature of the carbon-metal bond. These interpretations
are perhaps different in degree rather than in kind. For magnesium compounds in
diethyl ether [5,7,8,14] and for lithium compounds in diethyl ether or non-polar
solvents such as toluene or hexane,[6,13,15,16] investigators have favored localized structures involving polar σ bonds between carbon and the metal. For Grignards,
this interpretation is based upon the vicinal coupling, J_{12}. This coupling is averaged at all temperatures and, compared to the changes in J_{23}, it varies little

with change of the alkyl group at carbon-3.[14] This suggests low bond order between carbons 1 and 2 and substantial sp^3 character at carbon-1. In contrast, delocalized, "ionic" structures have been favored for allyllithiums dissolved in don-
or solvents such as THF. Magnetic resonance is unable to give a more definitive

$$(\underline{1Z}) \qquad\qquad (\underline{1E})$$

answer but the overall trends are clear. The tendency toward delocalized, monomeric, "ionic" structures and higher rotational barriers increases from magnesium
to lithium and from non-polar to polar environments.

Carbon-13 spectra for alkylallyl carbanions are limited to lithium [22-24] and
other alkali metal salts [24-26] dissolved in THF (Table 2). In non-donor solvents
like benzene, chemical shifts are much different, carbon-3 being much more shielded and carbon-1 being much more deshielded (No. 21). This shows the influence of
aggregation and perhaps a greater degree of localized character in non-polar environments. The carbon-13 shifts of the allyl carbons alternate: upfield, downfield, upfield, similar to the trends noted for proton shifts but over a much
larger shift range. Chemical shift changes due to alkyl substitution at carbon-3
cannot be accounted for solely on the shift changes expected for replacing hydrogen by alkyl. For example, α-alkyl substitution deshields by about 9 ppm at an sp^3
carbon and by about 11 ppm at an sp^2 carbon.[27] α-Alkyl substitution causes a small
shielding of about 2 ppm at the γ-position. In going from allyllithium to crotyl-
lithium (No. 14 vs 16), carbon-3 is deshielded by about 26 ppm and carbon-1 is
shielded by about 20 ppm by α-methyl substitution. These differences, greater deshielding at carbon-3 and greater shielding at carbon-1, are primarily due to the
redistribution of electron density toward carbon-1 upon alkyl substitution at car-
bon-3.

Carbon-13 shifts for alkylallyl carbanions are noticeably influenced by the
alkali metal cation. Carbon-1 becomes more deshielded as the cation becomes larger
(No. 16Z vs 17Z; 22Z, 23Z, 24Z, 25Z, and 26Z).[22,24,26] Shieldings of similar magnitude are observed at carbon-3. Cation solvation becomes less favorable as the
size of the carbanion's π-system decreases and as the size of the cation increases.
Lithium salts of carbanions with π-systems larger than allyl, such as benzyl and
α-trimethylsilylbenzyl, are dominantly contact ion pairs even down to -50° in THF.
[28] Therefore, it can be assumed that allyl and alkylallyl carbanions exist as con-

tact ions in THF. If this assumption is valid, deshielding at carbon-1 shows that the cation is less effective in polarizing the electron density toward carbon-1 as it becomes larger. The opposite shift trend at carbon-3 suggests that the alk-

TABLE 2

Carbon-13 Chemical Shifts for Alkylallyl Carbanions

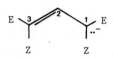

No.	R_3		C_1	C_2	C_3	Z:E	Conditions M^+ Solv.		Ref.
14	H		51.2	147.2			Li	THF	22
15	H		52.8	144.0			K	THF	25
16	CH_3	Z	32.0	142.6	76.0		Li	THF	22
		E	29.9	145.2	79.3				
17	CH_3	Z	45.3	139.1	62.8	100:0	K	THF	26
18	CH_3CH_2	Z	45.8	137.5	73.7	86:14	K	THF	26
		E	43.5	141.1	75.2				
19	$(CH_3)_2CH$	Z	45.5	136.8	81.0	65:35	K	THF	26
		E	44.1	139.1	81.6				
20	$(CH_3)_3C$	E	44.2	136.6	84.9	0:100	K	THF	26
21	$(CH_3)_3CCH_2$	Z	20.0	140.3	103.0	23:77	Li	PhH	23,24
		E	20.7	144.3	103.3				
22	$(CH_3)_3CCH_2$	Z	31.0	142.5	81.9	65:35	Li	THF −20°	24
		E	30.7	146.0	79.6				
23	$(CH_3)_3CCH_2$	Z	35.7	138.8	72.3	77:23	Na	THF −20°	24
		E	34.5	145.0	70.9				
24	$(CH_3)_3CCH_2$	Z	45.0	137.5	67.5	100:0	K		
25	$(CH_3)_3CCH_2$	Z	47.4	138.2	67.5	100:0	Rb	THF −20°	24
26	$(CH_3)_3CCH_2$	Z	51.4	139.5	69.0	100:0	Cs		
27	2-CH_3-3-$(CH_3)_3CCH_2$	Z	31.8	149.3	83.9	100:0	Li	THF −20°	23,24

ali metal cations are located closer to the less substituted, electron rich carbon-1 in the contact ions.

In contrast to proton NMR, individual Z and E conformers are observed with carbon-13 even at room temperature. However, allyl Grignards have not yet been studied. For allylpotassium compounds, this contrast may be due to an increase in the rotational barrier. Rotational barriers have not been determined with variable temperature carbon-13 for the potassium compounds because reaction with solvent becomes rapid at the higher temperatures required. For allyllithium compounds,

this contrast between proton and carbon-13 results is difficult to rationalize.
Conformer populations for alkylallylpotassium compounds are similar to those
found for allyl Grignards with proton NMR, the E conformer becoming dominant as
the size of the 3-alkyl group increases.[26] For neopentylallylmetal compounds,
conformer populations show a marked dependence upon the cation, with the Z conformer being favored with increasing cation size (No. 22-26).[23,24]

B. Phenylallyl Carbanions

The introduction of one or more phenyls at carbons 1 or 3 makes phenylallyl
carbanions easier to prepare and more stable in donor solvents than allyl or alkylallyl carbanions. Other structural features of carbanions in solution such as the
equilibrium between contact ions and solvent separated ions and the slow rotation
about phenyl carbon-allyl carbon bonds come into play and can be studied with magnetic resonance. NMR studies have been reported for alkali metal salts but not for
phenylallyl Grignards.

Proton shifts in the allyl portion alternate but protons 1 and 3 are less shielded compared to allyl carbanions because of delocalization of negative charge into
the benzene ring(s) (Table 3). This results in shielding at the ortho and para
hydrogens. For example, the para hydrogens of monophenylallyl carbanions are shielded by one to two ppm compared to their uncharged precursors. 1-E hydrogens are consistently more shielded than 1-Z hydrogens because the "inner" Z hydrogens lie in
the deshielding region of the carbon-2-carbon-3 bond. The shift of the 2-hydrogen
responds to stereochemistry in 1,3-diphenylallyl carbanions. In E,E conformers,
they are deshielded by about 0.7 ppm because of the influence of the two adjacent
phenyls (No. 32 vs 33; No. 37). Rotational barriers are high for monophenylallyl
carbanions and individual conformers can be observed when the equilibrium is favorable. Phenyls show a strong preference for the E position. This stereochemistry
is dictated by steric hindrance between the Z-3 phenyl and the Z-1 substituent
similar to the crowding observed for large alkyl groups in 3-alkylallyl carbanions.

3-Phenylallyl carbanion exists only as the E-conformer (2E) as the lithium,

(2E) (3E,E) (3E,Z)

sodium, or potassium salt in d$_8$-THF[29] or as the potassium salt in liquid ammonia.[30]
Only this conformer is observed even when the carbanion is generated at low
temperatures from three different precursors: allylbenzene, cis or trans-propenyl-
benzene. The observation of discrete resonances for the 1-Z and 1-E hydrogens with

cis and trans vicinal couplings, J_{12}, of 9.4 and 15.4 Hz shows that rotation about

TABLE 3

Proton Chemical Shifts and Couplings for Phenylallyl Carbanions

No.	R	H$_1$	H$_2$	H$_3$	H$_p$	J$_{1Z-2}$ (J$_{1E-2}$)	J$_{23}$	Conditions M$^+$ Solv.	Ref.
E-3-Ph:					_Z_				
28	H	Z 3.1 / E 2.7	6.7	4.1	5.7	15.4 (9.4)	12.2	Li THF 5°	29
29	H	Z 3.39 / E 2.93	6.63	4.22	5.48	15.4 (9.3)	12.2	K NH$_3$ -20°	30
30	E-1-CH$_3$ / Z-1-CH$_3$	Z 3.85 / E 3.29	6.24 / nr	3.92 / 3.86	5.19 / 5.35	13.8 (9.8)	11.4 / 12.5	K NH$_3$,-60° / K NH$_3$,-20°	30,31,35
31	E-1-OCH$_3$ / Z-1-OCH$_3$	Z 5.56 / E 4.93	6.08 / 5.37	3.61 / 3.79	5.09 / 5.19	11.2 (5.5)	11.6 / 12.1	K NH$_3$,-60° / K NH$_3$,-20°	33
32 33	E-1-Ph Z-1-Ph	Z 4.70 / E 4.40	7.30 / 6.60	4.70 / 5.35	5.98 / nr	13.0 (10.0)	13.0 / 14.6	M NH$_3$,THF / Li THF,-60°	30,34,35 / 36,37
34	Z-3-CH$_3$	Z 3.05 / E 3.01	6.81		5.54	15.2 (9.4)		K NH$_3$ -20°	38
35	Z-3-Ph	Z 4.26 / E 3.40	6.48		6.22	16.4 (10.4)		K NH$_3$ -20°	38
36	E-1-CH$_3$- / Z-3-CH$_3$	Z 3.59	6.52		5.21	13.5		K NH$_3$ -20°	38
37	E-1-Ph- / Z-3-CH$_3$	Z 4.49	7.26		5.98 / 5.82	13		M THF	37
Z-3-Ph:				_E_					
38	2-CH$_3$	Z 3.48 / E 3.19		3.75	5.73			K NH$_3$ -20°	30
39	2-Ph	Z 3.73 / E 3.40		4.01	5.85			K NH$_3$ -20°	30
40	2-CH$_3$- / E-1-Ph	Z 4.10		5.32	6.06			M THF	40
41	2-CN- / E-1-Ph	Z 4.65		5.40	6.50			Na DMSO 5°	41
42	2-Ph- / Z-1-Ph	E 4.70						Li TMEDA-Hex	42

the 1-2 bond is slow. Free energies of rotation, determined by observing the coalescence of the multiplets for hydrogens on carbons 1, 2, and 3 at higher temperatures, are sensitive to cation and solvent ($\Delta G^{\dagger}$ = Li, THF, 17.0 kcal/mol; Li, Et$_2$0, 15.7; Na, THF, >17.8; K, THF, >20.1).[29] Bond rotation about the carbon-3-phenyl bond can be slowed at low temperatures and the smaller free energies show a similar sensitivity to cation and solvent.

1-Methyl and 1-methoxy-3-phenylallyl carbanions show two conformers (3E,E $\rightleftharpoons$ 3E,Z). Proton abstraction from trans-1-phenyl-2-butene by potassium amide in liquid ammonia below -20° initially gives the expected E,E conformer, identified by its trans vicinal couplings of 13.8 and 11.4 Hz (R = CH$_3$).[31,32] Isomerization occurs slowly at 0° to give an equilibrium mixture of E,E and E,Z conformers (E,E:E,Z = 17:83).[32] Similarly, two conformers are observed for 1-methoxy-3-phenylallyl carbanion (3E,E $\rightleftharpoons$ 3E,Z; R = OCH$_3$).[33] Trans-1-methoxy-3-phenylpropene gives the expected E,E conformer with potassium amide in liquid ammonia at -60° and slowly isomerizes completely to the E,Z conformer at -20°. It has been proposed that rotation in the allyl fragment for allyl Grignards [5,7,8,9,14] and allyl alkali metal compounds [13,15,16,17,29] may involve a low, spectroscopically undetectable concentration of species with covalent carbon-metal bonds. However, the rate of isomerization of 1-methyl-3-phenylallylpotassium is insensitive to a large excess of potassium ion.[32] This result argues strongly against covalent intermediates and for ionic ones.

Three conformers are possible for 1,3-diphenylallyl carbanion (4Z,Z; 4E,Z; and 4E,E). On steric grounds, one would predict that the Z,Z conformer is higher in energy than the other two and it has not been observed. Only the E,E conformer is

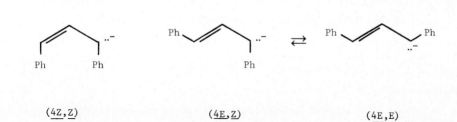

(4Z,Z) (4E,Z) (4E,E)

formed from 1,3-diphenylpropenes by proton removal with n-butyllithium,[35,36,37,39,40] with potassium amide in liquid ammonia [30] or by reduction with sodium, potassium, or rubidium.[36,37] The less stable E,Z conformer can be prepared by the reaction of cis-1,3-diphenylpropene with lithium cyclohexylisopropyl amide in THF at -45° or by the reaction of cis,trans-2,3-diphenyl-1-bromocyclopropane with lithium in THF at -60°.[34] The E,Z conformer is identified by its cis vicinal coupling of 10.0 Hz and its trans vicinal coupling of 14.5 Hz while the E,E conformer shows a trans vicinal coupling of 13 Hz. The barrier to rotation, determined by following the isomerization of the E,Z to the E,E conformer with proton NMR, is the same as for phenylallyllithium ($\Delta G^{\dagger}$ = 17.0 kcal/mol). Further, these kinetic data give a half life for the E,Z conformer of 3 min at -30° and this explains the difficulty earlier investigators had in observing the less stable E,Z conformer.

Phenylallyl carbanions with three 1,3-substituents such as 1,3-dimethyl-3-phenyl (5, R = CH$_3$) and 3-methyl-1,3-diphenyl (5, R = Ph) exist dominantly as the conformers that would be predicted from the trends established by the less substituted phenylallyl carbanions.[37,38] 2-Substituents perturb the equilibria toward

(5) (6) (7) (8)

conformers with terminal phenyls in the Z position. However, the evidence from proton NMR is weak because the vicinal couplings are lost upon substitution. For example, assignment of the Z conformer to 2-methyl-3-phenyl and 2,3-diphenylallyl carbanions (6, R = CH$_3$ or Ph) is based upon analogy to less substituted carbanions and upon the small, 3-bond coupling, J_{1E-3}, of 1.3 Hz.[30] The conformations of 2-methyl and 2-cyano-1,3-diphenylallyl carbanions were based only upon the appearance of nonequivalent 1-Z and 3-E proton singlets at low temperatures (7, R = CH$_3$ or CN).[40,41] The Z,Z stereochemistry proposed for 1,2,3-triphenylallyl carbanion (8) was based upon product stereochemistry after quenching rather than on NMR evidence.[42] Proton shift changes for 1,3-diphenylallyl carbanions of the alkali metals have also been used to study contact ion-solvent separated ion equilibria (Section V.E.).[36,37]

Carbon-13 data for phenylallyl carbanions are as yet quite limited (Table 4).

TABLE 4

Carbon-13 Chemical Shifts for Phenylallyl Carbanions

No.	R	C_1	C_2	C_3	C_{ipso}	C_o	C_m	C_p	Conditions M+ Solv.		Ref.
43	E-3-Ph	66.1	137.5	78.4	148.7	117.1	128.5	109.8	Li	THF	22
44	E-3-Ph	73.0	136.1	79.0	147.6	115.9	129.2	108.1	K	THF	25
45	E-1-Ph- E-3-Ph	90.3	129.0	90.3	146.9	118.5	128.9	112.1	K	NH$_3$	43,44

22,25,43,44 The high field shifts at carbons 1 and 3 show the high electron density

at these carbons. Delocalization of the charge into the benzene rings is seen
in the upfield chemical shifts of the <u>ortho</u> and <u>para</u> carbons. Similar to the
carbon-13 shifts for neopentylallyl carbanions (Table 2, No. 22-26), chemical
shifts at carbon-1 show a marked dependence on cation (Table 4, No. 43 vs 44).
This may be due to cation size or to differences in solvation.

III. LARGER ACYCLIC AND CYCLIC CARBANIONS

A. Acyclic Carbanions

Proton shifts for larger acyclic carbanions such as pentadienyl, heptatrienyl,
and nonatetraenyl follow the same general pattern of shift alternation but the
protons on the electron rich carbons are not quite as shielded because the negat-

TABLE 5

Proton Chemical Shifts and Couplings for Pentadienyl, Heptatrienyl, and Nonatetraenyl Carbanions

No.			H_1	H_2	H_3	H_4	H_5	J_{1Z-2} (J_{1E-2})	J_{23}	Conditions M^+ Solv.	Ref.
Pentadienyl:											
46	H	Z	3.1	6.2	4.1			16	11	Li	45,46
		E	2.7					(9)		THF 15°	
47	H	Z	3.01	6.13	4.35			15.1	11.5	K	47
		E	2.58					(9.0)		NH$_3$ -20°	
48	4-CH$_3$		3.0	6.2	3.8		6.9	14	11.5	Li THF	45
49	Z-5-CH$_3$	Z	3.01	6.09	4.07	5.84	3.07	15.1	11.5	K	32
		E	2.45					(8.8)		NH$_3$ -20°	
50	E-5-CH$_3$	Z	2.71	6.02	4.09	5.75	3.39	15.2	11.9	K	48
		E	2.24					(9.0)		NH$_3$ -20°	
51	E,E-1,5-di-Ph	Z	5.20	nr	4.81			14.4	11.2	Li Et$_2$O	49
52	3-CH=CH$_2$	Z	3.7	6.2				16	nr	Li THF	50
		E	3.5					(10)			
Heptatrienyl:											
53	H	Z	3.4	6.1	4.5	6.0		16.0	12.0	Li	51
		E	3.2					(8.0)		THF -50°	
54	H	Z	3.56	6.14	4.57	6.01		16	12	K	52
		E	3.19					(8)		NH$_3$ -60°	
55	7-E-CH$_3$	Z	3.32	6.11	4.43	5.93	4.47	15.7	11.3	K	53
		E	2.93					(9.3)		NH$_3$ -60°	
56	7-Z-CH$_3$	Z	3.45	6.14	4.61	6.00	4.46	15.7	11.2	K	53
		E	3.08					(9.4)		NH$_3$ -60°	
Nonatetraenyl:											
57	H	Z	3.7	5.7	4.7	5.9	4.6	17	12.0	Li	54
		E	3.4					(8)		THF -60°	

ive charge is spread over a larger carbon framework (Table 5). Z hydrogens are
consistently downfield from E hydrogens and terminal vicinal couplings are slightly larger than internal vicinal couplings. Three conformations have been widely

discussed for. acyclic pentadienyl carbanions: "W" (9); "sickle" (10); and "U" (11).
Early it was suggested that the "U" conformation might be favored even for acyclic
systems because of the possibility of overlap between carbons 1 and 5 in this conformation.[55] The large _trans_ vicinal couplings, J_{1Z-2} and J_{23}, however, show that
acyclic carbanions prefer all _trans_, extended conformations. For pentadienyl carb-

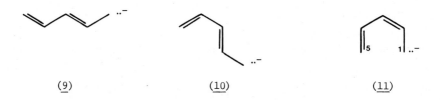

| (9) | (10) | (11) |

anions, (9) is most frequently observed. Only at low temperatures or with a few exceptional structures is the sickle conformer observed. For example, 1,3,5-triphenyl
pentadienyllithium exists as a mixture of "W" and sickle conformers at low temperatures in a ratio of about 2:1.[56] For acyclic pentadienyl carbanions, the "U" confo
mer has never been detected. Apparently, steric hindrance prevents acyclic pentadienyl carbanions from assuming the "U" conformation so that 1,5 overlap is not
possible. Rotational barriers in these larger acyclic carbanions are larger for
terminal rotation (15-20 kcal/mol) than for internal rotation (<14 kcal/mol).[45,50]

B. Cyclic Carbanions

Cyclic pentadienyl carbanions have been studied with proton NMR as models for
the acyclic pentadienyl conformers. Shifts and couplings for the sickle model (12)
the "U" model (13), and the larger ring cyclopentadienyl carbanions (14) and (15)

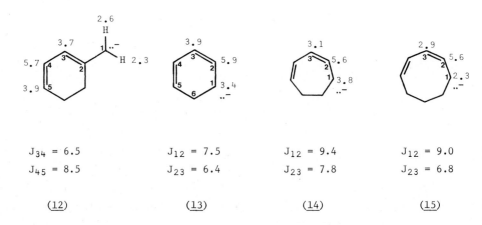

| J_{34} = 6.5 | J_{12} = 7.5 | J_{12} = 9.4 | J_{12} = 9.0 |
| J_{45} = 8.5 | J_{23} = 6.4 | J_{23} = 7.8 | J_{23} = 6.8 |

| (12) | (13) | (14) | (15) |

are for the lithium salts in THF[45,51,57] and these shifts change very little for
the potassium salts in liquid ammonia[52,58,59] or for alkyl substitution at the
sp^3 carbons.[50,53,58,60] The small _cis_ vicinal couplings for (12)-(15) are in con-

trast with the large _trans_ vicinal couplings observed for acyclic pentadienyl, heptatrienyl, and nonatetraenyl carbanions and this provides the principal spectral evidence that acyclic carbanions prefer all-_trans_, extended conformations.

Proton and carbon-13 shifts have been used to address the question of 1,5 overlap (homoaromaticity) in cyclic pentadienyl carbanions.[58,59] If 1,5 interaction were present for carbanions like (13), one would expect a decrease in the proton shift alternation due to the more even spreading of the charge around the homoaromatic system. Further, as the ring size increases with the insertion of sp^3 carbons as in (14) and (15), the extent of such interaction should decrease because the distance between carbons 1 and 5 increases. The similarity of the proton shifts and the shift alternation for six, seven, and eight-membered cyclic pentadienyl carbanions (13)-(15) argues strongly that homoconjugation is absent.

C. Homoaromatic Carbanions

Homoaromaticity does become important in cyclic carbanions with one sp^3 carbon, but with larger rings than (13) and for structurally rigid bicyclic carbanions. Potassium metal reduction of _cis_-bicyclo[6.1.0]-nona-2,4,6-triene in THF or DME proceeds through the monohomocyclooctatetraene anion radical[61-63] to the homocyclooctatetraene dianion (16).[64] This dianion may also be formed by removal of two protons from Z,Z,Z-1,3,6-cyclononatriene with n-butyllithium in TMEDA-hexane.

$$J_{12}, J_{23} = 8.7$$
$$J_{34} = 7.9$$
$$J_{45} = 9.1$$
$$J_{ab} = 12.9$$

(16)

$$J_{12} = 11.0$$
$$J_{23} = 8.9$$
$$J_{34} = 7.9$$
$$J_{ab} = 10.5$$

(17)

(18)

[65] In liquid ammonia, the 9-methyl and 9,9-dimethyl dianions of (16) may be observed with proton NMR at low temperatures but alkali metal reduction of unsubstituted _cis_-bicyclo[6.1.0]-nona-2,4,6-triene gives only cyclononatrienyl carbanion through protonation of (16) by solvent.[66] Proton NMR shifts and couplings convincingly demonstrate that there is substantial 1,8 overlap in (16). Qualitatively, the smaller shift differences between hydrogens of the eight π-carbons of (16)

compared to the shift differences for (13)-(15) show that the charge is more even-ly spread around the π-system in (16). The "inside" hydrogen, H_b, appears at -1.2 δ and the "inside" methyl in the 9,9-dimethyl dianion appears at -1.6 δ. These groups are in the shielding region above the diamagnetic ring current caused by the homoaromatic system. The proton-proton couplings were obtained for the more soluble lithium salt in d_8-THF [65] because couplings could not be observed for the much less soluble potassium salt.[64] The coupling between the methylene hydrogens, J_{ab}, is much too large for geminal hydrogens on a 3-membered ring and this rules out a structure in which there is a 3-membered ring between carbons 1, 8, and 9. The size and similarity of the vicinal couplings indicate a coplanar structure for carbons 1-8. However, the couplings (7.9 to 9.1 Hz) are slightly below the value expected for dihedral angles of 0° and on this basis a slightly bent con-formation has been proposed for (16).[65] The methylene bridged cyclodecatetraenyl carbanion (17) (R = CH_2SOCH_3 or CH_2SCH_3) has proton NMR characteristics similar to those of (16), indicating that it is a 10-electron, homoaromatic system.[67] The vicinal couplings suggest coplanarity for carbons 1-9 and the high field shifts for the methylene bridge hydrogens show that there is a diamagnetic ring current.

The proton NMR of bicyclic carbanions (18) and (19) shows that there is inter-action between the two isolated π-bridges.[68,69,70] Hydrogens 1 and 3 are not as shielded as the terminal hydrogens of allyl carbanions and hydrogens 5 and 6 are shielded by over 2 ppm compared to the uncharged hydrocarbon precursor. This shows

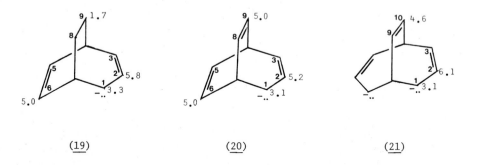

(19)   (20)   (21)

that the charge is delocalized around the 6-electron bishomocyclopentadienide anion. The methylene bridge hydrogens for (18) are shielded by the ring current of the homoaromatic system by approximately 1.2 ppm but the bridge hydrogens on carbons 8 and 9 of (19) are unchanged. The bridge hydrogens of (18) lie directly over the center of the homoaromatic ring where the shielding effect is large while in (19) they lie over the periphery of the ring close to the zero shielding region of the induced ring current.[69]

For bicyclic carbanions with more than two interacting π-systems, molecular orbital symmetry arguments have been used to develop the requirements for homo-

aromatic stabilization.[71,72] The topology of carbanions like (20), the 5,6-benzo
derivative of (20), and (21) has been termed "longicyclic" and the three π-bridges
must have either two 4n bridges and one 4n + 2 bridge as in (21) or two 4n + 2
bridges and one 4n bridge as in (20) for homoaromatic stabilization ("bicycloaro-
maticity").[72] Proton NMR shows the delocalization of the negative charge into both
ethylenic bridges of (20) by the magnetic equivalence and upfield shifts of the
hydrogens on carbons 5, 6, 8, and 9.[69,70,73,74] The bicyclo[3.3.2]-decatrienyl dianion (21) was prepared by the reduction of bullvalene with sodium-potassium alloy
in DME and the upfield carbon-13 and proton shifts for carbons 9 and 10 and for
the hydrogens on these carbons show that the ethylenic bridge bears a substantial
amount of the negative charge.[75]

D. Reactions of Acyclic Carbanions

The eight electron, acyclic carbanions undergo interesting cyclizations which
may be followed with proton NMR. Heptatrienyl anions as lithium salts in THF[51] or
as potassium salts in liquid ammonia[52,53] are observed when prepared below -50°
(Table 5, No. 53-56). Above -30°, these anions undergo thermal, conrotatory closure
to cycloheptadienyl anions.[51-53] The cis-R conformer of 3-vinylpentadienyl carbanion (22, R = CH$_2$CH$_3$) cyclizes to cycloheptadienyl carbanion (23) at room temper-

(22)   (23)

ature in approximately seven minutes.[50] This conversion probably takes place by
rearrangement of the acyclic carbanion to a 2-vinylpentadienyl carbanion to a
2-ethylheptatrienyl carbanion followed by heptatrienyl-cycloheptadienyl cyclization. Although proton NMR shows that these acyclic carbanions exist dominantly in
all-trans conformations, the ease of these cyclizations indicates that the cis
conformations required for ring closure must be energetically accessible.

Unlike heptatrienyl and vinylpentadienyl carbanions, the 10-electron nonatetraenyl carbanion does not cyclize even when heated to 70° for prolonged periods.[54]
6-(1-Butenyl)-1,4-cycloheptadiene reacts with n-butyllithium and then ring opens
to 7-ethylnonatetraenyl carbanion, probably through a cycloheptadienyl carbanion.
These different pathways have been rationalized as due to the greater delocalization energy in the nonatetraenyl carbanion compared to that in the heptatrienyl
carbanion.[54]

286

E. Reactions of Cyclic Carbanions

Cyclic carbanions also undergo reactions that may be followed with proton NMR. The spirocyclopropylcyclohexadienyl anion (24) is not observed when the diene is treated with potassium amide in liquid ammonia at -65° or with n-butyllithium in

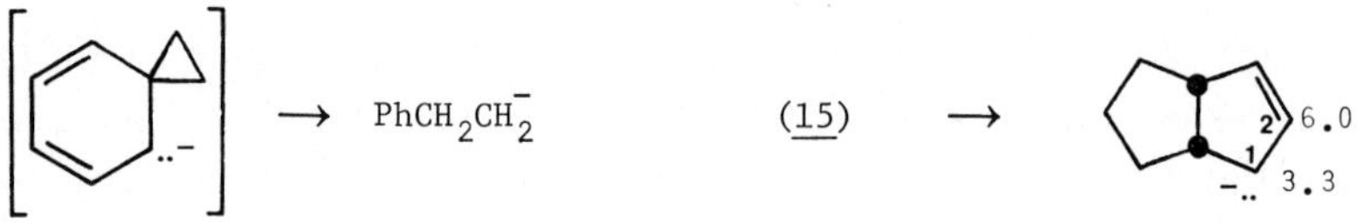

PhCH$_2$CH$_2^-$ (15)

(24)

$J_{12} = 3.5$

(25)

THF but undergoes rapid cyclopropyl ring opening to 2-phenylethyl anion.[76] The 6-π-electron cyclooctadienyl carbanion (15) cyclizes in a disrotatory manner to the bicyclic allyl carbanion (25).[57]

Cyclic carbanions containing 8-π-electrons within a 7-membered ring are potentially "antiaromatic" and attempts to prepare them have resulted in further reactions. Reaction of cycloheptatriene with potassium amide in liquid ammonia at -33° results in the dimer (26).[77] Deuterium labelling was employed to show that this

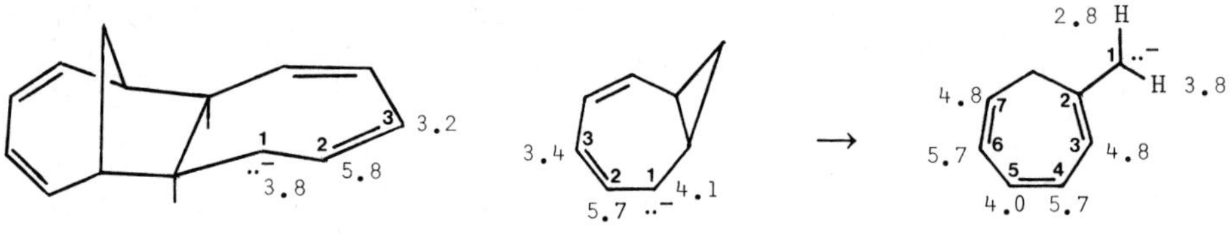

$J_{12} = 10.5$
$J_{23} = 8.0$

(26)

$J_{12} = 9.3$
$J_{23} = 8.3$

(27)

$J_{34} = 9.5$ $J_{45} = 10.0$
$J_{56} = 6.9$ $J_{67} = 8.4$

(28)

cycloaddition probably occurs through the reaction of cycloheptatrienyl carbanion with cycloheptatriene. Bicyclo[5.1.0]-octa-2,5-diene reacts with potassium amide in liquid ammonia initially to give the bicyclic cycloheptadienyl anion (27).[78] This anion does not undergo the thermally forbidden, electrocyclic ring opening to a cyclooctatrienyl carbanion but rearranges to anion (28). Photolysis of (27) at -70° results in the formation of cyclooctatetraene dianion, probably through the intermediacy of cyclooctatrienyl carbanion.[79]

The instability of 8-electron cyclooctatrienyl monoanions toward disproportionation to 10-electron, aromatic cyclooctatetraene dianion and cyclooctatriene
may be thwarted by blocking one of the carbons. Reaction of potassium amide with
7-chloro-3,3-dimethyl-1,4-cyclooctadiene results in the formation of a relatively
stable cyclooctatrienyl carbanion (29).[80] Photolysis of (29) establishes a photo-
equilibrium between (29) and 8,8-dimethylcycloheptadienyl anion (27).[80] If the sp^2
carbons of (29) lie in the same plane and allow appreciable antibonding interaction between the π-orbitals on carbons 1 and 7, this anion is potentially "anti-

$J_{12} = 12.4$
$J_{23} = 9.0$
$J_{34} = 11.0$

(29)

$J_{12} = 12.5$
$J_{23} = 10.0$
$J_{34} = 10.9$

(30)

$J_{12} = 12.5$
$J_{23} = 10.2$
$J_{34} = 10.8$

(31)

homoaromatic". The methyls of (29) are magnetically equivalent down to −77° and
this is compatible with either a planar or a rapidly flipping, folded conformation. The small difference in the coupling, J_{23}, in (29) compared to the same coupling in (31) is used to argue that (29) is non-planar and folded due to undesirable
bond angle strain in the planar form.[81] Since (29) is probably non-planar, then
the question of "antihomoaromatic" character in this system can not be answered.

Unlike the spirocyclopropylcyclohexadienyl carbanion (24), the analogous cyclo-
propylcyclooctatrienyl carbanion (30) is relatively stable.[82] The size of the vicinal couplings for (30) and (31) suggests that both anions are close to planar.
The downfield position of the cyclopropyl hydrogens of (30) compared to those in
similar hydrocarbons (δ = 0.5 to 0.8) indicates polarization of electron density
out of the cyclopropyl ring into the 8-membered ring. Despite gaining electron
density from the cyclopropyl ring, hydrogens on carbons 2-6 of (30) are downfield
by about 0.7 ppm when compared to the corresponding hydrogens of the similar anions
(29) and (31). These downfield chemical shifts for (30) are attributed to a substantial diamagnetic ring current.[82] Therefore, if aromaticity is experimentally
defined as the development of a diamagnetic ring current, (30) would be "more"
aromatic than (31). This interpretation of the proton shift data is opposite to

the conclusions based on resonance energy arguments.[82]

Anion formation from cis-bicyclo[6.1.0]-nona-2,4,6-trienes takes different
pathways depending upon the reaction conditions and the substituents on the
triene. Reduction of the unsubstituted cis-triene with alkali metals gives monohomocyclooctatetraene anion radical and then homocyclooctatetraene dianion (16)
in THF or DME.[61-64,66] In liquid ammonia, protonation of (16) by solvent gives

J_{12} = 10.5

J_{23} = 7.6

J_{34} = 11.6

(32)

(33)

cyclononatrienyl carbanion (32).[66] This anion has also been prepared by deprotonation of 1,3,6-cyclononatriene.[83] Proton removal from unsubstituted or 9-phenyl
substituted cis-bicyclo[6.1.0]-nona-2,4,6-trienes gives methylenecyclooctatrienyl
carbanions (31).[81,82,84] However, reduction of 9-phenyl cis-trienes gives benzyl-
cyclooctatetraene dianions (33).[85]

In the methylenecyclooctatrienyl carbanion (31), there is little interaction
between the π-orbitals of the exo-methylene and the orbitals of the 7-membered
ring and this anion has been used as an example of a "4n + 1" atropic system in
contrast to "aromatic" 4n + 2 systems (diatropic) and "antiaromatic" 4n systems
(paratropic).[81] If the ring proton shifts of (31) are calculated using an initial
chemical shift of 6.1 δ, HMO charge densities, and a proportionality constant of
10.7 ppm/electron,[86] the calculated shifts agree well with the experimental values.
[81] Thus, (31) is an example of an atropic system, one in which there is no induced
paramagnetic or diamagnetic ring current.

In contrast to the reactions of cis-bicyclo[6.1.0]-nonatrienes, cis-bicyclo-
[6.2.0]-deca-2,4,6-triene (34) forms cyclooctatetraene dianion (35) with amide
ion [87] and ring opens to cyclodecatrienyl anion (36) upon reduction with potassium
metal.[88] Similar to the cyclizations of cyclooctadienyl carbanion (15), (36)
cyclizes to (37) completely at -41° in about 23 min.

$$J_{12} = 11.7$$
$$J_{23} = 9.9$$
$$J_{34} = 12.8$$

(35)   (34)   (36)

$$J_{12} = 10.0$$
$$J_{23} = 8.2$$

(37)

E. Carbon-13 NMR of Larger Acyclic and Cyclic Carbanions

A number of different pentadienyl, cyclohexadienyl, and cycloheptadienyl carbanions have been characterized using carbon-13 (Table 6). The chemical shifts alternate, showing high electron density at carbons 1, 3, and 5. Methyl substitution causes a large upfield shift change at carbon-1, remote to the substitution,
due to the polarization of the electron density toward this carbon (No. 58 vs 65
and 66).[89-91] The chemical shifts of unsubstituted pentadienyl carbanions are
cation sensitive.[46,89] As the cation increases in size, carbon-1 moves downfield
while carbon-3 moves upfield (No. 58-61). If the cation is closest to carbon-1,
this effect is due to the decrease in the cation's ability to polarize the electron density toward carbon-1 as it becomes larger, similar to the effect of cation
size on the chemical shifts of allyl carbanions. Pentadienyl carbanions are probably contact ions at room temperature and changes in chemical shift with temperature are probably due to solvation. However, variable temperature magnetic resonance has not yet been employed to study the ion pair equilibria for pentadienyl
carbanions.

The chemical shifts of pentadienylzinc disolvates are exceptional and are best
described as σ-bonded rather than delocalized pentadienyl anions (No. 62 and 63).[92]
The position of σ-bonding depends upon the solvating ligand and the temperature. The TMEDA solvate is terminally σ-bonded at 6° and changes to a mixture
of terminally and 3-σ-bonded structures at higher temperatures. The THF solvate
is terminally σ-bonded at -60° and becomes dominantly 3-σ-bonded at 6° in benzene.

Carbon-13 shows that all the pentadienyl anions except 5,5-dimethylpentadienyl-
lithium (No. 69) are mainly in the extended "W" conformation (9). For unsubstituted pentadienyl anions, this interpretation is based upon the appearance of
only three carbon-13 resonances. The sickle conformation (10) requires five and
the "U" conformation (11), even though it would also show only three resonances,

TABLE 6

Carbon-13 Chemical Shifts for Pentadienyl, Cyclohexadienyl, and Cycloheptadienyl Carbanions

No.	R	C_1	C_2	C_3	C_4	C_5	Conditions M^+ Solv.		Ref.
Pentadienyl:									
58	H	66.2	143.8	86.9			Li	THF,$-41°$	89,90
59	H	77.2	135.5	77.4			Na	THF, $0°$	46
60	H	79.9	137.6	78.6			K	THF	25,46
61	H	76.4	135.0	76.8			Rb	THF	46
62	H	65.3	139.2	115.3			Zn–THF,PhH,$6°$		92
63	H	20.5	141.0	118.2	147.1	105.0	Zn–TMEDA,PhH,$6°$		92
64	4–CH$_3$	79.1	133.5	79.7	142.3	76.0	K	THF	46
65	Z–5–CH$_3$	56.7	143.6	81.4	137.3	85.7	Li	THF,$-37°$	89
66	E–5–CH$_3$	51.5	142.9	83.8	139.6	89.2	Li	THF,$-37°$	89
67	Z–3–CH$_3$	63.4	144.4	91.6			Li	THF,$-37°$	89,90
68	(38)	50.8	142.7	81.9	133.1	94.7	Li	THF,$-37°$	89
69	(39)	49.2	138.2	77.2	126.4	101.2	Li	THF,$-37°$	89
Cyclic:									
70	(13)	75.8	131.8	78.0			K	NH$_3$,$-60°$	58
71	(13) R$_6$ = CH$_3$	90.9	127.0	78.0			K	NH$_3$,$-60°$	58,90
72	(14)	93.0	133.8	77.3			K	NH$_3$,$-60°$	58,90

is excluded because earlier proton NMR results showed it to be absent.[45] For 5,5-dimethylpentadienyllithium, ten carbon-13 resonances show that two conformers are present.[89] The dominant conformer (80%) is assigned to the "W" structure (38)

(38)   (39)

while the minor conformer is assigned to the sickle structure (39). 5-Methylpenta-dienyllithium exists as a mixture of "W" conformers with the conformer having the the methyl in the Z position accounting for 65% and the conformer with an E methyl accounting for 21%. The remaining minor components were assigned to sickle con-formers of unknown structure.[89]

The carbon-13 shifts for cyclic carbanions offer strong evidence that there is little if any 1,5 overlap.[58,90] In both the cyclohexadienyl and cycloheptadienyl carbanions, the shifts alternate, showing high electron density at carbons 1, 3, and 5 and little charge density at carbons 2 and 4. Carbon-13 shifts for homo-aromatic carbenium ions such as homotropylium ion show that the charge is quite evenly spread over the olefinic carbons.[93-95] For cyclohexadienyl, cyclohepta-dienyl, and acyclic carbanions, the similarity of the carbon-13 chemical shifts strongly suggests that these cyclic anions are not analogous to the homoaromatic carbenium ions. Cyclohexadienyl carbanion (13) is not a homoaromatic cyclopenta-dienide ion but should be regarded as a typical pentadienyl carbanion.[58]

IV. HETEROATOM SUBSTITUTED CARBANIONS

The chemistry and magnetic resonance of alkali metal enolates has recently been reviewed.[4] In this section, proton NMR data for heteroatom substituted carb-anions, mainly enolates, will be presented and these data will be compared to their all-carbon analogs. The proton shifts and couplings of the 1-oxygen anal-ogs of allyl, pentadienyl, heptatrienyl, and nonatetraenyl carbanions are com-pared in Table 7.

The proton shifts for the enolates (40)-(46) show the shift changes that occur when the terminal methylene carbon is replaced by oxygen. The oxygen takes on a substantial amount of the charge both inductively and through resonance and the protons on the remaining carbons are all less shielded when compared to the all-carbon systems. The inductive influence is seen in the deshielding at hydrogen-2 (0.5 to 2.4 ppm). The resonance influence of oxygen on the electron distribution is displayed by the deshielding of the hydrogens on carbons remote to oxygen. For example, the terminal hydrogens of the heptatrienyl analog (44) are deshielded by 0.91 and 1.08 ppm compared to the all-carbon system. The anisotropic effect of the π-system on Z hydrogens compared to E hydrogens is similar to that observed for allyl carbanions, with Z hydrogens always downfield from E hydrogens in the enolates.

As with the all-carbon systems, interpretation of _cis_ and _trans_ vicinal coup-lings is crucial in defining enolate stereochemistry. The vicinal couplings are all smaller in the enolates but the approximate 2:1 ratio of the size of the _trans_

(40)   (41E)   (41Z)

to cis coupling is maintained. The E conformer of the enolate of phenylacetaldehyde (41E, R = H) has a trans vicinal coupling of 11.2 Hz compared to a cis vicinal coupling of 5.0 Hz for the Z conformer (41Z, R = H). Unlike the all-carbon analog, 3-phenylallyl carbanion (which exists exclusively as the E conformer), the enolate of phenylacetaldehyde is a 3:2 mixture favoring the Z conformer. This increase in the Z conformer is due to a decrease in the 1,3 steric

TABLE 7

Proton Chemical Shifts and Couplings for Enolate Ions: Oxygen Analogs of Allyl, Pentadienyl, Heptatrienyl, and Nonatetraenyl Carbanions

No.	H_2	H_{3Z} H_{3E}	H_4	H_{5Z} H_{5E}	H_6	H_{7Z} H_{7E}	H_8	H_{9Z} H_{9E}	Terminal J's J_{trans} J_{cis}		J_{23}	Ref
Allyl:												
73 (40)	6.92	3.60 3.15							13.4	5.4		96
1	6.38	2.24 1.78							15.2	8.6		6,10
74 (41E)	8.54	4.91							11.2			30
29 (2E)	6.63	4.22							12.2			30
Pentadienyl:												
75 (42)	7.79	4.82	6.35	4.11 3.78					16.5	10.7	10.5	47
47 (9)	6.13	4.35	6.13	3.01 2.58					15.1	9.0	11.5	47
76 (43)	7.32	4.30	6.82	4.22 3.86					17.2	10.2	4.5	96,102
Heptatrienyl:												
77 (44)	7.91	4.80	6.29	5.36	6.24	4.47 4.27			16.7	9.9	10.3	103
54	6.14	4.57	6.01	4.57	6.14	3.56 3.19			16	8	12	52
78 (45)	7.61	4.69	6.60	5.03	6.71	4.75 4.57			16.9	9.8	4.4	105
Nonatetraenyl:												
79 (46)	8.08	4.92	6.39	5.38	6.21	5.54	6.33	4.77 4.58	16.5	10.0	10.2	104
57	5.7	4.7	5.9	4.6	5.9	4.7	5.7	3.7 3.4	17	8	12.0	54

interaction when oxygen replaces the methylene carbon. This bias toward the Z conformer is even greater for enolates with substituents on carbon-2. Thus, the enolate of phenylacetone as the potassium salt in liquid ammonia [30] or as the lithium, sodium, or potassium salts in ether, THF, or DME [97,98] exist dominantly as the Z conformer. Similarly, only the Z conformer is observed for the lithium enolate of N,N-dimethyl-α-trimethylsilylacetamide. [99,100] Carbon-13 spectra have recently been reported for the alkali metal enolates of phenylacetone and for other enolate systems. [101]

Only the extended "W" conformer (42) is observed when crotonaldehyde reacts

with potassium amide in liquid ammonia.[47] This assignment is based upon a _trans_
vicinal coupling, J_{23}, of 10.5 Hz. 2,5-Dihydrofuran reacts with potassium amide
[102] or with n-butyllithium [96] to give the sickle enolate (43). This conformer is
distinguished from (42) by its _cis_ vicinal coupling of 4.5 Hz. Remarkably, these

(42)   (43)

conformers do not equilibrate. When the lithium salt of (43) is heated to 150° in
a sealed tube, it is not converted into (42) indicating a barrier to rotation about
the 2,3 bond greater than 23 kcal/mol.[96] Only the extended conformers (44) and (46)
are observed for the heptatrienyl and nonatetraenyl enolates when they are prepared from all-_trans_ precursors, _trans_-2-_trans_-4-hexadienal and _trans_-2-_trans_-4-_trans_-
6-octatrienal.[103,104] Unlike heptatrienyl carbanions, which undergo cyclizations to

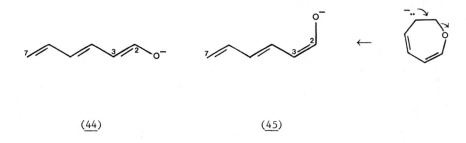

(44)   (45)

cycloheptadienyl carbanions, the anion from 2,3-dihydrooxepin ring opens to give the
sickle conformer (45), characterized by a _cis_ vicinal coupling, J_{23}, of 4.4 Hz.[105]
Again, sickle conformer (45) and extended conformer (44) do not equilibrate. The
cycloreversion of 2,5-dihydrofuran and 2,3-dihydrooxepin to open, sickle enolates
may be explained by the destabilization of the initially formed cyclic, α-carban-
ion by oxygen and by the stabilizing influence of oxygen in accomodating negative
charge in the enolates.[105] The high barriers to equilibration between (42) and
(43) and between (44) and (45) compared to the all-carbon systems is caused by
higher 2,3 bond order due to the resonance influence of oxygen.

Heteroatom analogs of cyclohexadienyl carbanions have been studied with proton
NMR. The alkali metal and magnesium salts of 4,4-dimethyl-1,4-dihydropyridine
(47) are prepared by the cleavage of N-carboethoxydihydropyridines with n-butyl
organometallics.[106] The spirocyclopropyl anion ((48), n = 2) behaves the same as
the all carbon analog (24), suffering ring opening and forming 2-(4-pyridyl)ethyl

organometallics. For larger rings ((48), n = 3-6), stable 3-N-cyclohexadienyl
carbanions are formed.[107] Interesting 6-heteroatom substituted cyclohexadienyl

X =	P	As	Sb
H_3 =	4.3	4.0	4.0
H_2 =	6.1	6.1	6.2
H_1 =	3.3	3.6	4.0

(47) (48) (49)

carbanions are formed by the addition of methyllithium to phosphabenzene, arsa-
benzene, and stibabenzene ((49), X = P, As, or Sb).[108] The proton shifts for these
heteroatom substituted cyclohexadienyl carbanions are very similar to shifts for
the all-carbon systems, showing only small variations due to the presence of the
heteroatom. Carbon-13 shifts have also been reported for some of these hetero-
cyclohexadienyl anions.[107,108]

V. ARYLMETHYL, INDENYL, AND FLUORENYL CARBANIONS

A. Proton and Carbon-13 Shifts for Arylmethyl Anions

Arylmethyl anions are easily prepared from readily available precursors. Solutions of these anions in polar, aprotic solvents are relatively stable. Benzyl
and α-alkylbenzyl anions, the most reactive toward solvent protonation, may
be studied. With two or three aryl groups on the α-carbon, aryl methyl anions
are even more stable. Because of these desirable qualities and because of the
synthetic importance of benzyl anions and of styrene and 1,1-diphenylethylene
dimer dianions, arylmethyl anions have been studied extensively with proton and
carbon-13 magnetic resonance to determine the response of chemical shifts to
changes in π-electron density, to changes in solvation with cation, solvent, and
temperature, and to study barriers to rotation about aryl carbon-α-carbon bonds.

Proton and carbon-13 shifts for arylmethyl anions, including α-alkyl substituted anions (R_2 = neopentyl, n-propyl, or n-pentyl), and dimer dianions of styrene,
α-methylstyrene, and 1,1-diphenylethylene (R_2 = $-CH_2)_2$) are presented in Tables
8 and 9. The shifts were determined in THF unless otherwise noted. Proton-proton
couplings are not shown in Table 8 because they are only used in assigning the
ortho, meta, and para resonances.

Proton shifts for monophenylmethyl anions show that the charge is substantially
delocalized into the ring (No. 80-83). Compared to benzene (δ = 7.27), the para
hydrogen is shielded by 1.8 ppm, the ortho hydrogens by over 1 ppm and the meta
hydrogens by about 1 ppm. The α-hydrogen, when it is not obscured by solvent, is
also at high field and therefore bears a substantial share of the negative charge.
Alkyl substitution at the α-carbon increases delocalization into the ring and the

TABLE 8

Proton Chemical Shifts for Phenyl, Diphenyl, and Triphenylmethyl Anions

No.	R_1	R_2	H_α	H_2	H_3	H_4	M^+	Ref.
Monophenyl:								
80	H	H	1.62	6.09	6.30	5.50	Li	109-112
81	H	$-CH_2)_2$	2.36	5.87	6.32	5.12	Li	113,114
82	CH	$-CH_2C(CH_3)_3$	5.24 5.58	6.12 6.22	4.48		Li	115
83	CH	$-CH_2)_2$	5.19 5.57	6.10	4.46		Li	113,114
84	H	H	0.88	6.41	6.77	6.48	Li,PhH	113
85	H	H	2.24	5.59	6.12	4.79	K	116
86	H	CH_3	nr	5.03 5.46	5.99 6.23	4.55	K	116
87	CH_3	CH_3		5.16	6.11	4.40	K	113,116-118
88	CH_3	$-CH_2)_2$		4.83 5.40	5.89 6.01	4.22	K	113,118,119
Diphenyl: R_1 = Ph								
89		H	4.22	6.51	6.54	5.65	Li	109,111
90		$-(CH_2)_4CH_3$		6.84	6.42	5.55	Li	112,120,121
91		$-CH_2)_2$		7.03	6.49	5.66	Li	118,119,122
92		H	nr	7.28	6.80	6.31	Li,Et$_2$O	123
93		$-(CH_2)_2CH_3$		7.05	6.82	6.08	Li,PhH	120
94		$-CH_2)_2$		7.18	6.61	5.75	Na	118,119,122
95		$-CH_2)_2$		7.01	6.55	5.67	K	118,119,122
Triphenyl: R_1, R_2 = Ph								
96				7.28	6.48	5.93	Li	109,123,124
97				7.30	6.58	6.03	Na	123
98				7.30	6.60	6.05	K	123
99				7.28	6.63	6.07	Rb	123
100				7.23	6.64	6.09	Cs	123

ortho and para hydrogens occur at higher field. Similar shift trends are observed
at the para hydrogen for diphenyl and triphenylmethyl anions but the shielding is
attenuated because the charge is spread over more than one ring. Ortho hydrogens
are not as shielded as might be expected in the diphenyl and triphenylmethyl anions
and appear downfield from the meta hydrogens. This deshielding at the ortho hydrogens is due to the ring current in the adjacent phenyl(s) and is found to be a
maximum when the angle of twist between the phenyls is approximately 30°.[118]

Carbon-13 chemical shifts show much larger changes (Table 9). Para carbons for
phenylmethyl anions are shielded by 12 to 37 ppm compared to benzene (δ = 128.7)
and ortho carbons by 5 to 23 ppm. Similar to the proton shift trends, shielding
in the ring(s) increases with alkyl substitution at the α-carbon and is attenuated

TABLE 9

Carbon-13 Shifts and Couplings for Phenyl, Diphenyl, and Triphenyl Anions

No.	R_1	R_2	C_α	C_1	C_2	C_3	C_4	$J_{C_\alpha-H_\alpha}$	M^+	Ref.
Monophenyl:										
101	H	H	36.7	161.0	116.7	128.3	104.4	132	Li	22,28,111,112,125
102	H	Si(CH$_3$)$_3$	40.9	159.6	120.1	127.8	107.9	117	Li	28,126
103	CH$_3$	-CH$_2$)$_2$	63.1	148.9	108.7[a]	128.8[a]	97.0		Li	23
104	H	H	30.1	157.8	120.7	130.8	113.6	116	Li,PhH	110,112,125
105	H	H	52.8	153.0	110.9	130.7	95.7	153	K	25,125
106	H	CH$_3$	62.3	145.2	107.4[a]	130.6[a]	91.9		K	126
107	H	Si(CH$_3$)$_3$	53.8	156.9	116.0[a]	130.0	101.7	134	K	28,126
108	CH$_3$	-CH$_2$)$_2$	78.1	137.1	105.2[a]	130.4[a]	87.5		K	23,119
109	H	Si(CH$_3$)$_3$	55.7	157.5	116.0[a]	130.0	101.6	130	Rb	127
110	H	H	22.2	155.1	123.4	127.3	116.1		Mg,Et$_2$O	128
Diphenyl: R_1 = Ph										
111		H	78.5	147.4	117.5	128.1	107.1	143	Li	22,111,125
112		H	68.7	147.9	118.9	130.2	112.0		Li,PhH	125
113		H	78.8	145.7	116.9	129.4	108.2		K	25,28,125,129
114		-CH$_2$)$_2$	86.9	145.8	117.5	129.3	108.1		K	119
Triphenyl: R_1, R_2 = Ph										
115			90.5	149.9	124.0	128.0	113.1		Li	22,28,111,125
116			87.1	150.4	125.1	129.5	115.3		Li,PhH	125
117			88.3	148.8	123.7	128.9	114.3		K	25,125

[a] These resonances are nonequivalent at approximately 25° and have been averaged (Reference 130).

in diphenyl and triphenyl anions. Unlike the shielding of meta hydrogens, meta carbons are unchanged compared to their precursors. This indicates that meta proton shifts if uncorrected for ring current effects give an unrealistically high estimate of electron density at the meta carbon (Section V.C.). It is very important to note that carbon-1, the ipso carbon, an "unobserved" site in proton NMR, is deshielded by as much as 23 ppm when compared to the ipso carbon of toluene (δ = 137.8) or styrene (δ = 138.2). This shows qualitatively that carbon-1 loses electron density in the carbanion compared to the uncharged precursor. In proton NMR, α-hydrogens have frequently not been reported because of solvent interference or because of complete substitution. Carbon-13 shifts for α-carbons of phenyl, diphenyl, and triphenyl anions cover a very large range of over 65 ppm and these shifts are particularly sensitive to electron density, cation size, and the state of solvation of the cation.

Both proton shifts and carbon-13 shifts are influenced by the nature of the cation. The α-hydrogens of phenylmethyl anions are less shielded and the ortho and para hydrogens are more shielded in going from the small cation, Li$^+$, to the larger cation, K$^+$ (Table 8, No. 80 vs 85). Similarly, but with larger shift changes, carbon-13 shifts are less shielded at the α-carbon and more shielded at the ortho and para carbons as the cation becomes larger (Table 9, No. 101 vs 105; 102 vs 107 vs 109; and 103 vs 108). If it is assumed that phenylmethyl anions are dominantly contact ions in THF at room temperature (Section V.E.), these shift changes show the decrease in the cation's ability to polarize the electron density toward the α-carbon as it becomes larger.

For diphenyl and triphenylmethyl anions of similar structure, proton shifts for para hydrogens are more shielded for the lithium salts than for salts of the larger alkali metal cations (Table 8, No. 91 vs 95; 96-100). Carbon-13 shifts also appear to have reversed order of shielding compared to the monophenylmethyl anions. The α-carbons have similar shifts while the para carbons of the lithium salts are more shielded than the potassium salts (Table 9, No. 111 vs 113; 115 vs 117). However, for the anions of the larger diphenyl and triphenyl π-systems, lithium and sodium cations are appreciably solvated in THF at room temperature and the solvated cations influence the electron distribution in the anion as if they were large cations (Section V.E.).

B. The Nature of Carbon-Lithium Bonding in Benzyllithium

Proton and carbon-13 shifts and the α-carbon-hydrogen couplings change substantially for phenyl and diphenylmethyl anions in different solvents. α-Carbons and hydrogens are more shielded and para and ortho carbons and hydrogens are more deshielded in benzene than in THF (Table 8, No. 80 vs 84; Table 9, No. 101 vs 104). The α-carbon-hydrogen coupling decreases from 132 Hz in THF to 116 Hz in benzene. One-bond carbon-hydrogen couplings have long been used as a qualitative measure of hybridization.[131] The "normal" range for carbon-hydrogen coupling at an uncharged sp^2 carbon is approximately 160 to 170 Hz and for an sp^3 carbon, 120 to 130 Hz. For negatively charged sp^2 carbons, the coupling is somewhat smaller. For example, couplings at the sp^2 carbons in cyclopentadiene and cyclooctatetraene are 170 and 155 Hz while in cyclopentadienide anion, cyclooctatetraene dianion, and cyclononatetraenyl anion they are 157, 145, and 137 Hz, respectively.[132-134]

Early carbon-13 and proton investigations interpreted the ring proton and α-carbon shifts and the α-carbon-hydrogen coupling to show that the α-carbon is sp^2 hybridized with the electron pair in an orbital having predominantly p character for benzyllithium in polar solvents like THF.[109,111] For benzyllithium and 1,1-diphenyl-1-hexylmethyllithium in benzene, it was concluded that the α-carbon gains appreciable sp^3 character with decreasing solvent polarity.[110,112] The excess electron density in the phenyl ring of benzyllithium was estimated using the empirical relationship between shift and electron density with a proportionality constant of 10.7 ppm/electron [86] and was found to <u>decrease</u> from about 0.4 to 0.2 electrons in going from THF to benzene.[110] A missassigned resonance at 2.55 δ for the α-hydrogens of benzyllithium was deshielded compared to the shift in THF. From this shift comparison and the decrease in the α-carbon-hydrogen coupling, it was surprisingly concluded that electron density also <u>decreases</u> at the α-carbon in going from THF to benzene and that benzyllithium is substantially sp^3 hybridized at the α-carbon in non-polar solvents. Later work showed that the α-hydrogens of benzyllithium are shifted upfield from 1.62 δ in THF to 0.88 δ in benzene [113] and that benzyllithium is monomeric in THF [115] but dimeric in benzene.[113]

The early proton and carbon-13 investigations suffered from lack of complete NMR information. α-Carbon-13 enriched benzyllithium gave carbon-13 information only for the α-carbon. Empirical electron densities from proton shifts overestimate density at the <u>meta</u> carbons and underestimate density at the <u>ortho</u> carbons and the question of the electron density change at the "unobserved" ipso carbon is left unanswered. The more complete information provided by Fourier transform carbon-13 NMR shows that there is only a small redistribution of electron density toward the α-carbon of benzyllithium in non-polar solvents (Table 9, No. 101 vs 104, Δδ = -6.6 ppm). This increase at the α-carbon is compensated for by a decrease in electron density at the <u>ortho</u> and <u>para</u> carbons as indicated by downfield shift changes of 4.0 and 9.2 ppm. This small redistribution of electron density does not seem to require a change in hybridization at the α-carbon and the α-carbon may be sp^2 hybridized even in non-polar solvents. Until more is understood about the influence of aggregation on carbon-13 shifts at the α-carbon and the influence of charge on the α-carbon-hydrogen coupling, the exact nature of metal-carbon bonding in arylmethyllithiums in non-polar solvents will remain in doubt. Reminiscent of the arguments concerning the type of bonding in allyl organometallics (Section II.A.), magnetic resonaence may not be able to give a more definitive answer, but the trends are clear: in polar solvents, phenylmethyl anions tend toward delocalized, monomeric, "ionic" structures while in non-polar solvents, they tend toward aggregated structures perhaps with more sp^3 character at the electron rich α-carbon.

C. Proton and Carbon-13 Shifts and π-Electron Density in Carbanions

It was recognized very early that proton and carbon-13 shifts for π-systems tend to reflect π-electron density. In substituted benzenes, electron-withdrawing groups decrease shielding while electron-donating groups increase shielding at ring carbons and hydrogens. In magnetic resonance investigations of allyl, acyclic, cyclic, and arylmethyl anions, it is always implied that the high field shifts at alternate positions in the carbanion's framework at least qualitatively show high electron density. For cyclooctatetraene dianion, cyclopentadienide anion, benzene, and tropylium ion, proton and carbon-13 shifts are linearly related to π-electron density according to eqn 1.[86,132,135] Within each of these π-systems, the π-electron density, ρ , is the same at each carbon and equal to the number of π-electrons divided by the number of π-carbons (ρ = 1.25, 1.20, 1.00, and 0.86, respectively). The constant, k, shows the sensitivity of the chemical shifts to changes in π-

$$\delta = a - k\rho \qquad \begin{array}{l} ^1H: \quad a = 18.2, \; k = 10.7 \\[2mm] ^{13}C: \quad a = 290, \; k = 160 \end{array} \qquad (1)$$

electron density, 10.7 ppm/electron for proton shifts and approximately 160 ppm/ electron for carbon-13 shifts. It must be emphasized that the purpose of this section will be to examine the applicability of these two empirical expressions for determining electron distributions in delocalized carbanions from experimen- tally measured chemical shifts. The prediction of proton and carbon-13 shifts from calculated π-electron densities and the many other factors that are required to predict chemical shifts will not be discussed.

π-Electron densities calculated from proton and carbon-13 shifts are presented in Table 10 and compared to densities calculated from simple molecular orbital

TABLE 10

π-Electron Densities for Arylmethyl and Indenyl Anions

Carbanion		α	1	2	3	4	Σρ
	ρ_H	1.55		1.12	1.10	1.18	
	ρ_C	1.51	0.88	1.14	1.02	1.24	7.9
	ρ_{scf}	1.50	0.87	1.14	1.07	1.23	8.0
	ρ_H	1.31		1.09	1.09	1.17	
	ρ_C	1.35	0.92	1.11	1.02	1.16	14.0
	ρ_{scf}	1.32	0.86	1.07	1.06	1.23	14.0
	ρ_H			1.02	1.09	1.15	
	ρ_C	1.29	0.90	1.06	1.03	1.12	19.9
	ρ_{scf}	1.25	0.85	1.05	1.06	1.19	20.0
						β	
	ρ_H	1.19		1.05	1.11	1.11	
	ρ_C	1.27	1.03	1.09	1.12	1.11	10.1
	ρ_{hmo}	1.25	1.10	1.04	1.06	1.11	10.0
	$\Delta\delta_{e^-}$	-1.80		-0.33	-0.96	-0.91	
	$\Delta\delta_r$	+0.48		+0.46	+0.18	+0.27	

methods.[136] The proportionality constant for proton shifts, 10.7 ppm/electron, is caused by an increase in electron density on the hydrogen due to polarization of the carbon-hydrogen σ bond by excess charge on the carbon atom.[135] However, other factors in addition to π-electron density contribute to proton shift changes in carbanions and can be of similar magnitude. These other factors must be accounted for to obtain reliable estimates of electron density from proton shifts with eqn 1. Factors which contribute to proton shift changes in carbanions include: ring current shifts due to neighboring rings, magnetic anisotropy and electronegativity of substituent and ring heteroatoms; and effects due to cation and solvent. The influence of heteroatoms on proton shifts through anisotropy and through polarization of the σ framework of the carbanion may cause large proton shift changes, particularly close to the heteroatom. Few calculations of π-electron density from proton shifts have been carried out for carbanions containing heteroatoms within or directly attached to the carbanion's framework. Shift changes due to the cation and solvent are usually small at least at sites far removed from the cation-anion interaction and have usually been ignored either by applying eqn 1 only to sites remote to these influences or by comparing proton shifts only for carbanions with the same counterion in the same solvent.

Proton shift changes will be influenced by ring currents in neighboring rings of polycyclic carbanions and the size of the ring current proton shift change is frequently comparable to the size of the shift change caused by an increase in π-electron density. Eqn 1 was derived using π-systems with six π-electrons so that proton shift changes caused by ring currents in this sized π-system is accounted for in the constant, 10.7 ppm/electron. For polycyclic, fused carbanions, ring current shifts can be calculated using eqn 2, where $\Delta\delta_r$ is the ring current shift

$$\Delta\delta_r = \frac{e^2}{2mc^2}\left(\frac{a^2}{R^3}\right) \quad (2) \qquad \Delta\delta_r = 12.0\left(\frac{a^2}{R^3}\right) \quad (3)$$

change, $\underline{a}$ is the radius of the ring, and R is the distance from the center of the ring to the proton in question.[137,138,139] This equation gives a downfield proton shift change for benzene due to ring current of 1.75 ppm and is thought to slightly overestimate the ring current effect.[140] The simpler equation 3 and an improved value for benzene is obtained by comparing the proton shift for benzene to the olefinic proton shifts for 1,3-cyclohexadiene.[86] Equation 3 gives reliable estimates of ring current shifts for monocyclic and bicyclic carbanions and has been used to correct for ring current in indenyl, fluorenyl, pentalenyl, and azulenyl anions and dianions.[86] Table 10 shows the diamagnetic ring current contributions to the proton shifts for indenyl carbanion ($\Delta\delta_r$) and compares them to the upfield shifts due to increase in electron density ($\Delta\delta_{e^-}$). It can be seen that low values for π-electron density would be obtained for indenyl anion with eqn 1 if no ring

current correction is made, especially at carbons 2 and α. For larger carbanions
containing several fused rings, electron currents circulate around the periphery
of the ring and eqn 3 does not properly account for ring current. Peripheral ring
currents are probably responsible for the unusually large upfield shifts in the
dianions of anthracene, tetracene, acenaphthylene, fluoranthene, and perylene.[141,
142] A much larger proportionality constant than 10.7 ppm/electron was required
to fit the proton shifts to the calculated π-electron density because no correction was made for the paramagnetic ring current in these dianions. For larger
carbanion systems such as these, it is important to separate proton shift changes
due to π-electron density from proton shift changes due to ring current. This
separation is necessary in order to use proton NMR as a criterion of aromatic
character from the ring current shifts in (4n + 2) and 4n π-systems (Section VI).

While proton shift changes are small and are influenced by other factors such
as ring current, changes in π-electron density are primarily responsible for the
very large carbon-13 shift changes in carbanions. However, a number of empirical
correlations have been reported with different proportionality constants. A very
early investigation showed that carbon-13 shifts are proportional to π-electron
density for π-systems with equivalent carbons ($C_8H_8^{2-}$, $C_5H_5^-$, C_6H_6, and $C_7H_7^+$; k =
160 ppm/electron).[132] If cyclononatetraenide anion is included, a slightly different slope of 167 ppm/electron is obtained.[133,134] These early correlations were
extended to include three carbenium ions and eight carbanions in which the carbons
need not be equivalent by plotting the average chemical shifts against the average
π-electron densities. A slope of 156 ppm/electron was obtained.[25] For these three
correlations, it should be noted that no molecular orbital calculation is necessary to establish the π-electron density coordinate.

A constant of 167 ppm/electron correlates the carbon-13 shifts for cyclopropenium, cyclobutenium, and tropylium ions and three carbanions with HMO charge
densities [143] and the para carbons of monosubstituted benzenes and phenylcarbenium
ions with CNDO charge densities.[144] A much different constant of 306 ppm/electron
is used to correlate four hydroxycarbenium ions with HMO charge densities.[145] In
this correlation, the central carbon of trimethylcarbenium ion was used as a shift
reference to represent the carbon-13 shift of a carbon with unit positive charge.
Dications of polycyclic aromatic hydrocarbons give a correlation with CNDO charge
densities with a slope of 200 ppm/electron [146] and xanthylium ions give a slope
of 152 ppm/electron.[147]

A number of explanations can be offered for these variations in slope. Theoretical treatment of carbon-13 shifts for aromatic hydrocarbons,[148-152] substituted
benzenes,[153] and heteroaromatics [154-156] show that σ electron density and polarization of the σ framework by heteroatoms make important contributions to the
carbon-13 shifts in π-systems. Since different approaches were used to establish
the π-electron density coordinate for the empirical carbon-13 correlations (HMO

or CNDO charge densities or defined as the number of π-electrons divided by the
number of π-carbons), the differences in slope are probably due at least in part
to these different approaches. Frequently, for both proton and carbon-13 shifts,
the correlation has been based upon chemical shift differences from a model compound. With this approach, the slope of the relationship may depend critically
upon the model selected.

Despite these variations, the dominant influence on the carbon-13 shifts for
delocalized carbanions is π-electron density. Estimating electron densities from
carbon-13 shifts offers significant advantages over the use of proton shifts. Much
larger shift changes occur compared to proton shift changes and carbon-13 shifts
are not influenced by ring currents. Within the same carbanion, carbon-13 shifts
give excellent estimates of _relative_ π-electron density. For carbanions of similar
structure in the same solvent and with the same cation, carbon-13 shifts probably
still give very good estimates. For proton NMR, densities at quaternary carbons
must be estimated by difference while all the carbons are observable with carbon-
13. This is particularly important when it is noted that carbon-13 shifts show
that quaternary carbons lose electron density in the carbanion compared to the
precursor (Table 10, $\rho < 1.0$ at carbon-1). More work should be done to extend
the relationship between carbon-13 shifts and π-electron density to other systems,
particularly to account for the influence of α-substitution and to estimate densities in carbanions containing heteroatoms.

D. Proton and Carbon-13 Shifts for Indenyl and Fluorenyl Carbanions

Indenyl and fluorenyl carbanions have been extensively studied with proton
and carbon-13 NMR. The equilibrium between contact and solvent separated ion
pairs has been determined for the lithium and sodium salts of these carbanions
along with those for diphenylmethyl, triphenylmethyl, benzyl, and 1,3-diphenyl-
allyl salts with variable temperature NMR. Delocalized carbanions with 10 to 20
π-electrons, indenyl to triphenylmethyl, are the right sized systems to undergo
appreciable solvation of the cation at low temperatures in ethereal solvents such
as MeTHF, THF, and DME. The NMR results may be compared to similar UV studies of
solvation for fluorenyl,[157] diphenylmethyl,[158] triphenylmethyl,[159] and 1,3-di-
phenylallyl [160] alkali metal salts.

Room temperature proton shifts for indenyl carbanions show only slight differences with different cations in ether, THF, or DME (Table 11). Only the sodium
salt in HMPA shows substantial changes, probably due to the formation of solvent
separated ion pairs. Fluorenyl salts show a slightly greater sensitivity to solvent and cation. For fluorenyl salts, the α-hydrogen and the 4-hydrogen, _para_ to
the α-hydrogen, are the most shielded. This is consistent with these sites having
the highest electron densities. However, the 2-hydrogens, _ortho_ to the negative
charge, are further downfield than the 3-hydrogens due to ring current. For fluorenyl salts, the downfield ring current shifts are large: 1.0, 0.8, and 0.6 ppm

TABLE 11

Proton Chemical Shifts for Indenyl and Fluorenyl Carbanions

No.		H_α	H_β	H_2	H_3	H_4	H_5	M^+	Solv.	Ref.
Indenyl:										
118		5.95	6.45	7.36	6.53			Li	Et$_2$O	161
119		5.94	6.49	7.33	6.48			Li	THF	161-164
120		5.90	6.45	7.31	6.48			Li	DME	164
121		5.94	6.61	7.34	6.43			Na	THF	85,123,161,164
122		5.72	6.37	7.05	6.07			Na	HMPA	165
Fluorenyl:										
123		5.89		7.40	6.98	6.67	7.98	Li	Et$_2$O	123,166
124		5.81		7.21	6.73	6.33	7.80	Li	THF	166,167
125		5.90		7.23	6.73	6.34	7.81	Li	DME	123,166
126		6.00		7.37	6.87	6.51	7.98	Na	THF	85,123,167
127		5.89		7.27	6.81	6.44	7.87	K	THF	167,168
128		5.88		7.25	6.81	6.44	7.82	Rb	THF	167
129	α-Ph			7.85	6.85	6.49	7.87	Li	THF	157(m)
130	α-Ph			7.93	6.96	6.61	7.98	Na	THF	157(m)
131	α-Ph			7.89	6.95	6.60	7.95	K	THF	157(m),169
132		6.05		7.41	7.35	7.00	7.53	K	THF	168

for the α, 5, and 2-hydrogens, respectively.[86]

Carbon-13 shifts cover a much larger range and more closely reflect the electron distribution in indenyl and fluorenyl carbanions (Table 12). The electron rich α-carbon is furthest upfield followed by carbons 3 and 2 for indenyl and by carbons 4 and 2 for fluorenyl anions. The chemical shifts of these electron rich carbons also show the largest chemical shift changes with temperature. For indenyllithium in DME, a downfield shift change of 4.9 ppm is observed at carbon 3 when the temperature is raised 90°.[170,171] A smaller, downfield change occurs at carbon-2 while the α-carbon moves upfield slightly. For fluorenyllithium in MeTHF, the directions of the shift changes are the same but the largest change occurs at the α-carbon, an upfield shift change of 5.5 ppm. These temperature dependent chemical shift changes are due to the formation of solvent separated ion pairs at low temperatures. At high temperatures, where contact ions dominate the ion pair equilibria, the α-carbon chemical shifts for the fluorenyl salts vary with the size of the cation, from 80.6 δ for the lithium salt to 84.3 δ for the cesium salt (Table 12, No. 140-144).

TABLE 12

Carbon-13 Chemical Shifts for Indenyl and Fluorenyl Carbanions

No.	C_α	C_1	C_2	C_3	C_4	C_5	C_β	M$^+$ Solv.	Ref.
Indenyl:									
133	91.8	127.5	120.6	116.4			114.5	Li Et$_2$O	170,171
134	91.5	129.4	119.9	114.4			115.5	Li THF +60°	
	91.8	130.0	118.2	111.7			116.0	Li THF −65°	170,171
135	90.6	127.8	118.6	113.8			114.2	Li DME +30°	
	91.5	129.1	116.5	108.9			116.2	Li DME −60°	172,173
136	90.9	128.2	117.9	111.4			115.1	Na DME +30°	
	91.4	128.8	116.6	109.1			116.0	Na DME −60°	172,173
137 β−CH$_3$	92.2	129.4	118.4	113.8			127.3	Li THF	162,171
138 α,α−di−CH$_3$	97.1	125.8	117.5	112.9			116.9	Li THF	171
Fluorenyl:							C_6		
139	77.4	136.3	117.2	121.0	111.3	119.7	122.5	Li MeTHF+70°	
	82.9	137.3	116.2	119.0	107.8	118.6	122.8	Li MeTHF−60°	28,171
140	80.6	137.8	116.3	118.6	108.3	119.2	123.3	Li THF +57°	
	82.6	137.4	116.1	118.6	107.7	118.9	122.7	Li THF −42°	126
141	80.4	136.5	116.6	119.3	109.5	120.1	121.8	Na THF +45°	
	82.7	137.3	116.2	119.0	107.8	118.7	122.7	Na THF −46°	126
142	82.9	136.5	116.8	119.4	109.5	120.2	121.5	K THF	126
143	83.3	136.2	116.8	119.3	109.6	120.4	121.1	Rb THF	126
144	84.3	137.0	117.3	119.8	110.0	120.7	122.0	Cs THF	126

E. The NMR Study of Ion Pairing

The equilibrium between contact ions at high temperature and solvent separated ions at low temperatures was first studied in detail for fluorenyl salts with ultraviolet absorption.[157] Fluorenyl contact ions show bathochromic shifts of the absorption maxima with increasing cation size, reaching a value of 368 nm for the cesium salt compared to a limit of 373 nm for fluorenyl solvent separated ions. [157(b)] For fluorenyllithium and sodium, the absorption maxima of the contact ions, 349 and 356 nm, respectively, are well separated from the maximum for the solvent separated ion and variable temperature measurements establish the position of equilibrium as a function of cation and solvent. An important advantage of the UV method over NMR is the ability to measure precise concentrations of each species in relatively dilute solutions ($\sim 10^{-4}$ M) from these individual absorption maxima. For proton and carbon-13 NMR, considerably higher concentrations are necessary ($> 10^{-1}$ M) and only a single, averaged resonance is observed. UV measurements are not interfered with by paramagnetic species so that solutions of anion radicals and dianions, where anion radicals may be present, may also be studied. With NMR, resonances are broadened and lost at relatively low concentrations of paramagnetic species. However, UV absorption has been extended to relatively few other carb-anionic systems (diphenylmethyl,[158] triphenylmethyl,[159] and 1,3-diphenylallyl[160]) because with larger π-systems it is frequently difficult to distinguish between contact ions and solvent separated ions because of overlap of absorptions. Further, UV gives little information concerning what is occuring within the carbanion as it undergoes solvation.

Proton and carbon-13 NMR gives additional information about the cation's position and the electron distribution in the contact ion. Proton shifts are related to the size of the cation, particularly at the α-hydrogen and at the hydrogens ortho and para to the α-hydrogen. For example, the para hydrogen of triphenylmethyl anion in diethyl ether, where it is a contact ion for all alkali metal cations, is at 6.31, 6.17, and 6.09 δ for the lithium, sodium, and cesium contact ions, respect-ively.[123] Similar relationships have been observed for the contact ions of fluor-enyl,[167] 1- and 2-naphthylmethyl,[174,175] and 1,3-diphenylallyl carbanions.[36,37,40] Contact ion proton shift changes with cation size are relatively small, 0.5 ppm at the largest, and frequently the shifts of the lithium salts appear out of order because an appreciable amount of solvation occurs even at room temperature in more polar solvents such as THF or DME (Table 11, No. 124, 126-128).

Carbon-13 shifts show large differences with cation size that reflect electron distribution changes in the contact ions.[28,129,173] The α-carbon goes upfield while the ortho and para carbons go downfield as the size of the cation increases. If the cation is presumed to reside closest to the α-carbon, these shift changes show that the cation is less able to polarize the electron density toward the α-carbon as it becomes larger. The carbanion responds by spreading the electron density more evenly throughout the carbanion, decreasing density at the α-carbon and delocalizing more density into the ring(s). For triphenylmethyl, diphenylmethyl, fluorenyl, and α-tri-methylsilylbenzyl anions, the α-carbon shifts of contact ions are linear with the reciprocal of the distance between cation and carbanion.[129] The size of the α-carbon shift difference between the lithium and cesium contact ions depends upon the size of the carbanion's π-system. The shift difference is small for the 20 π-electron triphenylmethyl anion (5.2 ppm) and large for the 8 π-electron α-trimethylsilyl-benzyl anion (17.1 ppm), showing that electron density is more easily polarized toward the α-carbon by the positive charge as the size of the π-system decreases.

For lithium, sodium, and potassium salts of carbanions with π-systems of 8 to 20 π-electrons, lowering the temperature results in proton and carbon-13 shift changes as the ion pair equilibria become dominated by solvent separated ions. Plotting the shifts of the most sensitive sites against temperature gives sigmoidal curves. Ion pair equilibrium constants can be calculated from these curves using equation 4, where δ_o is the observed chemical shift, and δ_c and δ_s are shift limits for the contact ion and the solvent separated ion, respectively. The temperature range over which the conversion from contact ions at high temperatures to solvent separated ions at low temperatures is quite large and it is usually not possible to cover the entire range experimentally. Therefore either one or the other shift limits, δ_c or δ_s, must be estimated.[123,129,173] For carbon-13, inaccessible contact limits were estimated from the linear plots of contact shifts with interionic distance. [129] Solvent separated limits, unlike contact shift limits, are cation and solvent

$$K \quad = \quad (\delta_o \; - \; \delta_c)/(\delta_s \; - \; \delta_o) \tag{4}$$

independent so that inaccessible solvent separated limits may be estimated from low temperature spectra in more polar solvents. However, the need to estimate at least one of these limits is probably the principal source of error in the equilibrium constants and thermodynamic values for solvation obtained from proton or carbon-13 measurements.

Qualitatively, the thermodynamic values compare well for the three different methods but it is difficult to make exact comparisons because the errors that contribute to each method are likely different and in only a few cases have values been determined by all three methods for the same carbanion with the same cation in the same solvent (Table 13). The enthalpy change is determined by the balance between the energy required to separate two oppositely charged ions and the energy gained from the ion-dipole interaction between cation and and the donor sites of the solvent. Solvation for a given carbanion in the same solvent is most exothermic for the lithium salt, slightly less for the sodium salt, and smallest for the potassium salt because the energy gain from solvent-cation interaction decreases as cation size increases. The enthalpy change also depends upon the size of the carbanion's π-system. For the same cation in the same solvent, it is slightly smaller for indenyl than for fluorenyl and markedly smaller for diphenylmethyl than for triphenylmethyl anions because the energy required to separate the cation decreases with greater delocalization in the carbanion. The enthalpies probably do depend upon the solvent for the same carbanion and cation. However, the spread of values caused by different errors in the different methods obscures such a relationship. The large, negative entropies reflect the increased order upon solvation with the "freezing out" of solvent molecules around the cation. These entropies show a slight solvent dependence, being less negative in DME than in the other solvents. Since DME has two coordination sites, fewer solvent molecules are immobilized upon solvent separation.

Slow rotation about aryl carbon-α-carbon bonds as indicated by nonequivalent ortho hydrogens or carbons has been observed for phenylmethyl,[113-116,118] 1- and 2-naphthylmethyl,[175] diphenylmethyl,[176] 1-phenylallyl,[29,30] and various 1,3-diphenylallyl anions.[34,40,41,43,44] Determination of rotational barriers for carbanions with different alkali metal cations with variable temperature NMR leads

TABLE 13

Thermodynamics of Solvation from Ultraviolet, Proton NMR, and Carbon-13 NMR

M^+	Solv.	ΔG	ΔS	Method	Ref.	M^+	Solv.	ΔG	ΔS	Method	Ref.
Fluorenyl:						Triphenylmethyl:					
Li	MeTHF	-7.7	-26	C13	28	Li	Et_2O	-11.9	-46	UV	159(b)
Li	THF	-7.0		UV	157(c)	Li	MeTHF	-15.5	-44	C13	28
Li	THF	-4.9	-14	C13	28	Li	THF	-9.2	-24	UV	159(b)
Li	CHA	-8.5	-23	UV	157(q)	Li	CHA	-11.8	-32	UV	157(q)
Li	DME	-5.6	-15	H1	123						
Na	THF	-7.6	-33	UV	157(c)	Na	THF	-8.2	-28	H1	123
Na	THF	-7.9	-32	C13	28	Na	THF	-11.7	-44	C13	28
Na	THF	-6.7	-27	H1	123						
Na	DME	-5.4	-17	H1	123	K	THF	-6.7	-21	UV	159(b)
						K	THF	-6.7	-23	H1	123
K	DME	-4.6		UV	157(h)	K	DME	-11.8	-36	UV	159(b)
K	DME	-4.1	-16	H1	123	K	DME	-5.3	-16	H1	123
Indenyl:						Diphenylmethyl:					
Li	CHA	-8.0	-26	UV	157(q)	Li	MeTHF	-7.1	-23	C13	28
Li	DME	-5.0	-15	H1	123	Li	DME	-7.2	-20	C13	28
Na	DME	-3.5	-15	H1	123	Na	THF	-7.6	-31	C13	28
						Na	DME	-6.6	-20	C13	28
1,3-Diphenylallyl:											
Na	MeTHF	-2.8	-9	H1	37						
Na	THF	-6.1	-22	H1	37						
K	THF	-4.1	-16	H1	37						

to contrasting results: barriers are sometimes cation independent [34,41,43] and sometimes cation dependent. [29,114,115,175] This contrast is due to differences in the solvation state of the carbanion. Those carbanions having cation independent barriers invariably were studied in solvents where solvent separated ions dominate such as DMSO or liquid ammonia. Cation dependence was found in THF or less-polar solvents such as TMEDA-isooctane where contact ions dominate. [177]

VI. ANNULENYL AND POLYCYCLIC ANIONS AND DIANIONS

Completely conjugated, cyclic polyenes have been given the name "annulenes". These substances will be aromatic if they have a reasonably planar carbon skeleton and contain (4n + 2) out of plane π-electrons. [178] Electron delocalization in aromatic systems generates a diamagnetic ring current in an applied magnetic field. [138] This causes downfield proton shift changes for "outer" protons and upfield changes for "inner" protons. Molecules showing this effect are termed "diatropic". Conversely, annulenes containing 4n π-electrons sustain a paramagnetic ring current, moving outer protons upfield and inner protons downfield. Such nonaromatic ("anti-aromatic") systems have been termed "paratropic". Proton NMR has been the major experimental method for testing this concept of aromaticity in annulenes.

A. Aromatic Annulenyl Monoanions and Dianions

Monoanions belonging to the aromatic annulenes must have an odd number of ring carbons (5, 9, 13, and 17) while dianions must have and even number (4, 8, 12, 16) to contain $(4n + 2)$ π-electrons. Examples of all of these carbanions except the 13-carbon monoanion and the 4-carbon dianion have been characterized with proton NMR. With annulenes of ten or more ring carbons, bond angle strain prevents all-cis stereochemistry and the alternative structures with two or more trans double bonds cannot achieve planarity because of steric repulsion between inner hydrogens. Two structural modifications have been employed to obtain planar, sterically unperturbed larger ring annulenes. Steric repulsions are removed by replacing the inner hydrogens with a methylene or larger bridging unit or by re-placing ethylenic units by two or more ethyne units in the annulene ring system ("dehydroannulenes"). A number of monoanions and dianions of these modified annul-enes have been characterized with proton NMR. In this section the magnetic res-onance spectra, primarily proton NMR, of annulenyl monoanions and dianions will be compared. More concerning the chemistry of the dianions may be found in Chap-ter 1.

Cyclopentadienide anion ([5]-annulenyl anion) was perhaps the first organo-metallic studied with proton NMR.[179] The proton shifts for the alkali metal salts do not change appreciably with temperature and they move upfield regularly with increasing cation size.[123] These data show that the small cyclopentadienide anion is a contact ion even for the lithium salt in DME (Table 14, No. 145). Variable temperature proton NMR has been employed to study the Schlenk equilibria for the magnesium chloride and bromide.[180]

Cyclononatetraenyl anion ([9]-annulenyl anion, (52)) and several derivatives of this 10-electron aromatic system have been investigated. Alkali metal reduction of either anti-9-chloro or anti-9-methoxy-cis-bicyclo[6.1.0]-nona-2,4,6-triene gives the all-cis anion (Table 14, No. 146).[133,134,181-183] However, syn-9-meth-

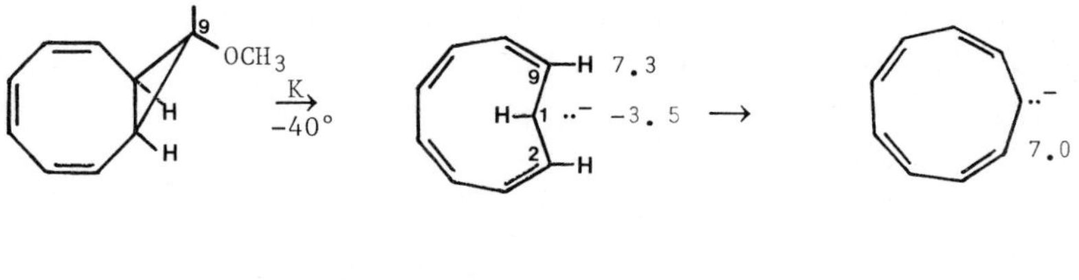

$$J_{12}; J_{19} = 15$$

(50)   (51)   (52)

oxy-cis-bicyclo[6.1.0]-nona-2,4,6-triene (50) is reduced with potassium metal at

TABLE 14

Proton and Carbon-13 Chemical Shifts for Aromatic Annulenyl Carbanions

No.	δ	M$^+$	Solv.	Ref.	No.	δ	M$^+$	Solv.	Ref.
Monoanions:					**Dianions:**				
145 $C_5H_5^-$	5.74	Li	DME	123	148 $C_8H_8^{--}$	5.73	Li	THF	181,187
	5.70	Na	DME	123,135,179		5.80	Na	THF	86,181
	5.55	K	DME	123		5.75	K	THF	181,187
	5.53	Rb	DME	123		5.70	Rb	THF	181
	6.45	)$_2$Mg	PhH	135,180	C-13:	90.6	K	THF	25
	6.18	)$_2$Mg	Et$_2$O	135,180					
	5.74	)$_2$Mg	THF	180	149 $C_{12}H_{12}^{--}$	6.98	Li	THF	188
	6.03	MgCl	THF	180		6.23		−80°	
						−4.60(I)			
C-13:	103.5	Li	THF	170					
	103.1	K	THF	180	150 $C_{12}H_8^{--}$	6.35	K	THF	189
	103.8	MgCl	THF	180		7.75		−35°	
						−6.88(I)			
146 $C_9H_9^-$	6.93	Li	THF	133,181-183					
	6.97	Na	THF	181	151 $C_{12}H_6^{--}$	6.74	K	THF,0°	189
	7.03	K	THF	181-183					
	6.92	Rb	THF	181	152 $C_{16}H_{16}^{--}$	8.77	Li	THF	190,191
						7.40		−30°	
C-13:	109.7	Li	THF	182,183		−8.07(I)			
147 $C_{17}H_{17}^-$	9.52	Li	THF	186	153 $C_{24}H_8^{--}$	6.12	K	THF	192
	8.21								
	−7.97(I)								

(I) = Proton shifts for "inner" hydrogens. Negative shifts are upfield from TMS.

−40° and then conrotatory ring opening leads to the trans,cis,cis,cis-cyclonona-tetraenyl anion (51).[184] This structure is confirmed by two spectral features: inner hydrogen-1 absorbs upfield at −3.5 δ due to the diamagnetic ring current of the aromatic ring and is coupled to hydrogens 2 and 9 with a trans vicinal coupling of 15 Hz. Anion (51) isomerizes to the all-cis anion (52) and kinetic measurements show a very high barrier to isomerization (29-34 kcal/mol), catalyzed photochemically and by excess alkali metal cation.[185]

Compared to the small cyclopentadienide anion, the proton shifts for the lithium and sodium salts of the 10-electron, all-cis cyclononatetraenyl anion (52) are out of order and upfield from the shift for the potassium salt, showing that appreciable solvation is occuring for this larger π-system in THF (Table 14, No. 146).[181] The proton shifts for cyclooctatetraene dianion are in regular order, the lithium salt furthest downfield and the rubidium salt furthest upfield in diethyl ether but in THF the lithium salt is upfield from the potassium salt. Therefore, cyclooctatetra-ene dianions are all contact ions in ether but the lithium salt is solvated in THF. Cyclooctatetraene dianion and derivatives of this anionic system have been charact-erized in many proton NMR investigations. Derivatives that have been investigated

310

include: methyl, trimethylsilyl, trimethylgermanyl, and trimethylstannyl substitute
dianions;[193,194] the dimer tetraanion;[195] benzo and dibenzo dianions;[196,197] bicyclo-
[3.3.0]-octatetraene dianions ("pentalene" dianion) and its benzo derivatives;[198–201] and ring-nitrogen substituted dianions (Chapter 1).[202]

The methylene bridged cyclononatetraenyl anion (53) has been characterized as
its sodium salt in DMSO.[203,204] Its ring proton shifts are slightly more shielded
than the proton shift for (52) but the shielding of the methylene hydrogens, located above the ring, indicates the presence of a diamagnetic ring current. The
shifts of this aromatic system can also be compared to the proton shifts of the

H_2, H_{5-8} = 5.4 to 6.0 δ

(53)

H_{1-7} = 6.5 to 7.6 δ

(54)

(55)

homoaromatic anion (17), which contains the same number of π-electrons separated
by one insulating sp³ carbon. Qualitatively, the ring proton shifts for (53) show
much less alternation and more even spreading of the electron density and the bridging methylene hydrogens are much more shielded than for (17) (-1.2 and -0.7 vs 0.9
and 0.4 δ). This decrease in ring current in (17) compared to (53) is perhaps due
to distortion of the ring from planarity caused by the intervening sp³ carbon. The
benzocyclononatetraenyl anion (54)[205] and its methylene bridged analog (55)[206]
show delocalization of electron density into the benzo moiety. For (54), all the
ring proton shifts are _downfield_ from the shifts of the uncharged precursor despite
the shielding effect expected from the negative charge and these systems may well
be viewed as 14 rather than 10-electron aromatic systems with substantial diamagnetic ring current.

Deprotonation of 6,7;8,9-dibenzocyclononatetraene with n-butyllithium in THF
first gives the non-planar, partially delocalized anion (56).[207] Note that the proton shifts of hydrogens 1 through 5 are highly shielded and the shifts and coupling
are quite close to the values for a typical cyclic pentadienyl anion like (15)
rather than the planar, aromatic anion (54). Anion (56) slowly disappears at room
temperature to give anion (57), characterized by _downfield_ proton shift changes
in the 9-membered and benzo rings. This shows that a large diamagnetic ring current
develops throughout the 17-carbon, 18-electron aromatic system as the benzo rings

flatten. The barrier to rearrangement (8.9 kcal/mol) is due to the twisting of the

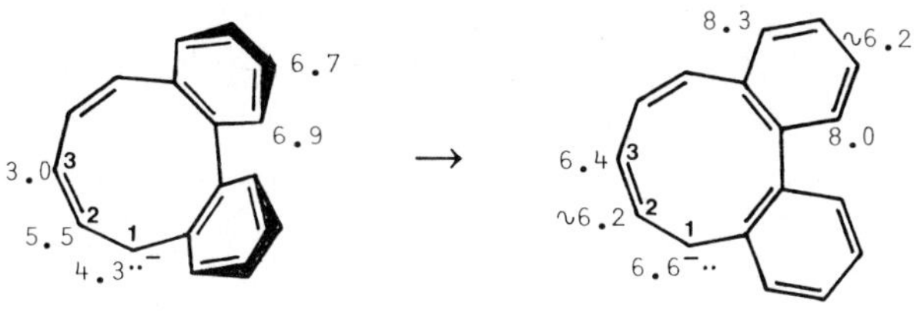

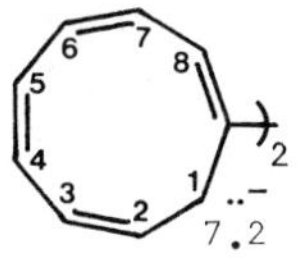

$J_{12} = 11$

$J_{23} = 8$

(56)

$J_{12} = 4$

(57)

$H_{2-7} = 6.6$

(58)

biphenyl portion of (56) required in achieving planarity in (57). The cyclononatetraenyl dimer dianion (58) has also been prepared as the potassium salt and characterized with proton and carbon-13 magnetic resonance.[208]

Compared to the all-carbon analog (52), hydrogens 2 and 9 of the nitrogen-substituted cyclononatetraenyl anion (59, "azonide") are deshielded by about 1.5 ppm
due to the inductive influence of the heteroatom on the σ-framework.[209,210] In
acetone, proton shifts of these hydrogens depend upon cation size, lithium furthest
upfield and rubidium furthest downfield. In DMSO, the lithium and sodium salts have
the same shifts as the rubidium salt. Therefore, the alkali metal azonides are all
contact ions in acetone but the lithium and sodium salts are solvent separated in

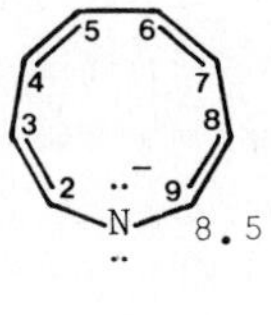

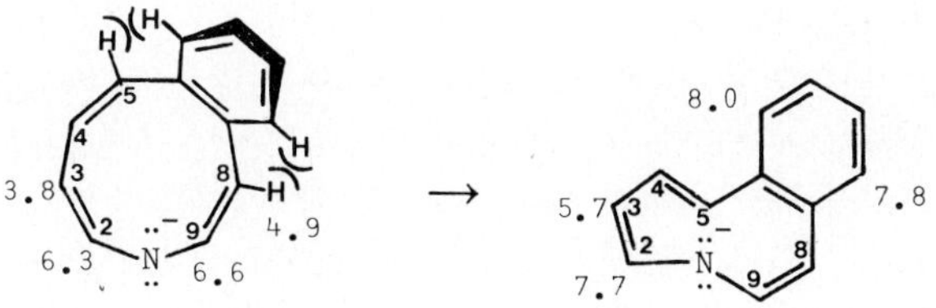

$H_{3-8} = \sim 6.5$

(59)

(60)

(61)

DMSO. The 6,7-benzoazonide anion (60) appears not to sustain a diamagnetic ring
current. This conclusion is based upon upfield proton shifts compared to (54),
particularly at hydrogens 3 and 8.[211] This all-cis anion rearranges to anion (61)
which has trans stereochemistry at the carbon 4-5 and nitrogen-carbon-2 bonds.
This stereochemistry is based upon the tentative assignment of a doublet at -0.95

δ ($J_{4,5}$ = 16 Hz) to the inner hydrogen on carbon-5 and the formation of a quench-ing product that contains one <u>trans</u> bond in the 9-membered ring. <u>Cis-trans</u> isomer-ization of (60) to (61) is in marked contrast to the <u>trans-cis</u> isomerization of (51) to (52).[184,185] The driving force for the azonide rearrangement is relief of <u>peri</u> interaction between the 5-hydrogen and the <u>ortho</u> benzo hydrogen and partial relief of the interaction between the 8-hydrogen and its <u>ortho</u> benzo hydrogen. In (60), these steric interactions prevent planarity and this explains its lack of aromaticity. The sizable downfield proton shift changes at hydrogens 2 and 3 in (61) compared to (60) show the development of a diamagnetic ring current and arom-aticity in (61).

The proton and carbon-13 characteristics of cyclononatetraenyl carbanions with an acetyl substituent depend upon cation and temperature.[213,214] With the large cation, potassium, charge resides primarily in the ring and the proton shifts are downfield due to diamagnetic ring current. With the small cation, lithium, the pro-ton shifts are consistent with a fulvene structure where the cation is associated with the enolate oxygen. For a sodium cation, the process is temperature depend-ent. At high temperatures in THF, the carbanion is a contact ion enolate while at low temperatures it is a solvent separated, delocalized carbanion.

In small ring annulenyl carbanions (6 to 10 ring atoms), diamagnetic ring cur-rent shift changes are smaller or comparable to shift changes due to charge. For example, at first it is surprising that the 10-electron, aromatic cyclooctatetra-ene dianion has almost exactly the same proton shift as its nonaromatic precursor, cyclooctatetraene, until it is realized that the upfield shift change due to charge is just balanced by the downfield shift change due to diamagnetic ring current. Small ring aromatic annulenyl carbanions, with the few exceptions that have been noted, prefer all-<u>cis</u> stereochemistry and the diamagnetic ring current is only dis-played in the proton NMR by the downfield shift changes for outer hydrogens. In larger ring aromatic annulenyl carbanions (12 or more ring atoms), the effect of charge on proton shifts diminishes because the charge is delocalized over a larger number of carbons and diamagnetic ring current shifts are large, particularly for inner hydrogens. For these reasons, the influence of ring current dominates and leads to rather remarkable shift changes when proton shifts of aromatic annulenyl carbanions are compared to their nonaromatic precursors. Large ring annulenes are mobile and frequently variable temperature measurements will show the presence of several stereoisomers. However, larger aromatic annulenyl dianions are much less conformationally mobile because delocalization of charge in one planar stereo-isomer becomes energetically more important than relief of steric interactions. A number of larger aromatic annulenyl dianions have been characterized with pro-ton NMR. These include [12]-annulenyl dianion,[188] 1,6 and 1,7-methylene bridged [12]-annulenyl dianions,[215] di- and tridehydro[12]-annulenyl dianions,[189] [16]-annulenyl dianion,[190,191] and octadehydro[24]-annulenyl dianion [192] (Table 14, No.

149-153; Chapter 1).

Fewer larger annulenyl monoanions with an odd number of ring atoms have been studied. This lack of data does not reflect any inherent lower stability for the monoanions compared to the dianions but only shows that the precursors to these systems are less synthetically accessible. The potassium salt of aza[13]-annulenyl anion (62) is formed through the reaction of potassium metal with aza[13]-annulene at -78° in THF.[216] Only the upfield, inner hydrogen on carbon-2 and the downfield hydrogen on carbon-13 α to nitrogen could be specifically assigned from the viscosity broadened, low temperature spectrum. This anion quickly isomerizes to (63) in order to relieve the steric repulsion between three inner hydrogens and places the sterically less demanding nitrogen in an inner position.[216,217] Despite the

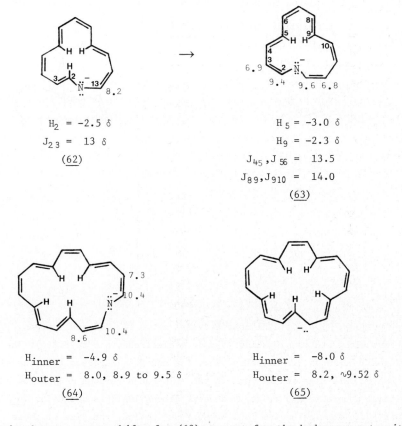

$H_2 = -2.5\ \delta$

$J_{23} = 13\ \delta$

(62)

$H_5 = -3.0\ \delta$

$H_9 = -2.3\ \delta$

$J_{45}, J_{56} = 13.5$

$J_{89}, J_{910} = 14.0$

(63)

$H_{inner} = -4.9\ \delta$

$H_{outer} = 8.0, 8.9\ to\ 9.5\ \delta$

(64)

$H_{inner} = -8.0\ \delta$

$H_{outer} = 8.2, \sim 9.52\ \delta$

(65)

difference in charge, proton shifts for (63), except for the hydrogens α to nitrogen, are quite comparable to the inner and outer shifts for [12]-annulenyl dianion. These similarities point out that diamagnetic ring current in these 14-electron, aromatic anions is the dominant factor influencing proton chemical shifts. Aza-[17]-annulenyl anion (64)[217] and [17]-annulenyl anion (65)[186] show inner hydrogens even further upfield and outer hydrogens even further downfield. Methoxy-tridehydro[17]-annulenyl anion has also been studied with proton NMR.[218]

B. Nonaromatic Annulenyl and Polycyclic Monoanions and Dianions

As would be expected, monoanions and dianions belonging to the category of non-aromatic ("antiaromatic") annulenes are somewhat limited but there are enough data to demonstrate the dramatic differences between proton shifts for 4n paratropic systems compared to (4n + 2) diatropic systems. Heptaphenylcycloheptatrienyl carbanion has been characterized as its potassium salt in DME.[219] However, the proton spectrum (broad multiplet, 6.5 to 7.1 δ) is not very informative becaues the 8-electron, 7-membered ring is completely substituted. Benzocycloheptatrienyl anion (66) has been prepared as the potassium salt in liquid ammonia at -50°.[220] The paramagnetic ring current of this 12-electron system causes all the proton shifts to be well upfield when compared to shifts for aromatic anions: cyclooctatetraene dianion (10

$$\Delta\delta_r$$

$J_{12} = 10.8$	$H_1 = -6.8$
$J_{23} = 8.2$	$H_2 = -5.7$
$J_{78} = 8.0$	$H_3 = -6.2$
$J_{89} = 6.4$	$H_8 = -5.4$
	$H_9 = -3.7$

(66)

$\Delta\delta_r$		$\Delta\delta_r$
$J_{12} = 10.4$	$H_1 = -3.9$	$H_{10} = -3.5$
$J_{23} = 10.2$	$H_2 = -4.6$	$H_a = +10.6$
$J_{89} = 9.0$	$H_3 = -4.4$	$H_b = +15.9$
$J_{910} = 4.7$	$H_9 = -3.3$	

(67)

π-electrons, ∿5.8 δ); cyclononatetraenyl anion (52, 10 π-electrons, 7.0 δ); and benzocyclononatetraenyl anion (54, 14 π-electrons, 6.5 to 8.2 δ). The size of the vicinal couplings in the benzo ring, J_{78} and J_{89}, suggests that the electron distribution with high double bond character between carbons 7-8, 9-10, and 11-6 and minimal double bond character between carbons 10-11 as shown for (66) is favored. In the aromatic carbenium ion, benzotropylium ion, the size of these couplings is reversed ($J_{78} = 7.0$ and $J_{89} = 8.4$ Hz) and this indicates high double bond character in the carbon 10-11 bond, maximizing the aromatic character of the tropylium moiety of the cation.[221] In (66), the electron distribution covering the 11-atom framework is favored because antiaromatic destabilization decreases with increasing size of the 4n π-electron ring.

The bicyclo[5.4.1]-dodecapentaenyl anion (67) is another example of a 12-electron paratropic anion.[222] The low value for the vicinal couplings, J_{910} and J_{78}, of 4.7 Hz suggests that the dihedral angles between the hydrogens on carbons 9 and 10 and on carbons 7 and 8 are greater than 40° and that carbons 8 and 9 are twisted out of the plane. Such twisting decreases bond angle strain and diminishes anti-aromatic character in (67). Compared to the methylene bridged cyclononatetraenyl anion (53, 10 π-electrons, 5.4 to 6.8 δ), all the ring proton shifts are quite shielded. The methylene bridge hydrogens are deshielded by an impressive 11.5 and 14.9 ppm compared to (53). Shift changes due to ring current ($\Delta\delta_r$) were determined by calculating proton shifts from charge densities and the empirical relationship between charge and proton shifts (10.7 ppm/electron) [86] and comparing calculated shifts to observed shifts. The difference at each hydrogen is attributed to para-magnetic ring current in (66) and (67). It can be seen that these paramagnetic shifts are an order of magnitude larger than the diamagnetic ring current shifts for indenyl anion (Table 10).

In polycyclic monoanions and dianions of three or more rings, the distinction between parpatropic and diatropic systems becomes blurred. For example, benzobicyclo[5.2.0]-nonatetraenyl anion (68) behaves both as a peripheral (4n + 2) system

7.3
7.9
6.5
5.8
-.. 4.2

$$\Delta\delta_r$$

$J_{12} = 7.6$	$H_1 = -0.1$
$J_{23} = 9.9$	$H_2 = -0.6$
$J_{78} = 7.1$	$H_3 = -0.6$
$J_{89} = 8.0$	$H_8 = +1.6$
	$H_9 = +1.7$

(68)

21.0 CH$_3$

CH$_3$

H_{ring} = -3.2 to -4.0 δ

(69)

5.3
6.3
6.7

(70)

6.8
6.0

(71)

encompassing all 14 π-electrons and a smaller 4n system in the 8-electron, 7-membered ring.[223] The effect is clearly seen in the estimated ring current shifts, ($\Delta\delta_r$). They are quite small compared to the $\Delta\delta_r$'s for (66) and (67), upfield in the 7-membered ring and downfield in the benzo ring. The dianion of trans-dimethyldihydropyrene (69), a 16 π-electron system, is clearly paratropic. Very large downfield shifts are observed for the methyl groups above and below the ring plane and the ring hydrogens are shifted upfield by the paramagnetic ring current.[224] Dibenzopentalene dianion (70)[142,225] and paracyclene dianion (71)[226] are also 16 π-electron systems but the downfield proton shifts for both are similar to the shifts for the aromatic [12]-annulenyl dianion (Table 14, No. 149).[188] Therefore, the proton shifts show that the negative charge resides in the 12-atom, 14 π-electron periphery of (70) and (71) with little, if any, charge delocalized over the central double bond.

Acknowledgement. Support of this work by the Robert A. Welch Foundation is gratefully acknowledged.

VII. REFERENCES

1   Earlier literature reviews and chapters in books that have treated various aspects of the magnetic resonance of carbanions include:
    (a) J. B. Stothers, "^{13}C NMR Studies of Reaction Mechanisms and Reactive Inter-mediates", in "Topics in Carbon-13 NMR Spcetroscopy", G. C. Levy, Ed., John Wiley and Sons, New York, 1974, Ch. 6, Vol. 1, pp.272-274.
    (b) L. D. McKeever, "Nuclear Magnetic Resonance Studies of Carbon-Lithium Bond-ing in Organolithium Compounds", in "Ions and Ion Pairs in Organic Reactions", M. Szwarc, Ed., Wiley-Interscience, New York, 1972, Ch. 6, Vol. 1, pp.263-287.
    (c) J. B. Stothers, "Carbon-13 NMR Spectroscopy", Academic Press, New York, 1972, pp.209-217.
    (d) S. W. Staley, "Pericyclic Reactions of Carbanions", in "Pericyclic Reactions" A. P. Marchand and R. E. Lehr, Ed., Academic Press, New York, 1977, Ch. 4, Vol. 1, pp.199-264.
2   Ring currents are long range shieldings (paramagnetic shifts) or deshieldings (diamagnetic shifts) due to anisotropic circulations of electrons about neigh-boring atoms and are particularly important in the proton NMR shifts of π-systems for delocalized carbanions (Reference 3).
3   L. M. Jackman and S. Sternhell, "Applications of Nuclear Magnetic Resonance Spectroscopy in Organic Chemistry", Pergamon Press, London, 1969, pp.61-98.
4   L. M. Jackman, Tetrahedron, 33 (1977) 2737.
5   J. E. Nordlander and J. D. Roberts, J. Am. Chem. Soc., 81 (1959) 1769.
6   C. S. Johnson, Jr., M. A. Weiner, J. S. Waugh, and D. Seyferth, J. Am. Chem. Soc., 83 (1961) 1306.
7   J. E. Nordlander, W. G. Young, and J. D. Roberts, J. Am. Chem. Soc., 83 (1961) 494.
8   G. M. Whitesides, J. E. Nordlander, and J. D. Roberts, Disc. Faraday Soc., 34 (1962) 185.
9   G. M. Whitesides, J. E. Nordlander, and J. D. Roberts, J. Am. Chem. Soc., 84 (1962) 2010.
10 P. West, J. I. Purmont, and S. V. McKinley, J. Am. Chem. Soc., 90 (1968) 797.
11 R. B. Bates and W. A. Beavers, J. Am. Chem. Soc., 96 (1974) 5001.
12 D. Seyferth and T. F. Jula, J. Organometal. Chem., 8 (1967) P13.
13 E. R. Dolinskaya, I. Y. Poddubnyi, and I. Y. Tsereteli, Dokl. Akad. Nauk SSSR, 191 (1970) 862.
14 D. A. Hutchison, K. R. Beck, R. A. Benkeser, and J. B. Grutzner, J. Am. Chem. Soc., 95 (1973) 7075.
15 W. H. Glaze and P. C. Jones, J. Chem. Soc., Chem. Commun., (1969) 1434.
16 W. H. Glaze, J. E. Hanicak, M. L. Moore, and J. Chaudhuri, J. Organometal. Chem., 44 (1972) 39.

17 W. H. Glaze, J. E. Hanicak, J. Chaudhuri, M. L. Moore, and D. P. Duncan, J. Organometal. Chem., 51 (1973) 13.
18 J. Klein and A. Medlik, J. Chem. Soc., Chem. Commun., (1973) 275.
19 In all tables, only the chemical shifts of the carbons or hydrogens attached to the carbons of the carbanion's framework are presented. The reader is referred to the literature for the chemical shifts of other carbons or hydrogens. All the chemical shifts have been converted to parts per million (ppm) downfield from tetramethylsilane, δ. Chemical shifts upfield from TMS are negative. Where several authors have reported shift values for the same carbanion under the same conditions of cation, solvent, and temperature or where the same author cites slightly different values for the same carbanion in different publications, the values have been averaged. Where there is a large discrepancy in the values of different authors, the more recent value is usually presented because most frequently the earlier literature does not cite the chemical shift reference used. The temperature at which the shifts in the tables were determined is ambient probe temperature (approximately 25° to 35°) unless otherwise shown. The abbreviations used in the tables are: nr, value not reported; M, several alkali metal cations were used and the shift values were not affected; THF, tetrahydrofuran; MeTHF, 2-methyltetrahydrofuran; DME, 1,2-dimethoxyethane; DMSO, dimethylsulfoxide; TMEDA-hex, tetramethylethylene-diamine-hexane; HMPA, hexamethylphosphortriamide; Et_2O, diethyl ether; CHA, cyclohexylamide; PhH, benzene; $PhCH_3$, toluene.
20 Reference 3, pp.128-137.
21 Carbanions are numbered for convenience of comparing chemical shifts and are not necessarily according to systematic rules. Proton chemical shifts on figures (12)-(71) have been rounded to the nearest 0.1 ppm in order to save space. Electron distributions shown on the figures are for ease of "electron accounting" and do not imply a favored distribution.
22 J. P. C. M. van Dongen, H. W. D. van Dijkman, and M. J. A. de Bie, Rec. Trav. Chim., 93 (1974) 29.
23 S. Bywater, P. Lachance, and D. J. Worsfold, J. Phys. Chem., 79 (1975) 2148.
24 S. Bywater and D. J. Worsfold, J. Organometal. Chem.,
25 D. H. O'Brien, A. J. Hart, and C. R. Russell, J. Am. Chem. Soc., 97 (1975) 4410.
26 D. H. O'Brien, C. R. Russell, and A. J. Hart, Tetrahedron Lett., (1976) 37.
27 Reference 1(c), p.58 and p.75.
28 D. H. O'Brien, C. R. Russell, and A. J. Hart, J. Am. Chem. Soc., 101 (1979) 633.
29 V. R. Sandel, S. V. McKinley, and H. H. Freedman, J. Am. Chem. Soc., 90 (1968) 495.
30 G. J. Heiszwolf and H. Kloosterziel, Rec. Trav. Chim., 86 (1967) 1345.
31 H. Kloosterziel and J. A. A. van Drunen, Rec. Trav. Chim., 87 (1968) 1025.
32 G. J. Heiszwolf, J. A. A. van Drunen, and H. Kloosterziel, Rec. Trav. Chim., 88 (1969) 1377.
33 H. Kloosterziel and J. A. A. van Drunen, Rec. Trav. Chim., 89 (1970) 32.
34 G. Boche and D. R. Schneider, Tetrahedron Lett., (1976) 3657.
35 H. H. Freedman, V. R. Sandel, and B. P. Thill, J. Am. Chem. Soc., 89 (1967) 1762.
36 J. W. Burley, R. Ife, and R. N. Young, J. Chem. Soc., Chem. Commun., (1970) 1256.
37 J. W. Burley and R. N. Young, J. Chem. Soc., Perkin II, (1972) 1006.
38 H. Kloosterziel and J. A. A. van Drunen, Rec. Trav. Chim., 89 (1970) 37.
39 J. W. Burley and R. N. Young, J. Chem. Soc. (C), (1971) 3780.
40 J. W. Burley and R. N. Young, J. Chem. Soc., Perkin II, (1972) 1843.
41 G. Boche, D. Martens, and H-U. Wagner, J. Am. Chem. Soc., 98 (1976) 2668.
42 J. E. Mulvaney and D. Savage, J. Org. Chem., 36 (1971) 2592.
43 R. J. Bushby and G. J. Ferber, Tetrahedron Lett., (1974) 3701.
44 R. J. Bushby and G. J. Ferber, J. Chem. Soc., Perkin II, (1976) 1688.
45 R. B. Bates, D. W. Gosselink, and J. A. Kaczynski, Tetrahedron Lett., (1967) 205.
46 H. Yasuda and H. Tani, J. Macromol. Sci.-Chem., A9 (1975) 1007.
47 G. J. Heiszwolf and H. Kloosterziel, Rec. Trav. Chim., 86 (1967) 807.
48 H. Kloosterziel and J. A. A. van Drunen, Rec. Trav. Chim., 89 (1970) 270.

318

49 S. Brenner and J. Klein, Israel J. Chem., 7 (1969) 735.

50 R. B. Bates, S. Brenner, and C. M. Cole, J. Am. Chem. Soc., 94 (1972) 2130.

51 R. B. Bates, W. H. Deines, D. A. McCombs, and D. E. Potter, J. Am. Chem. Soc., 91 (1969) 4608.

52 H. Kloosterziel and J. A. A. van Drunen, Rec. Trav. Chim., 88 (1969) 1084.

53 H. Kloosterziel and J. A. A. van Drunen, Rec. Trav. Chim., 88 (1969) 1471.

54 R. B. Bates, S. Brenner, and B. I. Mayall, J. Am. Chem. Soc., 94 (1972) 4765.

55 R. Hoffman and R. A. Olofson, J. Am. Chem. Soc., 88 (1966) 943.

56 D. H. Hunter, R. E. Klinck, R. P. Steiner, and J. B. Stothers, Can. J. Chem., 54 (1976) 1464.

57 R. B. Bates and D. A. McCombs, Tetrahedron Lett., (1969) 977.

58 G. A. Olah, G. Asensio, H. Mayr, and P. v. R. Schleyer, J. Am. Chem. Soc., 100 (1978) 4347.

59 H. Kloosterziel and J. A. A. van Drunen, Rec. Trav. Chim., 89 (1970) 368.

60 E. Grovenstein, Jr., S. Akabori, and J-U. Rhee, J. Am. Chem. Soc., 94 (1972) 4734.

61 T. J. Katz and C. Talcott, J. Am. Chem. Soc., 88 (1966) 4732.

62 R. Rieke, M. Ogliaruso, R. McClung, and S. Winstein, J. Am. Chem. Soc., 88 (1966) 4729.

63 F. J. Smentowski, R. M. Owens, and B. D. Faubion, J. Am. Chem. Soc., 90 (1968) 1537.

64 M. Ogliaruso, R. Rieke, and S. Winstein, J. Am. Chem. Soc., 88 (1966) 4731.

65 M. Barfield, R. B. Bates, W. A. Beavers, I. R. Blacksberg, S. Brenner, B. I. Mayall, and C. S. McCulloch, J. Am. Chem. Soc., 97 (1974) 900.

66 S. V. Ley and L. A. Paquette, J. Am. Chem. Soc., 96 (1974) 6670.

67 W. A. Boll, Tetrahedron Lett., (1968) 5531.

68 S. Winstein, M. Ogliaruso, M. Sakai, and J. M. Nicholson, J. Am. Chem. Soc., 89 (1967) 3656.

69 M. V. Moncur and J. B. Grutzner, J. Am. Chem. Soc., 95 (1973) 6449.

70 J. B. Grutzner and S. Winstein, J. Am. Chem. Soc., 90 (1968) 6562.

71 M. J. Goldstein, J. Am. Chem. Soc., 89 (1967) 6357.

72 M. J. Goldstein and R. Hoffman, J. Am. Chem. Soc., 93 (1971) 6193.

73 J. B. Grutzner and S. Winstein, J. Am. Chem. Soc., 94 (1972) 2200.

74 M. V. Moncur, J. B. Grutzner, and A. Eisenstadt, J. Org. Chem., 39 (1974) 1604.

75 M. J. Goldstein, S. Tomoda, and G. Whittaker, J. Am. Chem. Soc., 96 (1974) 3676.

76 S. W. Staley, G. M. Cramer, and W. G. Kingsley, J. Am. Chem. Soc., 95 (1973) 5052.

77 S. W. Staley and A. W. Orvedal, J. Am. Chem. Soc., 96 (1974) 1618.

78 H. Kloosterziel and E. Zwanenburg, Rec. Trav. Chim., 88 (1969) 1373.

79 H. Kloosterziel and G. M. Gorter-la Roy, J. Chem. Soc., Chem. Commun., (1972) 352.

80 S. W. Staley and N. J. Pearl, J. Am. Chem. Soc., 95 (1973) 2731.

81 S. W. Staley and G. M. Cramer, J. Am. Chem. Soc., 95 (1963) 5051.

82 S. W. Staley and W. G. Kingsley, J. Am. Chem. Soc., 95 (1973) 5804.

83 S. W. Staley and N. J. Pearl, J. Am. Chem. Soc., 95 (1973) 3437.

84 S. W. Staley and G. E. Linkowski, J. Am. Chem. Soc., 98 (1976) 5010.

85 S. W. Staley. G. E. Linkowski, and A. S. Heyn, Tetrahedron, 31 (1975) 1131.

86 T. Schaefer and W. G. Schneider, Can. J. Chem., 41 (1963) 966.

87 S. W. Staley, G. M. Cramer, and A. W. Orvedal, J. Am. Chem. Soc., 96 (1974) 7433.

88 S. W. Staley and A. S. Heyn, J. Am. Chem. Soc., 97 (1975) 3852.

89 W. T. Ford and M. Newcomb, J. Am. Chem. Soc., 96 (1974) 309.

90 R. B. Bates, S. Brenner, C. M. Cole, E. W. Davidson, G. D. Forsythe, D. A. McCombs, and A. S. Roth, J. Am. Chem. Soc., 95 (1973) 926.

91 In footnote (8) of Reference 89, it is stated that carbon-13 shifts reported in Reference 90 may have been in error. Therefore, shifts for pentadienyl carbanion in Table 6 were taken from Reference 89.

92 H. Yasuda and H. Tani, Tetrahedron Lett., (1975) 11.

93 G. A. Olah, J. S. Staral, R. J. Spear, and G. Liang, J. Am. Chem. Soc., 97

(1975) 5489.

94 L. A. Paquette, M. J. Broadhurst, P. Warner, G. A. Olah, and G. Liang, J. Am. Chem. Soc., 95 (1973) 3386.
95 J. F. M. Oth, D. M. Smith, U. Prange, and G. Schroder, Angew. Chem. internat. Edit., 12 (1973) 327; Angew. Chem., 85 (1973) 352.
96 R. B. Bates, L. M. Kroposki, and D. E. Potter, J. Org. Chem., 37 (1972) 560.
97 H. O. House, R. A. Auerbach, M. Gall, and N. P. Peet, J. Org. Chem., 38 (1973) 514.
98 G. B. Trimitsis, J. M. Hinkley, R. TenBrink, M. Poli, G. Gustafson, J. Erdman, and D. Rop, J. Am. Chem. Soc., 99 (1977) 4838.
99 R. P. Woodbury and M. W. Rathke, J. Org. Chem., 43 (1978) 1947.
100 R. P. Woodbury and M. W. Rathke, J. Org. Chem., 42 (1977) 1688.
101 H. O. House, A. V. Prabhu, and W. V. Phillips, J. Org. Chem., 41 (1976) 1209.
102 H. Kloosterziel, J. A. A. van Drunen, and P. Galama, J. Chem. Soc., Chem. Commun., (1969) 885.
103 H. Kloosterziel, Rec. Trav. Chim., 89 (1970) 300.
104 H. Kloosterziel and J. A. A. van Drunen, Rec. Trav. Chim., 94 (1975) 1.
105 H. Kloosterziel and J. A. A. van Drunen, Rec. Trav. Chim., 89 (1970) 667.
106 G. Fraenkel, C. C. Ho, Y. Liang, and S. Yu, J. Am. Chem. Soc., 94 (1972) 4732.
107 G. Fraenkel and J. W. Cooper, J. Am. Chem. Soc., 93 (1971) 7228.
108 A. J. Ashe, III, and T. W. Smith, Tetrahedron Lett., (1977) 407.
109 V. R. Sandel and H. H. Freedman, J. Am. Chem. Soc., 85 (1963) 2328.
110 R. Waack, L. D. McKeever, and M. A. Doran, J. Chem. Soc., Chem. Commun., (1969) 117.
111 R. Waack, M. A. Doran, E. B. Baker, and G. A. Olah, J. Am. Chem. Soc., 88 (1966) 1272.
112 L. D. McKeever and R. Waack, J. Organometal. Chem., 28 (1971) 145.
113 S. Bywater and D. J. Worsfold, J. Organometal. Chem., 33 (1971) 273.
114 S. Brownstein and D. J. Worsfold, Can. J. Chem., 50 (1972) 1246.
115 G. Fraenkel, J. G. Russell, and Y-H. Chen, J. Am. Chem. Soc., 95 (1973) 3208.
116 K. Takahashi, M. Takaki, and R. Asami, Org. Magn. Resonance, 3 (1971) 539.
117 M. G. Pastor, B. Calas, B. Brun, and L. Giral, C. R. Acad. Sc. Paris, Serie C, 277 (1973) 1159.
118 K. Takahashi, M. Takaki, and R. Asami, J. Phys. Chem., 75 (1971) 1062.
119 K. Takahashi, K. Yamada, K. Wakata, and R. Asami, Org. Magn. Resonance, 6 (1974) 62.
120 Y. Okamoto and H. Yuki, J. Organometal. Chem., 32 (1971) 1.
121 R. Waack and M. A. Doran, J. Am. Chem. Soc., 85 (1963) 4042.
122 K. Takahashi and R. Asami, Bull. Chem. Soc. Japan, 41 (1968) 231.
123 J. B. Grutzner, J. M. Lawlor, and L. M. Jackman, J. Am. Chem. Soc., 94 (1972) 2306.
124 R. H. Cox, E. G. Janzen, and W. B. Harrison, J. Magn. Resonance,4 (1971) 274.
125 K. Takahashi, Y. Kondo, and R. Asami, Org. Magn. Resonance, 6 (1974) 580.
126 D. H. O'Brien, C. R. Russell, and A. J. Hart, unpublished results.
127 A. J. Hart, D. H. O'Brien, and C. R. Russell, J. Organometal. Chem., 72 (1974) C19.
128 D. Leibfritz, B. O. Wagner, and J. D. Roberts, Ann. Chem., 763 (1972) 173.
129 D. H. O'Brien, C. R. Russell, and A. J. Hart, J. Am. Chem. Soc., 98 (1976) 7427.
130 Shifts for nonequivalent ortho (C2,6) and meta (C3,5) resonances are: No. 103 C2,6 = 109.4 and 108.0, C3,5 = 129.0 and 128.6; No. 106, C2,6 = 112.2 and 102.7, C3,5 = 131.6 and 129.5; No. 107, C2,6 = 117.6 and 114.3; No. 108, C2,6 = 107.5 and 102.1, C3,5 = 131.1 and 129.1; No. 109, C2,6 = 118.0 and 116.0.
131 Reference 1(c), pp.332-348.
132 H. Spiesecke and W. G. Schneider, Tetrahedron Lett., (1961) 468.
133 E. A. LaLancette and R. E. Benson, J. Am. Chem. Soc., 87 (1965) 1941.
134 E. A. LaLancette and R. E. Benson, J. Am. Chem. Soc., 85 (1963) 2853.
135 G. Fraenkel, R. E. Carter, A. McLachlan, and J. H. Richards, J. Am. Chem. Soc., 82 (1960) 5846.
136 The π-electron densities calculated from proton shifts are all slightly higher than those that will be found in References 85 and 109 because eqn (1) (δ =

18.2 -10.7) was used rather than chemical shift differences from benzene.

137 J. A. Pople, J. Chem. Phys., 24 (1956) 1111.
138 J. A. Pople and K. G. Untch, J. Am. Chem. Soc., 88 (1966) 4811.
139 Reference 20, pp.141-145, pp.595-604, and p.770.
140 N. Jonathan, S. Gordon, and B. P. Dailey, J. Chem. Phys., 36 (1962) 2443.
141 R. G. Lawler and C. V. Ristango, J. Am. Chem. Soc., 91 (1969) 1534.
142 B. M. Trost and P. L. Kinson, J. Am. Chem. Soc., 92 (1970) 2591, footnote (3).
143 G. A. Olah and G. D. Mateescu, J. Am. Chem. Soc., 92 (1970) 1430.
144 G. A. Olah, P. W. Westerman, and D. A. Forsyth, J. Am. Chem. Soc., 97 (1975) 3419.
145 G. A. Olah and A. M. White, J. Am. Chem. Soc., 90 (1968) 1884.
146 D. A. Forsyth and G. A. Olah, J. Am. Chem. Soc., 98 (1976) 4086.
147 E. Dradi and G. Gatti, J. Am. Chem. Soc., 97 (1975) 5472.
148 P. C. Lauterbur, J. Am. Chem. Soc., 83 (1961) 1838.
149 M. Karplus and J. A. Pople, J. Chem. Phys., 38 (1963) 2803.
150 T. D. Alger, D. M. Grant, and E. G. Paul, J. Am. Chem. Soc., 88 (1966) 5397.
151 A. J. Jones, P. D. Gardner, D. M. Grant, and W. M. Litchman, and V. Boekel-heide, J. Am. Chem. Soc., 92 (1970) 2395.
152 A. J. Jones, T. D. Alger, D. M. Grant, and W. M. Litchman, J. Am. Chem. Soc., 92 (1970) 2386.
153 T. K. Wu. and B. P. Bailey, J. Chem. Phys., 41 (1964) 2796.
154 P. C. Lauterbur, J. Chem. Phys., 43 (1965) 360.
155 T. Tokuhiro and G. Fraenkel, J. Am. Chem. Soc., 91 (1969) 5005.
156 Correlations of charge density with carbon-13 chemical shifts are summarized in: G. J. Martin and M. L. Martin, Org. Magn. Resonance, 7 (1975) 2.
157 (a) J. Smid in Reference 1(b), pp.85-151; (b) T. E. Hogen-Esch and J. Smid, J. Am. Chem. Soc., 87 (1965) 669; (c) T. E. Hogen-Esch and J. Smid, J. Am. Chem. Soc., 88 (1966) 307; (d) L. L. Chan and J. Smid, J. Am. Chem. Soc., 89 (1967) 4547; (e) L. L. Chan and J. Smid, J. Am. Chem. Soc., 90 (1968) 4654; (f) T. E. Hogen-Esch and J. Smid, J. Am. Chem. Soc., 91 (1969) 4580; (g) T. Ellingsen and J. Smid, J. Phys. Chem., 73 (1969) 2712; (h) L. L. Chan, K. H. Wong, and J. Smid, J. Am. Chem. Soc., 92 (1970) 1955; (i) K. H. Wong, G. Konizer, and J. Smid, J. Am. Chem. Soc., 92 (1970) 666; (j) U. Takaki, T. E. Hogen-Esch, and J. Smid, J. Am. Chem. Soc., 93 (1971) 6760; (k) T. E. Hogen-Esch and J. Smid, J. Am. Chem. Soc., 94 (1972) 9240; (l) U. Takaki and J. Smid, J. Am. Chem. Soc., 96 (1974) 2588; (m) W. T. Ford, J. Am. Chem. Soc., 92 (1970) 2857; (n) A. Streitweiser, Jr., J. H. Hammons, E. Ciuffarin, and J. I. Brauman, J. Am. Chem. Soc., 89 (1967) 59; (o) A. Streitweiser, Jr., E. Ciuffarin, and J. H. Hammons, J. Am. Chem. Soc., 89 (1967) 63; (p) A. Streit-weiser, Jr., C. J. Chang, W. B. Hollyhead, and J. R. Murdoch, J. Am. Chem. Soc., 94 (1972) 5288; (q) A. Streitweiser, Jr., C. J. Chang, and D. M. E. Reuben, J. Am. Chem. Soc., 94 (1972) 5730.
158 (a) R. Waack, M. A. Doran, and P. E. Stevenson, J. Am. Chem. Soc., 88 (1966) 2109; (b) E. Buncel, B. C. Menon, and J. P. Colpa, Can. J. Chem., 57 (1979) 999.
159 (a) E. Buncel and B. C. Menon, J. Chem. Soc., Chem. Commun., (1978) 758; (b) E. Buncel and B. C. Menon, J. Org. Chem., 44 (1979) 317.
160 (a) J. W. Burley and R. N. Young, J. Chem. Soc., Chem. Commun., (1969) 1127; (b) J. W. Burley and R. N. Young, J. Chem. Soc. (B), (1971) 1018; (c) J. W. Burley and R. N. Young, J. Chem. Soc., Perkin II, (1972) 835; (d) G. C. Green-acre and R. N. Young, J. Chem. Soc., Perkin II, (1975) 1661.
161 W. H. Rhine and G. D. Stucky, J. Am. Chem. Soc., 97 (1975) 737.
162 G. A. Taylor and P. E. Rakita, Org. Magn. Resonance, 6 (1974) 644.
163 G. A. Taylor and P. E. Rakita, J. Organometal. Chem., 78 (1974) 281.
164 J. van der Kooij, N. H. Velthorst, and C. McLean, Chem. Phys. Lett., 12 (1972) 596.
165 H. W. Vos, Y. W. Bakker, N. H. Velthorst, and C. McLean, Org. Magn. Resonance, 6 (1974) 574.
166 J. A. Dixon, P. A. Gwinner, and D. C. Lini, J. Am. Chem. Soc., 87 (1965) 1379.
167 R. H. Cox, J. Phys. Chem., 73 (1969) 2649.
168 R. H. Cox, E. G. Janzen, and J. L. Gerlock, J. Am. Chem. Soc., 90 (1968) 5906.
169 R. H. Cox, J. Magn. Resonance, 3 (1970) 223.

170 U. Edlund, Org. Magn. Resonance, 9 (1977) 593.
171 U. Edlund, Org. Magn. Resonance, in press.
172 The exact chemical shifts were not reported in Reference 173. Shifts were obtained by interpolation of a plot of shifts vs temperatures.
173 J. van der Giessen, C. Gooijer, C. McLean, and N. H. Velthorst, Chem. Phys. Lett., 55 (1978) 33.
174 F. J. Kronzer and V. R. Sandel, Chem. Ind. (London), (1972) 210.
175 F. J. Kronzer and V. R. Sandel, J. Am. Chem. Soc., 94 (1972) 5750.
176 C. H. Bushweller, J. S. Sturges, M. Cipullo, S. Hoogasian, M. W. Gabriel, and S. Bank, Tetrahedron Lett., (1978) 1359.
177 For a complete discussion of rotational barriers in carbanions see Reference 1(d), pp.200-214.
178 F. Sondheimer, Accounts Chem. Res., 5 (1972) 81.
179 J. R. Leto, F. A. Cotton, and J. S. Waugh, Nature (London), 180 (1957) 978.
180 W. T. Ford and J. B. Grutzner, J. Org. Chem., 37 (1972) 2561.
181 R. H. Cox, L. W. Harrison, and W. K. Austin, Jr., J. Phys. Chem., 77 (1973) 200.
182 T. J. Katz and P. J. Garratt, J. Am. Chem. Soc., 85 (1963) 2852.
183 T. J. Katz and P. J. Garratt, J. Am. Chem. Soc., 86 (1964) 5194.
184 G. Boche, D. Martens, and W. Danzer, Angew. Chem. internat. Edit., 8 (1969) 984; Angew. Chem., 81 (1969) 1003.
185 G. Boche and A. Bieberbach, Tetrahedron Lett., (1976) 1021.
186 G. Schroder, G. Pinke, D. M. Smith, and J. F. M. Oth, Angew. Chem. internat. Edit., 12 (1973) 325; Angew. Chem., 85 (1973) 350.
187 T. J. Katz, J. Am. Chem. Soc., 82 (1960) 3785.
188 J. F. M. Oth and G. Schroder, J. Chem. Soc. (B), (1971) 904.
189 P. J. Garratt, N. E. Rowland, and F. Sondheimer, Tetrahedron, 27 (1971) 3157.
190 J. F. M. Oth, G. Antoine and J.-M. Gilles, Tetrahedron Lett., (1968) 6265.
191 J. F. M. Oth, H. Baumann, J.-M. Gilles, and G. Schroder, J. Am. Chem. Soc., 94 (1972) 3498.
192 R. M. McQuilkin, P. J. Garratt, and F. Sondheimer, J. Am. Chem. Soc., 92 (1970) 6682.
193 L. A. Paquette, S. V. Ley, R. H. Meisinger, R. K. Russell, and M. Oku, J. Am. Chem. Soc., 96 (1974) 5806.
194 L. A. Paquette, C. D. Wright, III, S. G. Traynor, D. L. Taggart, and G. D. Ewing, Tetrahedron, (1976) 1885.
195 L. A. Paquette, G. D. Ewing, and S. G. Traynor, J. Am. Chem. Soc., 98 (1976) 279.
196 L. A. Paquette, G. D. Ewing, S. Traynor, and J. M. Gardlik, J. Am. Chem. Soc., 99 (1977) 6115.
197 T. J. Katz, M. Yoshida, and L. C. Siew, J. Am. Chem. Soc., 87 (1965) 4516.
198 L. A. Paquette, J. F. Hansen, and T. Kakihana, J. Am. Chem. Soc., 93 (1971) 168.
199 T. J. Katz and M. Rosenberger, J. Am. Chem. Soc., 84 (1962) 865.
200 T. J. Katz, M. Rosenberger, and R. K. O'Hara, J. Am. Chem. Soc., 86 (1964) 249.
201 I. Willner and M. Rabinovitz, J. Am. Chem. Soc., 100 (1978) 337.
202 I. Willner, J. Y. Becker, and M. Rabinovitz, J. Am. Chem. Soc., 101 (1979) 395.
203 P. Radlick and W. Rosen, J. Am. Chem. Soc., 88 (1966) 3461.
204 W. Grimme, M. Kaufhold, U. Dettmeier, and E. Vogel, Angew. Chem. Internat. Edit., 5 (1966) 604; Angew. Chem., 78 (1966) 643.
205 A. G. Anastassiou and R. C. Griffith, J. Am. Chem. Soc., 96 (1974) 611.
206 R. J. Hunadi and G. K. Helmkamp, J. Org. Chem., 43 (1978) 1586.
207 P. J. Garratt and K. A. Knapp, J. Chem. Soc., Chem. Commun., (1970) 1215.
208 K. Hafner, S. Braun, T. Nakazawa, and H. Tappe, Tetrahedron Lett., (1975) 3507.
209 A. G. Anastassiou and S. W. Eachus, J. Am. Chem. Soc., 94 (1972) 2537.
210 A. G. Anastassiou and E. Reichmanis, J. Am. Chem. Soc., 98 (1976) 8266.
211 A. G. Anastassiou and E. Reichmanis, Angew. Chem. Internat. Edit., 13 (1974) 404; Angew. Chem., 86 (1974) 410.
212 A. G. Anastassiou and E. Reichmanis, J. Chem. Soc., Chem. Commun., (1975) 149.
213 G. Boche and F. Heidenhain, Angew. Chem. Internat. Edit., 17 (1978) 283; Angew. Chem., 90 (1978) 290.

322

214 G. Boche and F. Heidenhain, J. Am. Chem. Soc., 101 (1979) 738.
215 J. F. M. Oth, K. Mullen, H. Konigshofen, M. Mann, Y. Sakata, and E. Vogel, Angew. Chem. Internat. Edit., 13 (1974) 284; Angew. Chem., 86 (1974) 285.
216 A. G. Anastassiou, R. L. Elliot, and E. Reichmanis, J. Am. Chem. Soc., 96 (1974) 7823.
217 G. Schroder, G. Frank, H. Rottele, and J. F. M. Oth, Angew. Chem. internat. Edit., 13 (1974) 204; Angew. Chem., 86 (1974) 237.
218 J. Griffiths and F. Sondheimer, J. Am. Chem. Soc., 91 (1969) 7518.
219 R. Breslow and H. W. Chang, J. Am. Chem. Soc., 87 (1965) 2200.
220 S. W. Staley and A. W. Orvedal, J. Am. Chem. Soc., 95 (1973) 3382.
221 D. J. Bertelli and P. Crews, Tetrahedron, (1970) 4717.
222 S. W. Staley and A. W. Orvedal, J. Am. Chem. Soc., 95 (1973) 3384.
223 S. W. Staley, F. Heinrich, and A. W. Orvedal, J. Am. Chem. Soc., 98 (1976) 2681.
224 R. H. Mitchell, C. E. Klopfenstein, and V. Boekelheide, J. Am. Chem. Soc., 91 (1969) 4931.
225 B. M. Trost and P. L. Kinson, J. Am. Chem. Soc., 97 (1975) 2438.
226 B. M. Trost, D. Buhner, and G. M. Bright, Tetrahedron Lett., (1973) 2787.

CHAPTER 7

EQUILIBRIUM CARBON ACIDITIES IN SOLUTION

ANDREW STREITWIESER, JR., EUSEBIO JUARISTI AND LINDA L. NEBENZAHL

DEPARTMENT OF CHEMISTRY, UNIVERSITY OF CALIFORNIA, BERKELEY, CA 94720

CONTENTS

324

I. INTRODUCTION

Many organic reactions can be viewed essentially as acid-base
reactions. Correspondingly, acidity measurements and the effect
of structure on acidity have played an important role in the history
of physical organic chemistry. In recent years, increased attention
has been devoted to the quantitative study of carbon acidities. A
number of reviews of this topic are now available. The 1965 review
of Streitwieser and Hammons [1] has been amply supplemented by the
books of Cram [2], Jones [3], Bell [4], Buncel [5], Reutov, et al.
[6], and others [7], as well as by other extensive but more limited
reviews [8-13]. Much of the quantitative data on equilibrium carbon
acidities relate to the studies in the cyclohexylamine solvent
system in our laboratory. In the present review we summarize much
of the unpublished and published acidity determinations in our
laboratory and compare these results with those of other solvent
systems.

We consider the following equilibrium:

$$RH \quad \overset{K_a}{\rightleftharpoons} \quad R^- + H^+ \tag{1}$$

For some purposes one would prefer to have values for K_a in the
gas phase in order to study structural effects independently of solvation phenomena. Such K_a values can be determined from the bond
dissociation energy of the R-H bond (DH°), the ionization potential
of the hydrogen atom (IP) and the electron affinity of the alkyl
radical (EA).

$$
\begin{array}{ll}
RH \rightarrow R^{\cdot} + H^{\cdot} & \Delta H° = DH° \\
H^{\cdot} \rightarrow H^+ + e^- & \Delta H° = IP \\
R^{\cdot} + e^- \rightarrow R^- & \Delta H° = -EA \\
RH \rightarrow R^- + H^+ & \Delta Hg° = DH° + IP-EA
\end{array}
\tag{2}
$$

Application of eq. 2 has been feasible especially by direct and
indirect measurements with ion cyclotron resonance techniques [14],
and indicates the following order of intrinsic carbon acidities:

$CH_3NO_2 >$ cyclo-$C_5H_6 \gtrsim CHCl_3 > CH_3COCH_3 > CH_3CN > CH_2Cl_2$,

$CH_3SOCH_3 \gtrsim HC≡CH$, t-BuOH $>$ EtOH $> CH_3OH > C_3H_4$, $C_6H_5CH(CH_3)_2$

$> C_6H_5CH_3 > C_3H_6 > H_2O > C_6H_6 > C_2H_4$, $> (CH_2)_3$, CH_4

This sequence differs significantly from those obtained from solution studies (vide infra). For example, toluene is a stronger acid than water in the gas phase. It is also clear that in the gas phase alkyl substituents often increase the acidity of a molecule. Thus the acidity of alcohols in the gas phase increases in the opposite sequence, $\underline{t}\text{-}C_4H_9OH > C_2H_5OH > CH_3OH > H_2O$, compared to the acidity order of the same compounds in aqueous solution [15].

Nevertheless, only a relatively few gas phase carbon acidities are known and for more extensive studies of structural effects we must consider reactions in solution. The various methods for measuring such solution acidities have been reviewed by Cookson [16].

Carbon acidities in solution are conveniently dissected into the following categories:

kinetic   ionic   delocalized carbanions
equilibrium   ion pair   localized carbanions

In the present review we will not consider kinetic acidities but will instead restrict our scope to equilibrium acidity values. The effect of structure on acidity requires, in practice, the ionic acidity differences as defined by

$$RH + R'^- \xrightleftharpoons{K_i} R^- + R'H \qquad (3)$$

$$p\underline{K}_{R'H} - p\underline{K}_{RH} = \log \underline{K}_i \qquad (4)$$

Relative ion pair acidities refer to the following equilibrium:

$$RH + R'^- M^+ \xrightleftharpoons{K_{ip}} R^- M^+ + R'H \qquad (5)$$

$$p\underline{K}_{R'H} - p\underline{K}_{RH} = \log \underline{K}_{ip} \qquad (6)$$

The relative acidities measured in cyclohexylamine (CHA) solution are generally of the ion pair type with "p$\underline{K}$s" defined by eq. 6 relative to some standard.

II. IONIC ACIDITIES

Ionic acidities are available for carbon acids in a few solvents with the standard state defined in terms of the dilute solution in the solvent. For the evaluation of solvation effects it is additionally convenient to distinguish between hydroxylic solvents, which can stabilize the derived carbanion by hydrogen bonding, and polar aprotic (non-hydroxylic) solvents, which cannot.

A. Ionic Acidities in Hydroxylic Solvents

The most important hydroxylic solvent is, of course, water, but only one hydrocarbon has been both sufficiently soluble and sufficiently acidic for direct measurement in purely aqueous solution; the pK of cyclopentadiene has been found recently to be 16.0 (15.6 on a statistically corrected basis per H) [17]. A few other values have been derived from kinetic data; for example; the aqueous pK of chloroform has been estimated to be 24 [18]. However, by far the largest body of data is that derived from various aqueous organic solvent mixtures using the H_ technique [19]. Subject to the rather severe assumptions required by the H_ method and the dependence of the derived values on the choice of indicators [20], such pKs refer to the dilute aqueous standard state. Some carbon acidities derived in this manner for hydroxylic solvents are summarized in Tables 1, 2 and 3.

The principal factor responsible for the high acidity of most compounds in Tables 1-3 is the resonance stabilization of the carbanions, in which the important resonance contributions are those in which the negative charge resides on atoms more electronegative than carbon (oxygen, nitrogen). Because the charge density is concentrate largely on the heteroatom(s), interaction with the solvent, water or methanol, may well be substantial. The relative acidities presented in Tables 1-3 show that the ability of groups to acidify carbon-hydrogen bonds is in the order $NO_2 > CO > SO_2 > CO_2R > CN > H > R$, where R is an alkyl group.

Another important group of relatively acidic carbon acids is that derived from cyclopentadiene whose high acidity is well known to be associated with the 6π-electron aromatic sextet of the cyclopentadienyl anion. The influence of this carbanion aromaticity is still manifest in the benzo derivatives listed in Tables 2 and 3, fluorene, (1), fluoradene (2), and diphenylindene (3).

1a Y = H	1d $Y = COOCH_3$
1b $Y = C_6H_5$	1e $Y = CH_3$
1c Y = CN	1f $Y = CH_2C_6H_5$
	1g $Y = CH_2CH_3$
	1h $Y = CH(CH_3)_2$
	1i $Y = C(CH_3)_3$
	1j $Y = p-C_6H_4C_6H_5$

TABLE 1

p$\underline{K}_a$ data of some carbon acids in water at 25°

Carbon Acid	p$\underline{K}_a$[a]	Reference
Pentacyano-cyclopentadiene	-11	21
$CH(CN)_3$	-5.1	22
$CH(NO_2)_3$	0.2	23
$CH_2(NO_2)_2$	3.6	23
$O_2NCH_2COCH_3$	5.1	24
$CH_2(COCF_3)_2$	5.4	3
$CH(COCH_3)_3$	5.8	26
$C_6H_5CH_2NO_2$	6.8	27
$Me_2\overset{+}{S}CH_2\overset{+}{S}Me_2$	9.0	28
$CH_2(COC_6H_5)_2$	9.0	29
$CH_2(COCH_3)_2$	9.0	26
HCN	9.2	30
CH_3NO_2	10.2	31
$EtOCOCH_2COCH_3$	10.7	26
$CH_2(CN)_2$	11.2	24
$CH_2(SO_2C_6H_5)_2$	11.2	32
$CH_2(SO_2CH_3)_2$	12.5	33
$CH_2(CO_2Et)_2$	13.3	24
$C_6H_5COCH_3$	16	25
Cyclopentadiene	16.0	17
Cyclopentanone	17	33
Cyclohexanone	17	33
CH_3COCH_3	20	34
$CH_3SO_2CH_3$	23	24
CH_3CN	25	24

[a] Some of these acidity constants, particularly for the most weakly acidic carbon acids, have uncertainties of several p$\underline{K}$ units.

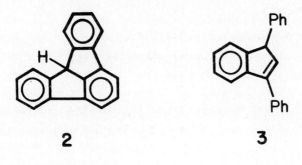

2　　　　**3**

328

TABLE 2

pK_a data of some carbon acids in aqueous sulfolane (H_)

Carbon Acid	pK$_a$ (ref. 35)
p-Nitrophenylacetonitrile	13.45
Bis-(p-nitrophenyl)methane	15.82
2-Nitrofluorene	17.59
9-Phenylfluorene, 1b	18.49

TABLE 3

pK_a data of some carbon acids in methanol

Compound	pK_a	Reference
9-Cyanofluorene, 1c	14.2	36
9-Methoxycarbonylfluorene, 1d	15.8	36
Fluoradene, 2	18.2	37
1,3-Diphenylindene, 3	19.8	37

B.   Ionic Acidities in Polar Aprotic Solvents

The most common polar aprotic solvent used for carbon acidity studies has been dimethyl sulfoxide (DMSO). Dilute solutions of carbanions in this solvent appear to involve essentially free ions or rather loose ion pairs [38,39]. Bordwell has pointed out recently that relative acidities of many compounds in DMSO are similar to gas phase acidity differences [40]. Thus, a plot of the relative gas phase acidities of several series of carbon acids such as CH_3CN, $PhCH_2CN$, and $CH_2(CN)_2$ against relative DMSO acidities show linear correlations with slopes near unity. It appears that the solvation of highly delocalized carbanions (e.g., $CH(CN)_2^-$, $PhCHCN^-$ and CH_2CN^-) by DMSO is nonspecific and relatively constant [12,40].

Several workers have established acidity scales in various DMSO solutions using the H_ technique [41-46]. All of the hydrocarbons studied by this method are referenced approximately to the aqueous standard state. These values are presented in Table 4. Kuhn and Rewicki [51] have measured the pKs of a number of highly conjugated fluorene derivatives in a variety of DMSO systems and a hexamethyl-phosphoric triamide (HMPT) system using the H_ technique. Their

TABLE 4

pK_a of carbon acids in DMSO mixtures

Compound	DMSO-EtOH	DMSO-MeOH	Aq. DMSO	CsCHA pK per H	LiCHA pK per H
	Reference				
	42,44	41,43	41,44 45,46	47	48
Malononitrile	(11.14)[a]	-	-	-	-
9-Cyanofluorene, 1c	11.41	-	-	-	-
9-Methoxycarbonyl-fluorene, 1d	12.88	-	-	-	-
Tris(p-nitrophenyl)methane	14.32	-	-	-	-
4-Cyano-9-phenylfluorene	-	-	15.40	-	-
4,4'-Dinitrodiphenyl-methane	15.85	-	-	-	-
7-Phenyl-7-H-benzo[c]-fluorene, 7	-	-	16.60	-	-
2,4'-Dinitrodiphenyl-methane	17.38	-	-	-	-
3,4'-Dinitrodiphenyl-methane	17.62	-	-	-	-
9-(m-Chlorophenyl)-fluorene	-	-	17.66	-	-
9-(m-Trifluoromethyl-phenyl)fluorene	-	-	17.69	-	-
2-Nitrofluorene	-	-	17.96	-	-
9-(p-Chlorophenyl)-fluorene	-	-	18.10	-	-
9-p-Biphenylyl-fluorene, 1j	-	-	18.21	-	-
9-(m-Anisyl)fluorene	-	-	18.47	-	-
9-Phenylfluorene, 1b	18.59	-	(18.59)[a]	(18.49)[a]	(18.49)[a]
9-(m-Tolyl)fluorene	-	-	18.84	-	-
2-Cyanofluorene	-	-	18.96	-	-
9-(p-Tolyl)fluorene	-	-	18.96	-	-
9-(p-Anisyl)fluorene	-	-	19.01	-	-
9-(1-Naphthyl)fluorene	-	-	19.2	-	-
Phenalene, 8	-	-	19.45	-	-
9-(p-N,N-Dimethyl-aminophenyl)fluorene	-	-	19.61	-	-
7-H-Benzo[c]fluorene, 9	-	-	19.62	19.75	19.68

TABLE 4

p$\underline{K}_a$ of carbon acids in DMSO mixtures

Compound	DMSO-EtOH	DMSO-MeOH	Aq. DMSO	CsCHA pK per H	LiCHA pK per H
	Reference				
	42,44	41,43	41,44 45,46	47	48
Indene	-	18.2	-	19.93	19.68
11-H-Benzo[a]-fluorene, 10	-	-	-	20.35	20.27
2-Bromofluorene	-	-	20.56	-	-
2-Chlorofluorene	-	-	20.59	-	-
9-Benzylfluorene, 1f	-	-	21.20	21.17[b]	-
9-H-Benzo[def]fluorene, 6	-	19.5	21.79	22.93	22.90
9-Methylfluorene, 1e	-	-	21.80	22.33[b]	22.55[b]
Fluorene, 1a	21.0	20.5	22.10, 20.5	23.04	22.85[b]
9-Ethylfluorene, 1g	-	-	22.22	22.60[b]	22.96[b]
9-Methoxyfluorene	-	-	22.36	-	-
9-Isopropylfluorene, 1h	-	-	22.70	23.20[b]	23.75[b]
10-H-Benzo[b]fluorene, 11	-	19.5	-	23.47	23.46
Tri-p-biphenylylmethane	-	22.8	-	-	-
9-$\underline{t}$-Butylfluorene, 1i	-	-	23.41	24.25[b]	24.82[b]
9-Phenylxanthene, 12b	-	24.2	24.3	28.5	-
p-Biphenylyldiphenyl-methane	-	25.3	-	30.20	-
Xanthene, 12a	-	27.1	-	-	-
4-Benzylbiphenyl	-	27.2	-	31.82[c]	-
Triphenylmethane	-	27.2	27.2	31.45[d]	-
9-Methyldihydroanthra-cene, 13b	-	27.7	-	-	-
Diphenylmethane	-	-	-	33.38	-

[a]Reference compound. [b]Ref. 49. [c]Ref. 97. [d]Ref. 50.

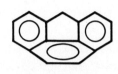

4

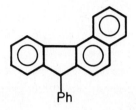

5

6

7

Ph

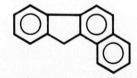

8

9

10

11

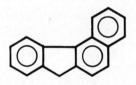

O

H Y

12a Y = H
12b Y = C$_6$H$_5$
12c Y = SC$_6$H$_5$

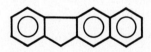

H$_2$

H Y

13a Y = H
13b Y = CH$_3$
13c Y = C$_6$H$_5$
13d Y = p-C$_6$H$_4$C$_6$H$_5$
13e Y = Cs

results are given in Table 5. Within the limits of the H_ approximations, these pKs refer to the dilute aqueous solution standard state;
however, see ref. 45 for additional limiations. Nevertheless, the
H_ method with solvent mixtures involving water and alcohols is now
much less important as a measure of carbon acidities, not only because
of the limitations and assumptions involved in the procedure, but
also because of the development of accurate pK values in polar aprotic
solvents, particularly dimethyl sulfoxide, DMSO.

Ritchie and Uschold [36,52] applied potentiometric titration
of the acids with standard cesium dimsyl to determine pKs with a
DMSO standard state. Some of their values for relatively acidic
carbon acids are summarized in Table 6.

More recently, Bordwell's laboratory has been determining many
carbon acidities in DMSO using the carbon acid indicator method of
eq. 3 [12,38,40,53-66]. These determinations supplant earlier
results. A number of these values are summarized in Table 7 with
emphasis on carbanion conjugate bases; Bordwell has published more
complete summaries of nitro compounds [65] and acetophenones [66].
The measurements of the Bordwell laboratories constitute the most
complete collection of ionic carbon acidity values available for a
single solvent. They are "absolute" values with DMSO as the standard
state. To emphasize this point, we refer to these values as "pK_{-DMSO}".
Nevertheless, the magnitudes of pK_{-DMSO} for carbon acids with delocalized conjugate bases are rather close to corresponding measures with
an aqueous solution standard state. In many of the summaries in
Table 7 as well as preceding Tables, comparisons with the CHA system
are included where available.

Shatenshtein and his collaborators in Moscow have also determined
a number of equilibrium carbon acidities in DMSO solution using the
indicator method of eq. 3. Their values are generally referenced to
an assumed value of 18.5 for the pK of 9-phenylfluorene; hence, the
absolute values differ from the pK_{-DMSO} values of Bordwell. Relative
values, however, are quite close. For example, Shatenshtein's pK
values [67] for 9 fluorene and polyarylmethane compounds are 0.5 ± 0.2
units higher than the pK_{-DMSO} of Bordwell. The Russian group has also
reported equilibrium DMSO acidities on a similar basis for acetylenes
[68], nitriles and esters [69,70], and a number of organophosphorus
compounds [71]. The group of Faleev [72] has also reported DMSO
acidities of nitroalkanes.

TABLE 5

pK_a of "very acidic" hydrocarbon acids. (Ref. 51).

Compound	DMSO/- HOAc/NaOAc	DMSO/- $N(C_3H_7)_3$	DMSO[a] EtOH/NaOEt	HMPT[a] $N(C_3H_7)_3$
	<7.0	-	-	-
	8.2	-	-	-
	9.1	-	-	-
	9.8	-	-	
	10.0	-	-	
	10.4	10.4	-	

TABLE 5

pK_a of "very acidic" hydrocarbon acids. (Ref. 51).

Compound	DMSO/- HOAc/NaOAc	DMSO/- $N(C_3H_7)_3$	DMSO[a] EtOH/NaOEt	HMPT[a] $N(C_3H_7)_3$
(structure: bis-fluorenylidene pentadienylidene)	11.2	-	-	-
(structure: dibenzofluorenyl-fluorenylidene methine)	11.2	11.1	-	-
9-Cyanofluorene, 1c	(11.4)[b]	(11.4)[b]	-	-
(structure: difluorenylidene propenyl)	12.3	12.3	-	-
(structure: diacenaphthylidene methine)	13.7	13.4	-	-
(structure: tricyclic fluoranthene-type)	14.0	13.8	-	-

TABLE 5

pK_a of "very acidic" hydrocarbon acids. (Ref. 51).

Compound	DMSO/- HOAc/NaOAc	DMSO/- $N(C_3H_7)_3$	DMSO[a] EtOH/NaOEt	HMPT[a] $N(C_3H_7)_3$
(9-phenylfluorenylidene-fluorene structure)	14.1	13.9	–	14.0
(fluorenyl-CH=acenaphthylene structure)	14.2	14.0	–	–
(difluorenylidenemethane =CH structure)	14.4	14.2	–	14.2[d]
(=CH–C(Ph)=CH– bis-fluorene structure)	14.9	14.7	–	14.7
(9-phenyl dibenzofluorene structure)	–	–	14.8	15.9
(dibenzofluorenyl-CH=indene structure)	~16.0	16.3	–	16.1

TABLE 5

pK_a of "very acidic" hydrocarbon acids. (Ref. 51).

Compound	DMSO/-HOAc/NaOAc	DMSO/-N(C$_3$H$_7$)$_3$	DMSO[a] EtOH/NaOEt	HMPT[a] N(C$_3$H$_7$)$_3$
	-	-	16.8	-
	-	-	17.3	-
	-	-	17.5	-
	-	-	19.1	-
	-	-	21.4	-

[a] pK_a values relative to pK_a of 9-phenylfluorene = 18.5.
[b] Assumed standard.

TABLE 6

pK_a data of carbon acids in DMSO using potentiometric methods

Compound	pK_{DMSO}
9-Cyanofluorene, 1c	8.4
1,3-Difluorenylidenepropane, 4	8.7
9-Methoxycarbonylfluorene, 1d	10.3
Fluoradene, 2	10.5
Malononitrile	11.0
Tris-(p-nitrophenyl)methane	12.2
Nitroethane	13.9

TABLE 7

Bordwell's acidities of carbon acids in DMSO, 25°.

Compound	pK_{DMSO}[a,b]	pK_{CsCHA} (per H)
Hydrocarbons (Ref. 39, 40, 57, 58, 59)		
9-Phenylfluorene, 1b	17.9	(18.49)[c]
Cyclopentadiene	18.1	16.25[d]
Indene	20.1	19.93[e]
9-H-Benz[def]fluorene, 6	22.4	22.93[e]
Fluorene, 1a	22.6	23.04[e]
10-H-Benz[b]fluorene, 11	23.2	23.47[e]
1,1,3-Triphenylpropene	25.9	26.49[e]
9-Phenylxanthene, 12b	27.7	28.49[e]
Phenylacetylene	28.7	
p-Biphenylyldiphenylmethane	29.4	30.17[e]
Xanthene,[f] 12a	30.0	
Triphenylmethane	30.6	31.45[g]
Diphenylmethane	32.3	33.38[g]
Toluene	42[h]	(42.2)[i]

TABLE 7 (continued)

Bordwell's acidities of carbon acids in DMSO, 25°.

Compound	pK_{DMSO} [a,b]	pK_{CsCHA} per H
Nitriles (Ref. 40, 56, 57, 60)		
$CH_2(CN)_2$	11.1	
$CH_3CH(CN)_2$	12.4	
Ph_2CHCN	17.5	
$PhSCH_2CN$	20.8	
$PhCH_2CN$	21.9	
$PhCHCNCH_3$	23.0	
$PhOCH_2CN$	28.1	
CH_3CN	31.3	
CH_3CH_2CN	32.5	
Sulfur Compounds (Ref. 55, 56, 57, 59, 60, 61)		
$PhSCH(SO_2Ph)_2$	5.6	
$PhSCH(SO_2Et)_2$	7.1	
$PhSCH_2SO_2CF_2$	11.0	
9-(Phenylthio)fluorene	15.4	
$PhSCH_2SO_2Ph$	20.3	
9-(Phenylthio)xanthene, 12c	22.8	
$(PhS)_3CH$	22.8	
$(PhS)_2CHPh$	23.0	
Ph_2CHSPh	26.7	
$PhCH(SCH_2CH_2CH_3)_2$	29.2	
4-Methyl-2,6,7-Trithiabicyclo-[2.2.2]octane	30.5	27.3
2-Phenyldithiane	30.7	29.6
$PhSCH_2SPh$	30.8	
$PhCH_2SPh$	30.8	
$(CH_3CH_2S)_3CH$	31.3	
$CH_2(SO_2Ph)_2$	12.2	
$CH_3CH(SO_2Ph)_2$	14.35	
$CH_2(SO_2Et)_2$	14.4	
$CH_3CH(SO_2Et)_2$	16.7	
$PhCH_2SO_2CF_3$	14.6	

TABLE 7 (continued)

Bordwell's acidities of carbon acids in DMSO, 25°.

Compound	pK_{DMSO} [a,b]	pK_{CsCHA} per H
$CH_3SO_2CF_3$	18.76	
$Ph_2PCH_2SO_2Ph$	20.2	
$CH_3CH_2SO_2CF_3$	20.4	
$(CH_3)_2CHSO_2CF_3$	21.80	
$Ph_2CHSO_2CHPh_2$	21.9	
Ph_2CHSO_2Ph	22.3	
$PhCH_2SO_2Ph$	23.4	22.5 [j]
$PhCH_2SO_2CH_2Ph$	23.5	
$PhOCH_2SO_2Ph$	25.7	
$CycloC_3H_5SO_2CF_3$	26.60	
$PhSCH_2SO_2Ph$	26.8	
$CH_3OCH_2SO_2Ph$	27.2	
CH_3SO_2Ph	29.04	27.18 [j]
$CH_3CH_2SO_2Ph$	31.0	29.13
$CH_3SO_2CH_3$	31.1	
$(CH_3)_2CHSO_2Ph$	32	
$Cyclo-C_3H_5SO_2Ph$	32	
$(CH_3CH_2)_2SO_2$	32.8	
$Ph_2CHSOPh$	24.9	
$PhCH_2SOPh$	25.6	
$PhCH_2SOCH_3$	29.1	
CH_3SOCH_3	35.1	

Substituted Fluorenes (Ref. 39, 59, 60, 62, 63)

Compound	pK_{DMSO} [a,b]	
$2-(CH_3)_2N$	24.2	
$2-CH_3$	23.1	
$2-CH_3O$	22.75	
H	22.6	
2-F	21.0	
$2-CH_3S$	21.65	
2-PhS	20.5	
2-Cl	20.25	

TABLE 7 (continued)

Bordwell's acidities of carbon acids in DMSO, 25°

Compound	pK_{DMSO}[a,b]	pK_{CsCHA} per H
2-Br	20.0	
2-CH$_3$SO	19.75	
2-PhCO	19.55	
2-Et$_2$NSO$_2$	18.8	
2-CH$_3$SO$_2$	18.5	
2-CN	18.2	
2-PhSO$_2$	18.1	
2,7-(CH$_3$O)$_2$	22.95	
2,7-(PhS)$_2$	18.5	
2,7-Br$_2$	17.9	
2,7-(Et$_2$NSO$_2$)$_2$	15.6	
2,7-(CN)$_2$	14.6	
9-CN	8.3	
9-COOCH$_3$	10.3	
9-SO$_2$C(CH$_3$)$_3$	10.55	
9-SO$_2$Ph	11.55	
9-SO$_2$CH(CH$_3$)$_2$	11.7	
9-SO$_2$CH$_2$CH$_3$	12.3	
9-SO$_2$CH$_3$	12.75	
9-SPh	15.4	
9-SC$_6$H$_4$CH$_3$-p	15.9	
9-SCH(CH$_3$)$_2$	16.9	
9-SCH$_2$CH$_3$	17.5	
9-Ph	17.9	18.49[c]
9-SCH$_3$	18.0	
9-OPh	19.9	
9-CH$_2$C(CH$_3$)$_3$	20.3	
9-CH$_2$CH(CH$_3$)$_2$	21.6	
9-OCH$_3$	22.1	
9-CH$_2$CH$_2$CH$_3$	22.2	
9-CH$_3$	22.34	22.33[k]
9-CH$_2$CH$_3$	22.6	22.60[k]
9-CH(CH$_3$)$_2$	23.2	23.3[k]
9-C(CH$_3$)$_3$	24.35	25.25[k]

TABLE 7 (continued)

Bordwell's acidities of carbon acids in DMSO, 25°.

Compound	pK_{DMSO}[a,b]	pK_{CsCHA} per H
9-Ph-2-SO$_2$Ph	13.8	
9-SC$_6$H$_4$CH$_3$(p)-2-SO$_2$Ph	11.9	
Substituted Toluenes (Ref. 64)		
p-NO$_2$	20.4	
p-SO$_2$CF$_3$	24.0	
p-PhCO	26.9	
p-PhSO$_2$	29.8	
p-CN	30.8	
Misc. (Ref. 55)		
Ph$_2$PCH$_2$PPh$_2$	29.9	31.07[l]

[a] pK_a values are not statistically corrected. [b] For a summary of Bordwell's results, see ref. 12. For summaries of nitro compounds and substituted acetophenones, not listed here, see refs. 65 and 66, resp. Note that because of a slight revision of the scale, earlier published values differ somewhat from more recent publications; compare ref. 39. [c] Reference standard. [d] Ref. 17. [e] Ref. 47. [f] This compound is an ether but is listed here for convenience. [g] Ref. 50. [h] Estimated. [i] Ref. 27. [j] Ref. 67. [k] Ref. 49. [l] Ref. 68.

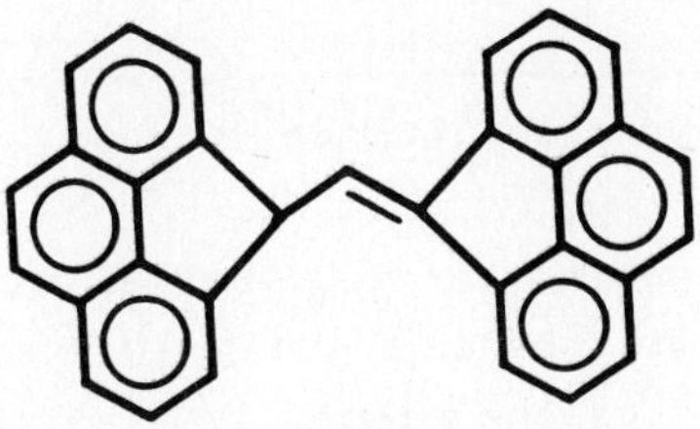

14

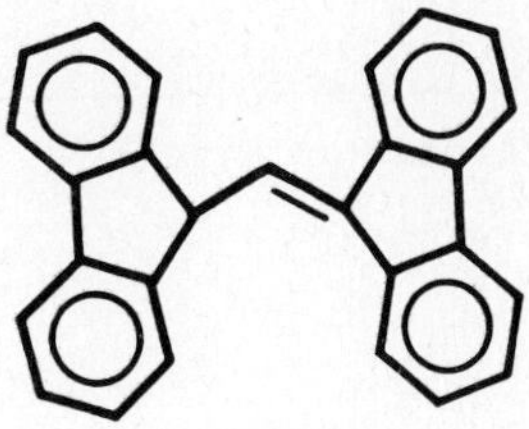

15

C. Measurement of Ionic Acidities by Electrochemical Methods

    1. Breslow's Electrochemical Method

An ingenious approach to the measurement of carbon acidities has been developed by Breslow and co-workers [73] and makes use of the thermodynamic cycle shown in eq. 7.

$$RH \xrightarrow{1} ROH \xrightarrow{2} R^+ \xrightarrow{3} R^\cdot \xrightarrow{4} R^- \ (\rightarrow RH) \tag{7}$$

From the potentials required in the 1-electron reductions of steps 3 and 4, and thermodynamic data applicable to steps 1 and 2, several pK_a values have been calculated (Table 8).

TABLE 8

pK_a determinations by electrochemical reduction in polar aprotic solvents. Ref. 73

Compound	pK_a (calcd)
Tris-(p-chlorophenyl)methane	28.9 ± 2
Triphenylmethane	31.5[a]
Tri-p-anisylmethane	34.6 ± 2
Tris-(p-dimethylaminophenyl)-methane	40.3 ± 2
Cycloheptatriene	36 ± 3
Triphenylcyclopropene	50 ± 4
Toluene	41 ± 1[b]
Trimethylcyclopropene	62 ± 5
Isobutane	~ 71

[a] Reference standard.   [b] R. Breslow, personal communication.

Values for delocalized carbanions appear to parallel the DMSO values but the derived pK_a values for localized carbanions are less simple to interpret. Breslow describes the electrolyte solution in the neighborhood of the electrode as "fused salt-like" and the standard state to which the pK's refer is not yet clear. Nevertheless, this valuable approach allows the determination of the acidity of hydrocarbons for which direct measurement of pK_a is impossible as well as the pK_a of a hydrogen which is not the most acidic in the molecule.

2. Polarographic Acidity Scale

A correlation between the cathodic reduction parameters of organomercury compounds, R_2Hg, and the pK_a values of the corresponding acids, RH, has been described by Reutov, Butin and Beletskaya [6,74].

$$R_2Hg + 2\ e^- \xrightarrow{\ \alpha E_{\frac{1}{2}}\ } 2R^- + Hg \tag{8}$$

$$\Delta(\alpha \underline{n}\ E_{\frac{1}{2}}) = \rho \cdot \Delta p\underline{K}_a \tag{9}$$

The method has the merit of allowing the measurement of acidities over a wide range of pK_a values in a polar solvent, even in one that is more acidic than the RH acid. Despite a number of limitations, eq. 9 (where $\Delta\alpha\underline{n}$ is the change in electrochemical transfer coefficient, $E_{\frac{1}{2}}$ is the half-wave reduction potential and ρ is a constant) was found to have apparent validity, and a polarographic acidity scale which includes RH acids having pK_a values of 7-60 has been developed (Table 9). However, many of the $p\underline{K}$ values used for their correlation were based on the Cram MSAD scale [2] which is now known to be seriously in error, especially at the low acidity end. There is also the question whether the derived values for localized carbanion systems are more appropriate as polar aprotic ionic or as ion pair values (vide infra).

TABLE 9
Polarographic acidity scale for some carbon acids

Compound	$p\underline{K}_a$ (ref. 6,75)	Compound	$p\underline{K}_a$ (ref. 6,75)
$(CF_3)_3CH$	7	$CH_3CO_2CH_3$	24
$HCBr_3$	9	$PhSO_2CH_3$	25
HCN	12	HCF_3	26
$HCCl_3$	15	C_6Cl_5H	31
Cyclopentadiene	16	Thiophene	35
$PhC\equiv CH$	19	Toluene	35
$F_2C=CFH$	20	Benzene	37
$\underline{t}$-BuCOCH$_3$	21	Methane	57
$CF_3CH_2CF_3$	22	Propane	60
C_6F_5H	23		

III. ION PAIR ACIDITIES

A. Introduction

The acidity measurements of carbon acids in aqueous and DMSO solutions provide an important body of knowledge on the effect of structure on the stability of carbanions. Nevertheless, most ionic organic reactions as actually performed in the laboratory are actually reactions of ion pairs. Studies of the effect of structure on the stabilities of ion pairs are an important complement to the more ionic studies of the previous section. Such ion pairs provide a useful bridge to the chemistry of organometallic compounds, especially of the alkali and alkaline earth metals [75]. Relative ion pair acidities, for example, are closely related to metallation reactions [11]. We shall also see that for some systems the role of solvent in stabilizing carbanions by hydrogen-bonding is similar to the electrostatic stabilization by the gegenion in the ion pair. There are important qualitative differences for delocalized and localized carbanions that lead to important tools for distinguishing these classes.

The study of ion pair equilibria (eq. 5) is often complicated by additional equilibria. For example, the solvent can participate as in eq. 10:

$$SH + R'H + R^-M^+ \underset{\overrightarrow{}}{\overset{K_1}{\rightleftharpoons}} SH + R'^-M^+ + RH \underset{\overrightarrow{}}{\overset{K_2}{\rightleftharpoons}} S^-M^+ + R'H + RH \quad (10)$$

As the effective pK of a hydrocarbon approaches that of the solvent, K_2 becomes increasingly important and can complicate the determination of the desired K_1. For hydrocarbon pKs higher than that of the solvent the amounts of carbanion salts present may be too low to measure (solvent leveling effect).

In principle, one can extend the range of carbon acidities measured by using solvents of higher pK. In practice, this procedure encounters important limitations. Solvents of high pK, such as hydrocarbons, have low ionizing power or dielectric constant and promote aggregation of ionic species. Equilibrium constants measured for such systems will not reflect K_{ip} (eq. 5) or K_1 (eq. 10) unless the dissociation constants for the aggregated species are the same for each carbon acid studied [10].

Even among monomeric ion pairs, the nature of the ion pair itself can vary with the carbanion, the cation and the solvent [76]. Ion pairs may be usefully dissected into contact, R^-M^+, and solvent-separated, $R^- \| M^+$, species, but even the solvent-separated ion pairs can vary in the degree of association or looseness. Relative ion pair acidities can be related in a clearcut fashion to structural effects or to corresponding ionic acidities only if the ion pairs involved are of the same type.

The first studies of ion pair equilibrium acidities were done by Conant and Wheland [77] and later by McEwen [78]. In their method, a hydrocarbon was mixed with an organosodium or organopotassium salt in ether or benzene (solvents of low dielectric constants in which ion association is important) and the position of equilibrium was estimated colorimetrically or by quenching with carbon dioxide assuming that the rates of carbonation were much greater than the rates of metal exchange. The results obtained for "p$\underline{K}$s" by Conant and Wheland and by McEwen are shown in Table 10 and referred to as pK_{-ether}. These values are compared with the p$\underline{K}$ values in cyclohexylamine for comparison. We see that despite the crudity of the methods of four decades ago, the results of Conant, Wheland and McEwen compare rather well with modern ion pair acidities.

Other RM equilibria have been used to study the acidities of hydrocarbon acids. Applequist and O'Brien [80] studied the equilibria in eq. 11 in ether and presented an order of carbanion stabilities.

$$RLi + R'X \rightleftharpoons RX + R'Li \tag{11}$$

The principal limitation of this method is the known aggregation of organolithium compounds in ether. Moreover, the degree and nature of the aggregation depends on structure; hence, this method, although important in principle is limited in practice.

Dessy and Salinger [81] studied the equilibria between organo-magnesium and organomercury salts in THF as shown in eq. 12. Here, the assumption was made that the more electronegative group (the more stable carbanion) is preferentially bonded to the more electro-positive metal.

$$R_2Hg + R_2'Mg \; \underset{}{\overset{\underline{K}_n}{\rightleftharpoons}} \; R_2Mg + R_2'Hg \tag{12}$$

The foregoing results were integrated by Cram [2] into his so-called MSAD (McEwen-Streitwieser-Applequist-Dessy) scale of carbon acidities. This scale is a mixture of ionic and ion-pair acidities but during the late 1960s served as a useful summary of the know-ledge of a decade and a half ago. Because of the importance of this scale in the development of the field and for comparison purposes

346

TABLE 10

p$\underline{K}_a$ data in ether of Conant, Wheland and McEwen

Compound	p$\underline{K}_{ether}$[a]	p$\underline{K}_{ether}$[b]	p$\underline{K}_{CsCHA}$ per H	p$\underline{K}_{LiCHA}$ per H
Phenylacetylene	22	21	-	23.20[c]
Indene	22	21	19.93[d]	20.24[e]
9-Phenylfluorene 1b	22	21	(18.49)[f]	(18.49)[f]
9-(1-Naphthyl)-fluorene	-	21	-	-
Fluorene 1a	24	25	23.04[d]	22.85[g]
Xanthene 12a	26	29	-	-
9-Phenylxanthene 12b	-	29	-	-
p-Biphenylyldi-phenylmethane	28	31	30.20[d]	-
Triphenylmethane	28.4	33	31.45[b]	-
1-Naphthyldiphenyl-methane	28.4	34	-	-
Diphenylmethane	29.5	35	33.38[h]	-
1,1-Diphenylpropene	30.0	36	-	-
Cumene	30.5-31.0	37	-	-

[a]Based on approximate equilibrium constants for RH + R'M = R'H + RM, M = K or Na, with the p$\underline{K}_a$ of the standard compound, acetophenone, taken as 20; ref. 77.

[b]Organosodium or -potassium equilibria in ether relative to p$\underline{K}_a$ (methanol) = 16; ref. 78.

[c]Ref. 79. [d]Ref. 47. [e]Ref. 48. [f]Standard. [g]Ref. 49. [h]Ref. 50.

it is reproduced in Table 11. Note that the scale is probably somewhat compressed at the upper (low-acidity) end.

A method for determining the p$\underline{K}$'s of weak carbon acids was
suggested by Schaeffer [82] based on a relation of chemical shift
differences between carbon acids and their lithium salts versus p$\underline{K}$s
in ether or THF. Unfortunately, this procedure groups together
localized and delocalized carbanions and is additionally complicated
by aggregation effects; hence, the derived p$\underline{K}$ values cannot be taken
seriously.

TABLE 11
Cram's MSAD scale (ref. 2; reproduced with permission)

Compound	pK_a	Compound	pK_a
Fluoradene	11	Ethylene	36.5
Cyclopentadiene	15	Benzene	37
9-Phenylfluorene	18.5	Cumene	37
Indene	18.5	Triptycene	38
Phenylacetylene	18.5	Cyclopropane	39
Fluorene	22.9	Methane	40
Acetylene	25	Ethane	42
1,1,3-Triphenyl-propene	26.5	Cyclobutane	43
Triphenylmethane	32.5	Neopentane	44
Toluene	35	Propane(2-H)	44
Propene	35.5	Cyclopentane	44
Cycloheptatriene	36	Cyclohexane	45

B. Ion pair acidities in cyclohexylamine

1. Definition

In this laboratory, equilibrium ion pair acidities have been measured in the solvent cyclohexylamine according to eq. 13:

$$RH + Cs^+R'^- \ \overset{K}{\rightleftharpoons} \ R'H + Cs^+R^- \tag{13}$$

The equilibrium constant values thus obtained are converted for convenience to absolute pK's for an appropriate aqueous standard state based on the value of 18.49 for 9-phenylfluorene which had been measured by H_- techniques in aqueous sulfolane [35]. Thus, we refer to such values as pK_{CsCHA} as defined by eq. 14. A similar definition applies to lithium salts and symbolized as pK_{LiCHA}.

$$pK_{CsCHA} = 18.49 - \log K \text{ (eq. 13)} \tag{14}$$
for R'H = 9-phenylfluorene

We first discuss the significance of such pK expressions and relate them to thermodynamic pKs.

Ionic acidities as in aqueous solution refer to the equilibrium constant expressed as eq. 15:

348

$$K_a = [R^-][H^+]/[RH] \tag{15}$$

Brackets in this equation refer to activities and $[H^+]$ refers to the activity of the protonated solvent. The essential point here is that K_a has units, conventionally moles per liter or M. Since the pK_a involves the logarithm, the value of pK_a depends on the units used. Since the conventional units are so universal this limitation entails no problems in practice.

The corresponding acidity in cyclohexylamine would be expressed as eq. 16:

$$RH \rightleftharpoons R^- + C_6H_{11}NH_3^+ \tag{16}$$

However, cyclohexylamine is so nonpolar that free ion concentrations are exceedingly small. Ion pair dissociation constants for lithium salts in cyclohexylamine are about 10^{-10} M [83]. The related ion pair acidity refers to eq. 17:

$$RH \rightleftharpoons R^- C_6H_{11}NH_3^+ \tag{17}$$

The corresponding equilibrium constant, $K=[R^-C_6H_{11}NH_3^+]/[RH]$, is unitless and the resulting pK_a value does not depend on the concentration units used. Some values of such "true" equilibrium ion pair pKs are summarized in Table 12.

TABLE 12
Ion pair pK values in cyclohexylamine

Hydrocarbon	pK (ref. 84)[a]
Fluoradene, 2	0.44
1,1,3,3-Bis(4,5-phenanthrylene)-propene, 14	1.38
1,1,3,3-Bis(biphenylene)propene, 15	2.05
1,3-Diphenylindene, 3	2.21

[a] Ion pair acidity for eq. 17.

The hydrocarbons in Table 12 are all relatively acidic and form colored solutions in cyclohexylamine because of the formation of highly colored carbanion ion pairs. The linear change in absorbance with concentration shows that the ionized species are present predominantly as ion pairs [84]. The ion pair dissociation constants are probably comparable to those of lithium salts, about 10^{-11} $\underline{M}$; hence, the p$\underline{K}$s of 0-2 in Table 12 correspond to ionic acidities expressed in the usual p$\underline{K}$ definition of 11-13. These numbers are rather similar to the ionic aqueous p$\underline{K}$s of these hydrocarbons as determined by H_- methods of about 14 (Table 5). That is, the approximate compensation of the greater basicity of cyclohexylamine by its reduced polarity results in net ionic acidities comparable to those in water itself. Moreover, these p$\underline{K}$ values are also comparable to the p$\underline{K}_{CsCHA}$ values (Table 13) available for three of the hydrocarbons in Table 12. Thus, "p$\underline{K}_{CsCHA}$" values are actually of the same magnitude as ionic acidities in cyclohexylamine, at least for highly conjugated hydrocarbons. Ion pair dissociation constants for highly delocalized carbanion ion pairs are not expected to change greatly, but some specific structural effects are known [9].

Cyclohexylamine, CHA, was chosen originally in our studies because of the several readily available and easily purified amines studied it alone dissolved its own lithium salt in reasonable concentrations. Its cesium salt is also soluble. It has several other important advantages. It is a good solvent for many organic compounds. As discussed in the chapter by E. Buncel and B. C. Menon in this volume, CHA solvates alkali metal cations much as does THF. It appears not to solvate cesium cations strongly; hence, cesium salts exist primarily as contact ion pairs in CHA [47,48,85]. It is a sufficiently weak acid that the involvement of solvent in competing equilibria as in eq. 10 is not important for many compounds. The equilibrium constant in eq. 18 has been found to be 68.8 ± 2.9 $\underline{M}^{-1}$ ($\underline{K}$=[RCs]/[RH][CsCHA]) for R=$\underline{p}$-biphenylylmethyl [86].

$$C_6H_{11}NH^-Cs^+ + RH \overset{K}{\rightleftharpoons} R^-Cs^+ + C_6H_{11}NH_2 \tag{18}$$

This number is equivalent to an effective p$\underline{K}_{CsCHA}$ for CHA of 41.6. In practice, carbon acids can be studied with p$\underline{K}_{CsCHA}$ up to about 38 before involvement of solvent becomes important; that is, it is possible to study quantitatively the equilibrium acidities of whole groups of compounds not feasible in the DMSO system.

Spectral studies in the visible region involve generally rather dilute solutions. Concentrations of cesium salts are generally on the order of 10^{-4} $\underline{M}$; hence, aggregation does not appear to be important. Studies of a number of organocesium compounds also show adherance to Beer's law over a concentration range of at least 10-fold and without change in the position of λ_{max}.

TABLE 13

pKs and Spectral Data of Cyclopentadienyl Derivatives at 34°

Compound	$\lambda_{max}(\varepsilon)$CsCHA	pK_{CsCHA} per H	$\lambda_{max}(\varepsilon)$LiCHA	pK_{LiCHA} per H
1,1,3,3-Bis(4,5-phenanthrylene)-propene, 14	552(112,000)[a]	12.96[b]	544(139,000)	11.91[b,c]
1,1,3,3-Bis(biphenylene)-propene, 15	553(141,000)[a]	13.47[b]	556(95,200)	12.50[b,c]
1,3-Diphenylindene, 3	384(21,500) 428(21,850)	13.62	376(22,200) 443(25,900)	13.62[b,c]
1,10-(o-Phenylene)-7,12-dihydropleiadene, 5	392(14,100) 446(11,350)	15.36[b]		
8,8-Dimethyl-8,12b-dihydrobenz[a]fluoranthene, 16	470(shoulder) 500(3062) 528(2538)	15.45[d]		
7-Phenyl-7-H-benz[c]-fluorene, 7	382(19,500) 446(1900) 496(4500)	15.67[b]		
Cyclopentadiene		16.25[e]		
14-H-5,6-Dihydrotribenz-[a,cd,h]azulene, 17	372(14,700) 402(24,000) 445(2285) 478(2600) 516(1677)	17.26[b]		
9-Phenylfluorene, 1b	398(22,300) 456(1738) 484(1677) 516(1677)	(18.49)[f]	452(1950) 487(2280) 520(1690)	(18.49)[f]
7-H-Benz[c]fluorene, 9	394(5070) 483(2720) 514(2250)	19.75[h]	397(4800) 455(2140) 465(2060) 477(2430) 487(2600) 508(1950) 519(2040)	19.68[g]
Indene	372(1140)	19.93[h]	371(1263)	20.24[g]
11-H-Benz[a]fluorene, 10	426(8780)	20.35[h]	425(8140)	20.27[g]
9-Benzylfluorene, 1f	476(1064) 500(1425) 536(1079)	21.27[i]		
9-Methylfluorene, 1e	477(953) 505(1170) 541(819)	22.33[i]	481(113) 513(1353) 552(994)	22.60[i]
9-Ethylfluorene, 1g	476(890) 505(1107) 541(775)	22.60[i]	481(1031) 513(1353)	22.96[i]

TABLE 13 (continued)

pKs and Spectral Data of Cyclopentadienyl Derivatives at 34°

Compound	$\lambda_{max}(\epsilon)$CsCHA	pK$_{CsCHA}$ per H	$\lambda_{max}(\epsilon)$LiCHA	pK$_{LiCHA}$ per H
9-H-Benz[def]fluorene, 6	7100[j]	22.93[h]	505(7360)	22.90[g]
Fluorene, 1a	477(984) 472(1200) 504(870)	23.04[h]	452(1080) 477(1300) 510(827)	22.85[i]
10-H-Benz[b]fluorene, 11	418(19,300) 599(1560) 648(1230)	23.47[h]	420(22,000) 605(1710) 657(1290)	23.46[g]
2,7-Diethylfluorene	464(1100)	23.55		
9-Isopropylfluorene, 1h	476(910) 504(1124) 540(769)	23.20[i]	481(1020) 513(1328) 552(916)	23.75[i]
2,7-Di-t-butylfluorene	460(1062)	24.04		
9-t-Butylfluorene, 1i	471(925) 496(1164) 532(795)	24.25[i]	476(1017) 508(1293) 546(903)	24.82[i]

[a]Extinction coefficients for DMSO (ref. 90). Accurate values are not available in CHA because of the formation of dianions. [b]Ref. 84. [c]Based on pK of diphenylindene=13.62 from results in CsCHA-CHA. [d]Ref. 91. [e]Ref. 17. [f]Reference value for aqueous standard state based on H_ studies. [g]Ref. 48. [h]Ref. 47. [i]Ref. 49. [j]This value was redetermined, and is a correction to the previously published value. [k]C. S. Chu, unpublished results.

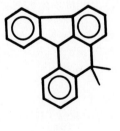

16

17

352

2. Experimental Results

Equilibrium constants for eqs. 13 and 14 are now available for a large variety of carbon acids. The experimental procedure makes use of CHA solutions prepared in a glove box with a recirculating atmosphere of helium or argon or on a vacuum line with careful exclusion of air and moisture using known amounts of the carbon acid and solvent and amounts of lithium or cesium cyclohexylamide such that measurable amounts of all four components are present. The concentrations of the two anions at equilibrium are determined from the visible spectra of the solutions [87]. This technique applies generally to highly conjugated hydrocarbons such as fluorene and polyarylmethane derivatives whose carbanions have electronic transitions in the visible region. For substrates without visible absorption spectra, that is, "invisible" carbanions, a single-indicator technique has been developed [79,88,89]. To a known mixture of a suitable indicator hydrocarbon and its lithium or cesium salt in CHA, a known amount of the test carbon acid is added. From the decrease in absorbance of the indicator carbanion the concentration of the test carbanion is calculated for evaluation of equilibrium 13. This method has now been applied to a variety of additional types of compounds such as acetylenes, fluorinated and chlorinated benzenes, fluorinated bicycloalkanes, sulfur- and phosphorus-containing carbon acids and heterocyclic compounds. The pKs measured in our laboratories by these methods are summarized in Tables 13 to 21. These pK values are statistically corrected and refer to pKs per hydrogen. This distinction is not always made clear in the original papers and the original data have been recalculated. The correction is based on the numbers of equivalent hydrogens that may be lost and on the number of equivalent positions in the carbanion to which a proton may return; thus, the statistical correction to the pK is given as eq. 19:

pK (per H) = pK (eq. 14) + log [(no. of equivalent ionizable hydrogens)/(no. of equivalent positions to which proton can return)] (19)

For example, the statistical correction for cyclopentadiene is 2/5, indene 2/2 and fluorene 2/1.

All of the results summarized in the following tables are on a consistent basis and may differ slightly from our previously published measurements, particularly of the carbanion spectra.

TABLE 14

pKs and Spectral Data of Benzenoid Aromatic and Polyarylmethane Derivatives

Compound	$\lambda_{max}(\varepsilon)$CsCHA	pK_{CsCHA} per H	$\lambda_{max}(\varepsilon)$LiCHA	pK_{LiCHA} per H
Tris-(pentafluorophenyl)methane				15.54[a]
Tris-(p-methyltetrafluorophenyl)methane				17.58[a]
Tris-(p-methoxytetrafluorophenyl)methane				18.98[a]
Phenalene, 8		18.49		
6-H-Benzo[cd]pyrene, 18	456(44,200) 523(10,400) 622(2650) 674(3100)	19.6[b]		
Bis-(pentafluorophenyl)methane				21.27[a]
Benzanthrene, 19	448(37,200)	21.43[c]	444(34,600)[d]	20.97[e]
1,1,2,2-Tetrakis(pentafluorophenyl)ethane				22.69[a]
1,1,3,3-Tetraphenylpropene			456(29,800) 495(18,400) 563(36,800)	25.9[c]
1,1,3-Triphenylpropene	470(23,500) 556(46,500)	26.59[c]	470(21,400) 556(46,200)	26.4[e]
10-p-Biphenylyl-9,9-dimethyl-9,10-dihydroanthracene, 20d	450(32,100)	27.72[f]		
10-Phenyl-9,9-dimethyl-9,10-dihydroanthracene, 20c	445(33,600)	28.01[f]		
9-Phenylxanthene, 12b	490(17,100)[g]	28.49[c]		
Bis(m-trifluoromethylphenyl)-methane	440 (48,000)	28.95[h]		
Bis(m-fluorophenyl)-methane	434(36,200)	29.83[g]		
p-Biphenylyldiphenylmethane	573(44,300)	30.17[a]	587[i]	
9,9-Dimethyl-9,10-dihydroanthracene, 20a	444(31,600)	30.25[f]		
9,9,10-Trimethyl-9,10-dihydroanthracene, 20b	452(31,100)	30.3[f]		
9,10-Dihydroanthracene, 13a	444(34,200)	30.6[j]		
Di-p-biphenylylmethane	557(102,000)	30.8[f]		
Dibenzocyclohepta-1,4-diene, 21	460(40,000)	31.2[f]		
Triphenylmethane	423(15,100)[g] 487(30,300)[g]	31.45[f]	488[i]	

354

TABLE 14 (continued)

p$\underline{K}$s and Spectral Data of Polyarylmethane Derivatives

Compound	$\lambda_{max}(\epsilon)$CsCHA	p$\underline{K}$_CsCHA per H	$\lambda_{max}(\epsilon)$LiCHA	p$\underline{K}$_LiCHA per H
3-Phenyl-dibenzo-cyclohepta-1,4-diene, 21b	462(39,200)	31.6[f]		
p-Benzylbiphenyl	525(65,000)	31.82[k]		
Di-m-anisylmethane	440(39,200)	32.7[h]		
Tri-p-tolylmethane	445(19,300) 496(27,500)	33.04[f]		
Diphenylmethane	443(47,100)	33.38[f]	443[f,i]	
o-Benzylbiphenyl	460(36,000)	33.51[k]		
3-Methyl-dibenzo-cyclohepta-1,4-diene, 21c	472(36,900)	33.6[f]		
Bis(m-cyclopropyl phenyl)methane	447(51,000)	33.71[l]		
Di-m-tolylmethane	447(47,900)	33.80[h]		
9,10-Dihydroanthracyl-9-cesium, 13e	633(18,300)	34.1[j]		
Bis(p-cyclopropyl-phenyl)methane	456(56,000)	34.74[l]		
Di-o-tolylmethane	449(50,500)	34.8[f]		
Di-p-tolylmethane	446(44,000)	35.1[f]		
Bis(2,4-dimethyl-phenyl)methane	445(37,700)[g]	36.3[f]		
p-Isopropylbiphenyl	494(17,000)	38.6[n]		
p-Ethylbiphenyl	482(33,400)	38.8[n]		
p-Methylbiphenyl	470(39,200)	39.0[f,n]		
Toluene	470	(41.2)[n,o]		

[a]Ref. 92. [b]Ref. 93. [c]Ref. 47. [d]Ref. 94. [e]Ref. 48. [f]Ref. 50. [g]This value was redetermined and is a correction to the previously published value. [h]Ref. 95. [i]Does not follow Beer's law. [j]Ref. 96. [k]Ref. 97. [l]Ref. 98. [m]For anthracene-dicesium. [n]Ref. 86. [o]Extrapolated result from kinetic acidities; ref. 99.

18

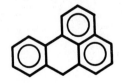

19

TABLE 15

pK data of acetylenes

Compound	$p\underline{K}_{LiCHA}$ (34°) (Ref. 79)
phenylacetylene	23.24
$CH_3\text{-}C\text{-}C\equiv C\text{-}H$ with CH_3 groups, tert-butylacetylene	25.52

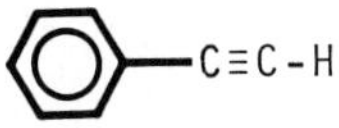

TABLE 16

pKs of some heterocyclic compounds

Compound	$p\underline{K}_{CsCHA}$ (34°) per H
Benzothiazole	28.08[a]
Thiazole	29.50[a]
Benzofuran	36.84[a]
Benzothiophene	37.05[a]
Thiophene	38.2[a,b]

[a] Ref. 89. [b] Ref. 86.

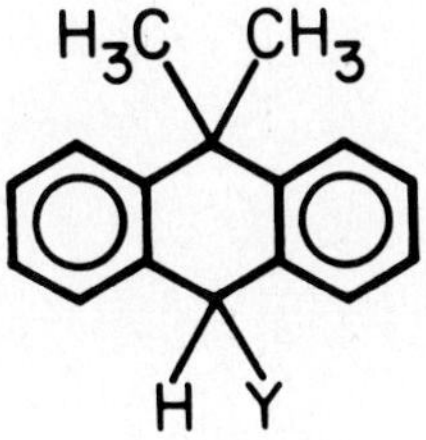

20a Y = H
20b Y = CH$_3$
20c Y = C$_6$H$_5$
20d Y = p-C$_6$H$_4$C$_6$H$_5$

356

TABLE 17

p$\underline{K}$s of some polyhalogenated benzenes

Compound	p$\underline{K}_{CsCHA}$ (34°) per H (Ref. 100)
	25.8
	29.9
	31.1
	31.5
	33.6
	34.0
	35.1
	(43.0)[a]

[a]Extrapolated p$\underline{K}_a$ value of benzene from a Br∅nsted correlation.

TABLE 18

p$\underline{K}$s of some dithiane derivatives

Compound	p$\underline{K}_{CsCHA}$ (25°)
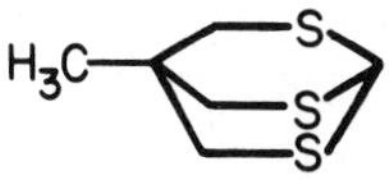	27.3[a]
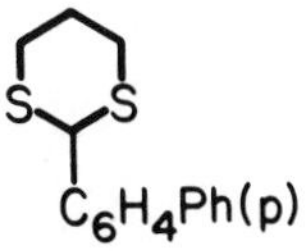 $C_6H_4Ph(p)$	27.5[b]
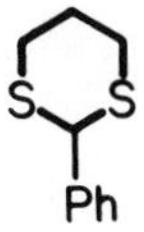 Ph	29.6[b]
	31.1[b]
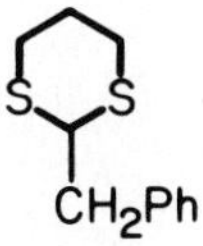 CH_2Ph	34.0[b]
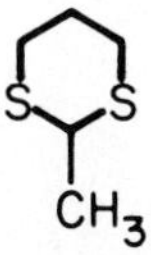 CH_3	37.8[b,c]
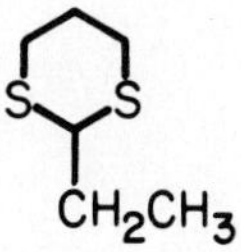 CH_2CH_3	>38.4[b,c]

[a]Reference 101.   [b]Reference 102.   [c]Reference 86.

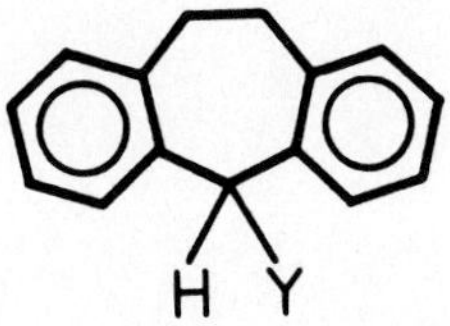

21a Y = H
21b Y = C_6H_5
21c Y = CH_3
21d Y = $p-C_6H_4C_6H_5$

TABLE 19

pKs of polyfluorinated bicycloalkanes

Compound	pK_{-CsCHA} (34°) per H (Ref. 103)
(bicycloalkane with F, H, F_{12})	18.3
(bicycloalkane with F, H, F_{10})	20.5
(bicycloalkane with CF_3, H, F_{10})	20.7
(bicycloalkene with F, H, F_8)	21.6
(bicycloalkane with H, H, F_{10})	22.3
(bicycloalkane with CH_3, H, F_{10})	23.4

TABLE 20

p$\underline{K}$s of some phosphines and phosphine oxides

Compound	$\lambda_{max}(\varepsilon)$CsCHA	p$\underline{K}_{-CsCHA}$ (25°) per H (ref. 68)
p-Biphenylylmethyldiphenyl-phosphine oxide	420 (30,000)	24.18
Benzyldiphenylphosphine oxide	325 (15,200)	24.89
p-Biphenylylmethyldiphenyl-phosphine	473 (12,000)	31.0
$Ph_2PCH_2PPh_2$		31.1
Diphenyl-p-tolylphosphine oxide	362 (20,100)	32.64
Diphenyl-p-tolylphosphine	365 (16,300)	38.0

TABLE 21

p$\underline{K}$s of some sulfones

Compound	p$\underline{K}_{-CsCHA}$ (25°) per H (ref. 67)
Benzyl phenyl sulfone	22.6
p-Biphenylyl methyl sulfone	27.1
Phenyl methyl sulfone	27.2
p-Tolyl methyl sulfone	27.5
Phenyl ethyl sulfone	29.1
Phenyl isopropyl sulfone	29.3

TABLE 22

Ion pair acidities in DME

Compound	$pK_{-Li^+,DME}$ [a]	pK_{-LiCHA}	$pK_{-Cs^+,DME}$ [a]	pK_{-CsCHA}
Conjugated Hydrocarbons [b]				
9-Phenylfluorene, <u>1b</u>	(18.5) [c]	(18.49) [c]	17.55	(18.49) [c]
Indene	20.3	20.24	19.0	19.93
Benzanthrene, <u>19</u>	20.9	20.97	20.65	21.43
9-Benzylfluorene, <u>1f</u>	21.95		20.95	21.27
9-(Dimethylamino)fluorene	23.25		22.1	
Fluorene, <u>1a</u>	23.65	22.85	22.3	23.04
9-Isopropylfluorene, <u>1h</u>	23.7	23.75	22.5	23.2
9-t-Butylfluorene, <u>1i</u>	24.85	24.82	23.75	24.25
1,1,3,3-Tetraphenylpropene	25.55	25.9	(25.55) [d]	
9-Phenylxanthene, <u>12b</u>	27.75		27.7	28.49
p-Biphenylyldiphenylmethane	29.15		29.3	30.17
9,10-Dihydroanthracene	30.85		30.3	30.6
Triphenylmethane	30.7		30.75	31.45
Acetylenes, $RC{\equiv}CH$ [b,e]				
R				
C_6H_5	23.7	23.24	26.9	
$(CH_3)_3Si$	24.6			
$(C_2H_5)_3Si$	24.9			
$(C_2H_5)_3Ge$	24.35			
$(C_2H_5)_3Su$	24.3			
$(CH_3)_2CHCH_2S$	22.65			
$(CH_3)_3C$	26.0	25.52		
$CH_3CH_2CH_2CH_2$	26.2			

[a] The Russian data were presented without statistical correction; they are changed in this table to a per hydrogen basis for direct comparison with our CHA results. [b] Ref. 104. [c] Taken as standard. [d] This value was taken as the standard to agree with $pK_{-Li^+,DME}$ because ion pair dissociation constants for the Li^+ and Cs^+ salts were closest for this compound. [e] Ref. 105.

C. Ion Pair Acidities in Ethers

In ether solutions acidities, including ion pair acidities, have no absolute meaning because the solvent is not a useful proton source. Relative acidities do have significance in the sense of the proton transfer equilibrium [3] or transmetallation equilibrium [5]. Indeed, such equilibria in ethers have especial importance in synthetic organic chemistry stemming from the widespread use of metallations in THF with butyllithium. The group of Petrov and Shatenshtein in Moscow has been especially active during the past decade in determining relative acidities of a range of compounds in 1,2-dimethoxyethane (DME). Because absolute p$\underline{K}$s have no real meaning in these solvents they have chosen to refer their values to standard compounds with assumed absolute p$\underline{K}$s appropriate for the aqueous solution. Their values include both lithium and cesium salts. A number of their values, symbolized as p$\underline{K}_{Li}{}^+$, DME and p$\underline{K}_{Cs}{}^+$, DME, are summarized in Table 22 and compared, when available, with corresponding p$\underline{K}_{LiCHA}$ and p$\underline{K}_{CsCHA}$ values. For most compounds where comparisons are possible the relative ion pair acidities with either Li$^+$ or Cs$^+$ gegenions are remarkably similar in CHA and DME.

The cesium salts are all contact ion pairs. Some of the lithium salts are also reported to be contact ion pairs but most of the lithium salts of highly delocalized carbanions are solvent separated ion pairs in DME [104]. Interestingly, the Russian workers report that equilibria with the cesium salts were established much more rapidly than for the lithium salts.

Values are also available for carboxyl compounds and nitriles [106, 107], phosphorus compounds [71] and organosodiums in hydrocarbons [118].

V. STRUCTURE AND CARBANION STABILITY

Available quantitative data on carbon acidity now cover a wide range of structure. A complete discussion of the effects of structure on carbanion stability is beyond the scope of this review. We will instead focus attention on a few areas, particularly where comparison between ionic and ion pair acidities plays a role.

A. Solvent Effects

As discussed above, the p$\underline{K}_{CsCHA}$ values for carbon acids having extensively delocalized carbanions are of the same order of magnitude as thermodynamic ionic p$\underline{K}_a$ values in both cyclohexylamine and in water. A further comparison of the carbon acidities of hydrocarbons in Table 4 between ion pair p$\underline{K}_{CsCHA}$ values and ionic p$\underline{K}$s for aqueous organic and DMSO mixtures shows generally excellent agreement in the

362

pK range of 18-25; the average deviation of either values is less than 0.5 pK units. This agreement shows that any of these compounds could have been chosen as the standard for pK_{-CsCHA} without much change in the assigned values.

The ionic pKs were determined with the H_ method and, given the assumptions of this method, these pKs represent those applicable to the dilute aqueous standard state; that is, they would represent pKs that would be obtained if one could measure them in pure water. Unfortunately, the H_ method depends on a cancellation of activity coefficients of the carbon acid and its carbanion with those of the indicator used to set up the H_ scale. The results, therefore, are sensitive to the type of indicator used and represent only approximately the pKs of an aqueous solution. For most purposes this suffices so long as a consistent set is used.

Nevertheless, the agreement between the ion pair pK_{-CsCHA} values with the "aqueous pKs" indicates that for highly delocalized carbanions the solvation interactions with solvent are comparable to the electrostatic interactions with the gegenion. All of these interactions are probably relatively small. For example, it has long been known that polarographic reduction potentials of polycyclic aromatic hydrocarbons to give conjugated radical anions have structural effects that are independent of solvent. In particular, hydrogen-bonding to solvent is probably unimportant. Cesium cation is a relatively large cation and its electrostatic interaction with a highly delocalized negative charge is rather small and non-specific. Specific ion pair effects can be found in comparisons with pK_{-LiCHA} and for carbanions that consist of two separated regions of charge [84,85,9], but these effects are all relatively small. For conjugated carbanions the cesium ion pairs are contact pairs and the lithium ion pairs are solvent separated [85].

These conclusions apply equally well to the ion pair acidities in DME (Table 22). The relative Li^+ and Cs^+ ion pair acidities are comparable in this solvent and also are similar to corresponding values in CHA. Moreover, a study of several ethers (DME, diethoxyethane, diglyme) showed little effect on solvent of ion pair acidities of several hydrocarbons having highly delocalized carbanions [108].

Another line of argument concerns cyclopentadiene. This hydrocarbon was measured in aqueous sodium hydroxide and the H_ extrapolation required was rather short [17]; hence, the pK of 15.6 (per H) undoubtedly corresponds closely to a true dilute aqueous standard state. The pK_{-CsCHA} found for cyclopentadiene, 16.25 (per H), involves

starting with the assumed aqueous p$\underline{K}$ of 18.5 for 9-phenylfluorene
and comparing ion pair equilibria for a chain of carbon acids. This
indirectly derived value is rather close to the measured aqueous
value and confirms that the p$\underline{K}$ assignments to hydrocarbons in this
region cannot be much in error; that is, they correspond to the dilute
aqueous solution standard state.

Much above p$\underline{K}$=25 the p$\underline{K}$ correspondence between the H$_-$ method
and CsCHA begins to break down; for example, the H$_-$ p$\underline{K}$ of triphenylmethane, 27.2, is much lower than the p$\underline{K}_{CsCHA}$ of 31.45 (Table 4).
This difference is in the wrong direction to be attributed to ion
pair interaction. Since triphenylmethane is a weaker acid than the
fluorene derivatives the charge is undoubtedly less delocalized and
specific ion pair association could well be greater--but this would
have the effect of lowering an ion pair p$\underline{K}$ relative to an ionic p$\underline{K}$.
We shall see this same phenomenon in discussing localized carbanions.
The observed difference probably represents a breakdown in the H$_-$
method; the extrapolation is apparently too long for the indicators
used. In effect, the indicators used in establishing the CsCHA
scale are carbon acids--the same as the compounds being measured.
It seems quite possible, therefore, that even the upper portion of
the CsCHA scale represents approximately the aqueous standard state.

The extensive set of p$\underline{K}_{DMSO}$ values determined in Bordwell's
laboratory provides an especially valuable comparison with p$\underline{K}_{CsCHA}$
values because of the extended p$\underline{K}$ range represented. Values for
ten compounds are compared in Table 23 over a range of 15 p$\underline{K}$-units.
The amazingly precise correlation between those values is summarized
in eq. 20 and illustrated in Fig. 1.

$$p\underline{K}_{DMSO} = (0.950 \pm 0.015)\ p\underline{K}_{CsCHA} + (0.821 \pm 0.400) \qquad (20)$$

r = 0.998

The standard deviation of the 10 values is only 0.23, hardly more
than the combined experimental error. This agreement is all the
more remarkable when we recall the difference in standard states.
Clearly, for this extensive series of conjugated carbon acids covering
a range of about 15 p$\underline{K}$ units, the electrostatic interaction between
the delocalized negative charge and the large cesium cation in the
contact ion pair is apparently comparable to the solvation of the
essentially free carbanion by DMSO solvent molecule dipoles.

Similarly, ion pair acidities for cesium salts in DME, the
p$\underline{K}_{Cs^+,DME}$ results in Table 22, parallel the p$\underline{K}_{CsCHA}$ results closely.

TABLE 23

Comparison of $p\underline{K}_{CsCHA}$ and $p\underline{K}_{DMSO}$

Compound	$p\underline{K}_{CsCHA}$[a]	$p\underline{K}_{DMSO}$[a,b]
9-Phenylfluorene	18.49	17.9
Indene	19.93	20.1
4,5-Methylenephenanthrene	22.93	22.4
9-Methylfluorene	22.33	22.3
Fluorene	23.04	22.9
Benzo[b]fluorene	23.47	23.2
1,3,3-Triphenylpropene	26.59	25.9
9-Phenylxanthene	28.49	27.9
p-Biphenylyldiphenylmethane	30.17	29.4
Triphenylmethane	31.45	30.6
Diphenylmethane	33.38	32.6

[a]per H.   [b]Ref. 39; see also Table 7.

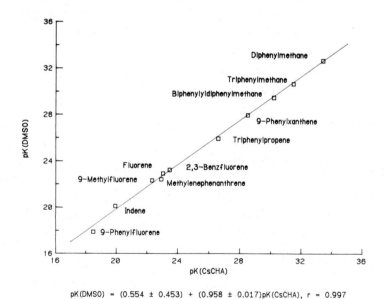

pK(DMSO) = (0.554 ± 0.453) + (0.958 ± 0.017)pK(CsCHA), r = 0.997

The comparison is described in eq. 21.

$$p\underline{K}_{Cs^+,DME} = 1.012\ p\underline{K}_{CsCHA} - (0.990 \pm 0.019) \tag{21}$$

$r = 0.999$

The important result of these studies is that the p$\underline{K}$s of these hydrocarbon acids with delocalized carbanions now form a background reference to which other types of carbon acids can be compared for identification of specific effects. Because of the close correspondences among H$_-$, DMSO, DME and CsCHA scales for these reference compounds, any of these scales can, in principle, be used and have, in fact, been used. At the high p$\underline{K}$ end the DMSO scale extends several units above the H$_-$ scale and the CsCHA scale extends approximately an additional 10 p$\underline{K}$ units. Cyclohexylamine is about 9 p$\underline{K}$ units weaker in acidity than DMSO.

The correspondence of p$\underline{K}$ scales in aqueous, DMSO, and ion pair systems found for delocalized carbanions breaks down completely for localized systems. In such systems negative charge is more concentrated and hydrogen-bonding solvation and ion pair electrostatic interactions become important. Such specific solvation effects are apparently less pronounced in DMSO; hence, p$\underline{K}_{DMSO}$ values tend to be higher than aqueous (H$_-$), p$\underline{K}_{M^+,DME}$ or p$\underline{K}_{CsCHA}$ values relative to delocalized standards. For example, phenylacetylene has p$\underline{K}_{DMSO}$ = 28.8 [39]; the p$\underline{K}_{CsCHA}$ is not available because of solubility but the closely related p$\underline{K}_{LiCHA}$ = 23.2 [79]. With the localized charge of the acetylide anion, Coulombic ion pair interaction is stronger and the ion pair acidity is higher than the analogous ionic acidity.

Not many such comparisons are yet available for unambiguously localized systems and a quantitative assessment is not now possible. Unfortunately, few such carbanions are sufficiently stable in DMSO for quantitative study. As such values do accumulate the comparisons of solvents will undoubtedly provide a useful tool for evaluating the degree of charge delocalization. An example is discussed below for sulfur-stabilized carbanions.

Still fewer pKs are available in hydroxylic solvents for localized carbanion species. The aqueous p$\underline{K}$ of phenylacetylene as estimated from kinetic exchange experiments is approximately 21 [58,109,110], not much different from the p$\underline{K}_{CsCHA}$ value. The hydrogen isotope exchange of highly halogenated benzenes catalyzed by methanolic sodium methoxide appears to provide a good measure of relative equilibrium acidities in methanol; the derived relative equilibrium ionic acidities correspond closely to relative ion pair pK_{CsCHA} values. It would appear that hydrogen-bonding stabilization of carbanions in hydroxylic solvents is comparable to cesium cation ion pair stabilization.

Cyclopentadiene provides an interesting comparison. Although the cyclopentadienyl anion is highly delocalized it still represents a rather concentrated volume of charge. It seems significant that the pK_{DMSO} of 18.0 (Table 7) is almost 2 pK units higher than the pK_{CsCHA} of 16.25; this difference is significantly greater than the correlation of Fig. 1. Moreover, both values are significantly higher than the aqueous pK_a value of 15.6. This comparison suggests that the cyclopentadienyl anion is stabilized by cesium cation to a greater extent than the reference indicators and that hydrogen-bonding stabilization is still more important. Nevertheless, the most important point is that for cyclopentadiene, pK_{aq}, pK_{CsCHA} and pK_{DMSO} are all relatively close in magnitude; small differences do exist that suggest interpretation by solvation phenomena but these differences are relatively small.

A related matter concerns the nature of ion pairs with localized carbanions. For the large cesium cation all of the carbanion ion pairs appear to be contact pairs; lithium, however, is more complex. With delocalized carbanions in coordinating solvents the solvent provides better solvation for Li^+ than does the carbanion and the resulting ion pairs are generally "loose" or "solvent-separated". CHA and DME are two such coordinating solvents. The more concentrated charge of localized carbanions increases the electrostatic interaction with the small lithium cation and equilibrium may now favor tight ion pairs. Temperature studies of pentafluorophenyllithium show, for example, that it is a tight or contact ion pair similar to pentafluorophenylcesium [111].

The same generalizations apply to lithium salts in DME. The ion pair acidity of phenylacetylene is 3 pK units greater towards its lithium salt than towards its cesium salt (Table 22). Phenylethynyllithium is undoubtedly a contact ion pair but its pK is referenced to a solvent separated standard; hence, the pK is lower than for cesium in which both substrate and reference standard are contact ion pair salts. Moreover, this interpretation is borne out by temperature and ionic dissociation studies of the Russian group. Lithium salts in DME that form tight ion pairs have lower ion dissociation constants than solvent separated analogs [112]. Correspondingly, the lithium tight ion pairs have more negative entropies of dissociation because additional solvent molecules must coordinate to the free Li^+.

In general, ion pair proton transfer equilibria in which the type of ion pair does not change--either contact or solvent separated on both sides of the equilibrium--have relatively small $\Delta S°$ values. A change in the type of ion pair involved shows up as a large entropy change [112].

The study of the nature of carbanion-lithium cation ion pairs will be an increasingly important tool for establishing the localized or delocalized nature of carbanions. Moreover, such study is also important in unraveling the complex behavior of lithium salts in synthetic organic chemistry. Further discussion of the nature of ion pairs is found in the chapter by E. Buncel and B. C. Menoy in this volume.

B. Delocalized Carbanions

There is no doubt that delocalization of charge in highly conjugated carbanions is principally responsible for the relatively high acidity of the corresponding hydrocarbons [8]. The results for nine systems with carbanions expected to be planar (Table 24) show a good correlation with a semi-empirical LCAO-MO SCF-π calculation of the π-energy difference between carbanion and hydrocarbon (Fig. 2). The deviations that do occur are probably largely associated with changes in structure and strain energy not considered in the calculations of π-electrons only.

In addition to the well-known acidifying effects of cyclopentadienyl anion moieties, the phenalenyl anion structure, 22, is almost equally effective. Note that the negative charge can be distributed to six equivalent carbons. This group contributes to the relatively high acidities of 6-H-benzo[cd]pyrene, 18, and benzanthrene, 19.

22

Delocalization of charge to phenyl substituents has a general acidifying effect but depends critically on steric effects, particularly the degree of coplanarity of the phenyl group and carbanion center. Using an extrapolation based on comparison of pK_{DMSO} of substituted toluenes with substituted anilines, Bordwell, Algrim and

368

TABLE 24

Correlation of pK_{-CsCHA} with SCF-π calculations

Hydrocarbon	pK_{-CsCHA}	E_{π_1} e.v.[a] Hydrocarbon	Carbanion	ΔE_{π}
Toluene	41.2	9.666	1.600	8.066
Phenalene	18.49	19.405	14.128	5.277
Indene	19.93	12.290	6.872	5.419
Fluorene	23.04	20.109	14.334	5.775
11-H-Benz[a]fluorene	20.35	27.215	21.794	5.421
10-H-Benz[b]fluorene	23.47	27.207	21.419	5.788
7-H-Benz[c]fluorene	19.75	27.243	21.738	5.505
Benzanthrene	21.43	27.235	21.536	5.699
9-H-Benz[def]fluorene	22.93	24.108	18.312	5.796
Cyclopentadiene	16.25	4.522	-.610	5.132

[a]J.S. Wright, Dissertation, University of California, 1968.

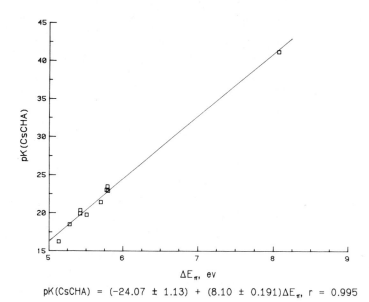

$pK(CsCHA) = (-24.07 \pm 1.13) + (8.10 \pm 0.191)\Delta E_{\pi}$, r = 0.995

Vanier [64] have estimated the $pK_{\overline{DMSO}}$ of toluene to be about 42. A Brønsted correlation of $pK_{\overline{CsCHA}}$ and hydrogen isotope exchange rates with LiCHA provides $pK_{\overline{CsCHA}}$ of toluene = 41.2 [99,86]. In both systems an additional phenyl substituent in diphenylmethane gives an increase in acidity of 8 (CsCHA) to 10 (DMSO) pK units. The further change to triphenylmethane gives an additional acidity increase of only 2.0 pK units in both systems. This effect is clearly due to the the non-planar structure of triphenylmethyl anion. One approach to assessing the degree of conjugation of a phenyl group involves evaluation of the effects of substituents in the phenyl ring.

Substituents on benzene rings have long been useful as probes of charge. The value of ρ in a Hammett $\sigma\rho$ treatment provides a measure of the charge near the aryl group and the enhanced effects of conjugating substituents over normal σ values provide a measure of the actual conjugation of the phenyl ring to the charged center. Cockerill and Lamper [46] have made use of this approach in their study of 9-arylfluorenes; they deduced that the phenyl ring in 9-phenylfluorenyl anion is twisted by 39° from coplanarity. In a comparison of this anion with related ring systems in which the 9-aryl group is constrained to greater coplanarity, Streitwieser and Nebenzahl [91] derived a twist angle of 50°.

The phenyl substituent itself can provide a useful probe since it has a relatively small polar effect (σ_m=0.06, σ_p=-0.01 [13]) but has an important conjugating effect. The $\Delta pK_{\overline{CsCHA}}$ for toluene and p-methylbiphenyl, 2.2, is substantial compared to that for toluene and diphenylmethane, 7.8, and provides a rough measure of the relative amounts of charge at the α and p positions of benzyl anion. Indeed, the ratio, 0.28, is rather close to the ratio of π-electron charges, 0.25, given for these two positions by a Hückel MO calculation on benzyl anion.

By comparison, the close $pK_{\overline{CsCHA}}$ values of 10-p-biphenylyl-, 20d, and 10-phenyl-9,9-dimethyl-9,10-dihydroanthracene, 20c, 27.7 and 28.0, respectively, shows that the aryl substituents in the corresponding carbanions must be strongly twisted from conjugation. Other examples of the use of phenyl groups as probes of carbanion character are found in Bordwell's research [57].

C. Alkyl Groups
    Alkyl substituents on an aromatic ring show typical electron-donating characteristics that may be associated primarily with the effective dipole of the $C_{sp}2$-$C_{sp}3$ bond. Such substituents invariably

370

have an acid-weakening effect. Typical examples are triphenylmethane
and tri-p-tolylmethane, ΔpK_{CsCHA} = 1.6, diphenylmethane and di-m-
tolylmethane, ΔpK_{CsCHA} = 0.4.

Alkyl substituents at the carbanion center, however, have a more
complex effect that is apparently a composite of steric effects (for
example, to coplanarity), hybridization changes and polarizability in
addition to an electron-donating inductive effect. The polarizability
factor is undoubtedly responsible for the acid-strengthening effect
of alkyl substituents in the gas phase acidity series such as t-BuOH
> i-PrOH > EtOH > MeOH > H_2O. The anionic charge produces an induced
dipole in the polarizable alkyl group that provides additional electro-
static stabilization represented symbolically as: ^-X-$\overset{\leftrightarrow}{Y}$. This induction
falls off rapidly with distance; it is the dominating effect for alkyl
groups close to the anion center in the gas phase but as the distance
increases the electron-donating effect of a permanent dipole becomes
increasingly important. These effects on gas phase acidities are
discussed in the chapter by M. J. Pellerite and J. I. Brauman in this
volume but the results summarized in Table 25 are particularly
instructive.

TABLE 25
Enthalpies for deprotonation in gas phase[a]

	Y=H $\Delta H°$ kcal mol^{-1}	Y=CH$_3$ $\Delta\Delta H°$ kcal mol^{-1}	Y=C(CH$_3$)$_3$ $\Delta\Delta H°$ kcal mol^{-1}
Y-OH	390.8	-11.7	-17.9
Y-SH	352.3	5.9	1.7
Y-C≡CH	374.0	5.0	2.1

[a]For RH   R$^-$ + H$^+$; J. E. Bartmess and R. T. McIver, Jr., in "Gas
Phase Ion Chemistry", Vol. 2, M. T. Bowers, ed., Academic Press
(1979).

In all three types of acids, alcohols, mercaptans and acetylenes, the
t-butyl compound is more acidic than the methyl but the difference is
smaller for the thiol and acetylene where the anionic charge is farther
from the substituent; moreover, the order of acidity of CH$_3$XH and
HXH reverses in the same manner along these series.

In solution, substituent polarizability is expected to play a
smaller role and alkyl substituent effects become still more complex.
In the 9-position of fluorene, acidity drops along the series Me > Et
> i-Pr >t-Bu, both in DMSO and in CHA. Most of this effect is probably
associated with increased strain involved in conversion to a planar
carbanion. It is remarkable that the reverse order is found when a
methylene group, sulfide or sulfone is inserted between the substituent and the fluorene [63]. Such reversed order may be indicative
of neopentyl-type strain in the carbon acid relieved on forming the
planar carbanion. In acetylenes, for example, $(C_2H_5)_3SiC\equiv CH$ is
slightly less acidic than $(CH_3)_3SiC\equiv CH$ (Table 22).

Replacement of an α-H at a carbanion center by a methyl frequently has but little effect on pK. 9-Methylfluorene is slightly
more acidic than fluorene in both CHA and DMSO. In CHA, p-ethyl and
p-isopropylbiphenyls are slightly more acidic than p-methylbiphenyl
(Table 14). Steric hindrance is probably not an important consideration in these cases but an effective hybridization change probably is
significant. The change from a tetrahedral methyl compound to the
methyl carbanion involves a bond strengthening change that may be
approximated as $C_{sp3}-C_{sp3} \rightarrow C_{sp3}-C_{sp2}$. This change is greater than
for hydrogen and is analogous to the stabilization of multiple bonds
by alkyl substituents. This effect opposes the electron-donating
destabilization of the $C_{sp3}-C_{sp2}$ dipole in the carbanion. When the
alkyl group is attached to an sp^2-carbon in both the carbon acid and
carbanion, as in ring-substituted aryl systems, the acid-weakening
effect is dominant.

D. Highly Halogenated Systems

The large anion-stabilizing effect of multiple fluorine substituents is evident in the relatively high acidities found by Filler
and Wang [92] for pentafluorophenylmethanes with LiCHA. Similarly,
perfluorophenyl and perfluorofluorenyl groups were found by Petrov
and Shatenshtein, et al, to have high acidifying effects in the DME
system [114]. The extraordinary electron-attracting character of
fluorine and even of chlorine is shown by the multiply halogenated
benzenes (Table 17) whose pK_{CsCHA} values are in a readily measurable
range. The pK_{CsCHA} values of these compounds give an excellent
Brønsted-type of plot with corresponding kinetic acidities measured
by methanolic sodium methoxide hydrogen isotope exchange and permit
an extrapolation to a pK_{CsCHA} value of benzene of 43.0 [88,100].

These large effects of halogen are primarily inductive effects associated with the high C-X dipole. Their magnitude is also demonstrated by the relatively low pK_{C_sCHA} values of highly fluorinated bicyclo[2.2.1]heptanes and bicyclo[2.2.2]octane (Table 19). Especially pertinent is the pK_{C_sCHA} difference of 2 units between the two series that is apparently simply attributable to the addition two more fluorines in the octane case.

The carbanions in these aryl and bicycloalkyl systems are undoubtedly localized and derive substantial stabilization from ion pair interactions. We may confidently expect that their gas phase and DMSO pK values relative to delocalized systems would be substantially higher. Unfortunately, suitable values are not yet available for comparison.

In addition to polar effects, other structural effects in localized carbanions are associated with the effective hybridization of the anion lone pair and polarization. The increase in acidity along the series ethane:ethylene:acetylene is usually attributed to increased s-character in the carbanion lone pair but recent ab initio MO calculations show that polarization of the multiple bond also plays an important role [115]. In the halogenated systems discussed here, fluorine is relatively non-polarizable and there is little doubt that polar effects dominate, but polarizability effects probably do contribute importantly to chlorine. The effects of halogens are also complicated by lone pair repulsions with the carbanion lone pair especially in π-type systems, but this effect is not important in the compounds in Table 17 and 19.

E. Third-Row Atoms

Sulfur, phosphorus and silicon are known to greatly stabilize adjacent carbanion centers. Documentation for sulfur and phosphorus is available in Tables 7, 18 and 20, and by extensive studies of Petrov, Shatenshtein, et al [71]. Less quantitative data are available for silicon. These groups are not highly electronegative and the large anionic stabilizing effects of these atoms are clearly not due to normal inductive effects. A continuing controversy concerns the relative roles of charge-transfer by conjugation in such systems by way of the vacant 3d orbitals on the third-row elements and of polarization. These differences can be associated with the following resonance descriptions:

$$\text{\Large{>}}\bar{C}-Y-R \longleftrightarrow \text{\Large{>}}\bar{C}-\overset{++}{Y}-R \longleftrightarrow \text{\Large{>}}C=\bar{Y}-R$$

$$\quad\quad a \quad\quad\quad\quad\quad\quad b \quad\quad\quad\quad\quad\quad c$$

23

Structure 23b shows the stabilizing effect of an induced dipole and 23c shows conjugation. One important difference that suggests operational criteria for distinction is that 23c implies delocalization with reduction of charge at carbon (charge-transfer) whereas 23b implies electrostatic stabilization without delocalization. All MO calculations on $HSCH_2^-$ show that d-orbitals have no special stabilizing role and that polarization of sulfur is the principal stabilizing factor [116]. The Streitwieser group interprets their data on dithianes (Table 18) on this basis [102], but the Bordwell group has considered that significant conjugation is also required to explain their results [60]. They point out, for example, that selenium is more polarizable than sulfur but is less anion-stabilizing ($PhSCH_2COPh$ is 1.5 pK_{DMSO} units more acidic than $PhSeCH_2COPh$) [60]; however, the generation of induced dipoles by polarization falls off rapidly with distance and the C-Se bond is appreciably larger than C-S.

In an important study of substituted acetylenes, Petrov and Shatenshtein and their coworkers [68,105] found that pK_{DMSO} are generally 5-6 units greater than $pK_{Li^+,DME}$ relative to delocalized indicators. This behavior is indicative of ethynyl anions that are essentially localized carbanions. For the series, $(C_2H_5)_3XC{\equiv}CH$ where X=Si, Ge, Sn, the $pK_{Li^+,DME}$ values were about 1.5 units lower than that for t-butylacetylene. This enhanced acidity indicated the existence of p_π-d_π conjugation to the Russian workers. However, in both DMSO and DME the pK differences along the series are rather small and not always monotonic, suggesting instead a dominant role of polarization effects.

Nevertheless, the mechanism of anion stabilization by third and higher row elements remains an unsettled and important problem. Operational criteria to distinguish charge transfer from polarization effects are difficult to devise, particularly with the limitations of working with real compounds. One interesting type of approach is suggested by 4-methyl-2,6,7-trithiabicyclo[2.2.2]octane, 24, which has pK_{DMSO} 3 units higher than pK_{CsCHA} (Table 7). This difference suggests the significant additional ion pair stabilization expected of a highly localized carbanion. By comparison, 2-phenyldithiane, 25,

has almost exactly the same pK_{-DMSO} as does 24 but is less acidic
towards CsCHA by 2 pK units. The carbanion from 25 is undoubtedly
delocalized via the benzylic system and ion pair interaction is
correspondingly reduced. These results suggest that the carbanion
from 24 is not extensively stabilized by delocalization to sulfur.
Nevertheless, the differences found are relatively small and this
criterion does not appear to be an especially sensitive one.

One further aspect of this topic concerns the possibility of
through-conjugation of the type 26, again by way of 3d orbitals.
The Bordwell group has interpreted their pK_{-DMSO} results for sulfones
as requiring conjugation of the carbanion with the SO_2 group [61].
Pagani, et al [117], have suggested that through-conjugation of
sulfone groups contributes significantly to the stability of anions
such as 27. However, through-conjugation of the type 26b is clearly
not significant; phenyl methyl sulfone and p-biphenylyl methyl sulfone
differ in pK_{-CsCHA} by only 0.1 units. If significant charge transfer
to the para-position had occurred we would anticipate a significantly
higher acidity for a p-phenyl substituent.

24

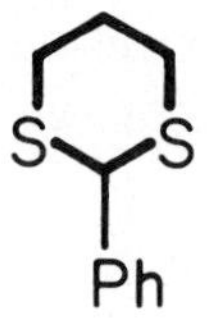

25

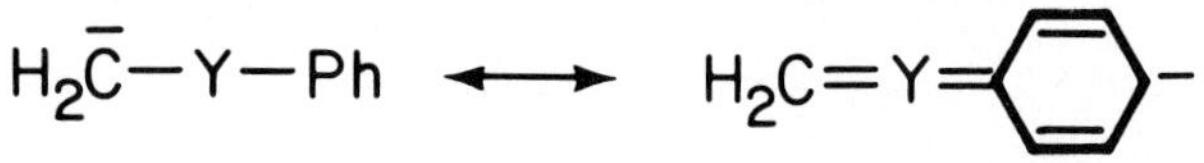

26

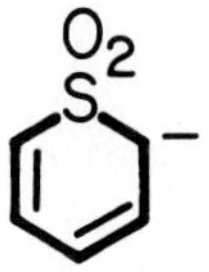

27

F. Dianions

Many dianions of aromatic systems are known through metallation studies and reactions with alkali metals. The formation of dianions had been noted in the CsCHA system with 9-benzylfluorene [49] and hydrocarbons of the 1,1,3,3-bis(biphenylene)propene, 15, type [84]. More recently, both the first and second pK_{CsCHA} values have been determined for 9,10-dihydroanthracene (Table 14) [96]. They differ by only 4 pK units. The implied relative stability of the dianion is in part related to the fact that it is actually anthracene dianion and receives some aromatic stabilization, but probably more important is the electrostatic stabilization present in the corresponding ion triplet, a structure with a cesium cation above and below the aromatic plane. Because of the two negative charges in the carbanion, the electrostatic attraction is four times that of a mono-anion cation pair, diminished only by the repulsion of two cesiums rather far from each other. Correspondingly, the pK of the purely ionic system would be expected to be far higher. Further discussion of dianions may be found in the chapter by R. B. Bates in this volume.

Acknowledgement

During the past decade the research in this laboratory on carbon acidity was supported by grant no GP-12855 of the National Institutes of Health, U.S. Public Health Service. It is presently supported by National Science Foundation grant no. CHE 79-10814. E. J. would like to thank his wife, Gabriela, for her patience during the preparation of this manuscript. We are also indebted to Professors Bordwell and McIver for communication of results before publication, and to G. W. Schriver for his assistance. Finally, this chapter would have been impossible without the superb secretarial services of Mrs. Lynne Gloria.

VI. REFERENCES

1 A. Streitwieser, Jr., and J.H. Hammons, Prog. Phys. Org. Chem., 3(1965)41.

2 D.J. Cram, Fundamentals of Carbanion Chemistry, Academic Press, New York, 1965.

3 J.R. Jones, The Ionisation of Carbon Acids, Academic Press, New York, 1973; cf also Quart. Rev. Chem. Soc., 25(1971)365; Prog. Phys. Org. Chem., 9(1972)241.

4 R.P. Bell, The Proton in Chemistry, 2nd Ed., Cornell University Press, Ithaca, N.Y., 1973.

5 E. Buncel, Carbanions. Mechanistic and Isotopic Aspects, Elsevier, Amsterdam, 1975.

6 O.A. Reutov, I.P. Beletskaya and K.P. Butin, CH-Acids, Pergamon Press, Oxford, 1978; cf also O.A. Reutov, K.P. Butin and I.P. Beletskaya, Russian Chem. Revs., 43(1974)1.

7 For example, H.F. Ebel, Die Acidität der CH-Sauren, Thieme Verlag, Stuttgart, 1969; M. Schlosser, Polare Organometalle, Springer-Verlag, Berlin, 1973.

8 H. Fischer and D. Rewicki, Prog. Org. Chem., 7(1968)116.

9 J.R. Murdoch and A. Streitwieser, Jr., Intra-Science Chem. Rept., 7(1973)45.

10 M. Scwarz, A. Streitwieser and P.C. Mowery, in Ions and Ion Pairs in Organic Reactions, M. Scwarz, ed., Vol. 2, Wiley-Interscience, New York, 1974, Ch. 2.

11 J. M. Mallan and R.L. Bebb, Chem. Rev., 69(1969)693.

12 F.G. Bordwell, Pure and Appl. Chem., 49(1977)963.

13 A. Collumeau, Bull. Soc. Chim. Fr. (1968)5087.

14 For example, J.I. Brauman and L.K. Blair, J. Am. Chem. Soc., 93 (1971)4315; D.K. Bohme, E. Lee-Ruff and L.B. Young, J. Am. Chem. Soc., 94(1972)5153.

15 J.I. Brauman and L.K. Blair, J. Am. Chem. Soc., 92(1970)5986; D.K. Bohme, E. Lee-Ruff and L.B. Young, J. Am. Chem. Soc. 93(1971) 4608; T.B. McMahan and P. Kebarle, J. Am. Chem. Soc., 98(1976)3399.

16 R.F. Cookson, Chem. Rev., 74(1974)5.

17 A. Streitwieser, Jr. and L.L. Nebenzahl, J. Am. Chem. Soc., 98 (1976)2188.

18 Z. Margolin and F.A. Long, J. Am. Chem. Soc., 95(1973)2757.

19 C.H. Rochester, Acidity Functions, Academic Press, New York,1970.

20 See Ref. 16, p. 6; E.M. Arnett, Prog. Phys. Org. Chem., 1(1963) 223; M.M. Kreevoy and E.H. Baughman, J. Am. Chem. Soc., 95(1973) 9178.

21 O.W. Webster, J. Am. Chem. Soc., 88(1966)3046.

22 R.H. Boyd, J. Phys. Chem., 67(1963)737.

23 V.I. Slovetskii, S.A. Shevelev, A.A. Fainzil'Berg and S.S. Novikov,
    Zhur. Vses. Khim. Obshch. Mendeleeva, 6(1961)599,707.

24 R.G. Pearson and R.L. Dillon, J. Am. Chem. Soc., 75(1953)2493.

25 M. Novak and G.M. Loudon, J. Am. Chem. Soc., 98(1976)3591.

26 G. Schwarzenbach and E. Felder, Helv. Chim. Acta, 27(1944)1701;
    G. Schwarzenbach and K. Lutz, Helv. Chim. Acta, 23(1940)1162.

27 V.M. Belikov, S.G. Mairanovskii, Ts.B. Korchemuaya, S.S. Novikov
    and V.A. Klimova, Izv. Akad. Nauk. SSSR, Otd, Khim. Nauk (1960)
    1787.

28 C.P. Lillya and P. Muller, J. Am. Chem. Soc. 88(1966)1559.

29 M. Laloi-Diard and M. Rubinstein, Bull. Soc. Chim. Fr., (1965)310.

30 R.H. Boyd and C.H. Wang, J. Am. Chem. Soc., 87(1965)430.

31 G.W. Wheland and J. Farr, J. Am. Chem. Soc., 65(1943)1433.

32 E.J. Corey, H. Konig and T.H. Lowry, Tetrahedron Lett. (1962)515.

33 R.P. Bell and P.W. Smith, J. Chem. Soc. B (1966)241; R.P. Bell
    and B.G. Cox, J. Chem. Soc. B (1971)652.

34 R.P. Bell, Trans. Faraday Soc., 39(1943)253.

35 C.H. Langford and R. L. Burwell, Jr., J. Am. Chem. Soc., 82(1960)
    1503.

36 C.D. Ritchie, J. Am. Chem. Soc., 91(1969)6749.

37 A. Streitwieser, Jr., C.J. Chang and A.T. Young, J. Am. Chem. Soc.,
    94(1972)4888.

38 F.G. Bordwell and W.S. Matthews, J. Am. Chem. Soc., 96(1974)1214.

39 W.S. Matthews, J.E. Bares, J.E. Bartness, F.G. Bordwell, F.J.
    Comforth, G.E. Drucker, Z. Margolin, R.J. McCallum, G. J. McCollum
    and N.R. Vanier, J. Am. Chem. Soc., 97(1975)7006, and references
    cited therein.

40 F.G. Bordwell, J.E. Bartness, G.E. Drucker, Z. Margolin and W.S.
    Matthews, J. Am. Chem. Soc., 97(1975)3226.

41 E.C. Steiner and J.M. Gilbert, J. Am. Chem. Soc., 87(1965)382.

42 K. Bowden and R. Stewart, Tetrahedron, 21(1965)261.

43 E.C. Steiner and J.D. Starkey, J. Am. Chem. Soc., 89(1967)2751.

44 K. Bowden and A.F. Cockerill, Chem. Commun., (1967)989; J. Chem.
    Soc. B (1970)173.

45 R.A. Cox and R. Stewart, J. Am. Chem. Soc. 98(1976)488.

46 A.F. Cockerill and J.E. Lamper, J. Chem. Soc. B, (1971)503.

47 A. Streitwieser, Jr., E. Ciuffarin and J.H. Hammons, J. Am. Chem.
    Soc., 89(1967)63.

48 A. Streitwieser, Jr., J.H. Hammons, E. Ciuffarin and J.I. Brauman, J. Am. Chem. Soc., 89(1967)59.

49 A. Streitwieser, Jr., C.J. Chang and D.M.E. Reuben, J. Am. Chem. Soc., 94(1972)5730.

50 A. Streitwieser, Jr., J.R. Murdoch, G. Hafelinger and C.J. Chang, J. Am. Chem. Soc., 95(1973)4248.

51 R. Kuhn and D. Rewicki, Justus Liebigs Ann. Chem. 704(1967)79; 706(1969)250.

52 C.D. Ritchie and R.E. Uschold, J. Am. Chem. Soc., 89(1967)1721, 2752; 90(1968)2821.

53 F.G. Bordwell, R.H. Imes and E.C. Steiner, J. Am. Chem. Soc., 89 (1967)3905.

54 F.G. Bordwell and W.S. Matthews, J. Am. Chem. Soc., 96(1974)1216.

55 F.G. Bordwell, W.S. Matthews and N.R. Vanier, J. Am. Chem. Soc., 97(1975)442.

56 F.G. Bordwell, J.E. Bartmess and J.A. Hautala, J. Org. Chem., 43

57 F.G. Bordwell, J.E. Bares, J.E. Bartmess, G.J. McCollum, M. Van Der Puy, N.R. Vanier and W.S. Matthews, J. Org. Chem., 42(1977)321.

58 F.G. Bordwell, D. Algrim and H.E. Fried, J.C.S. Perkin II, submitted.

59 F.G. Bordwell, J.E. Bares, J.E. Bartmess, G.E. Drucker, J. Gerhold, G.J. McCollum, M. Van Der Puy, N.R. Vanier, and W.S. Matthews, J. Org. Chem., 42(1977)326.

60 F.G. Bordwell, M. Van Der Puy and N.R. Vanier, J. Org. Chem., 41 (1976)1885.

61 F.G. Bordwell, N.R. Vanier, W.S. Matthews, J.B. Hendrickson, and P.L. Skinner, J. Am. Chem. Soc., 97(1975)7160.

62 F.G. Bordwell and G.J. McCollum, J. Org. Chem., 41(1976)2391.

63 F.G. Bordwell, G.E. Drucker and G.J. McCollum, J. Org. Chem., 41 (1976)2768.

64 F.G. Bordwell, D. Algrim and N.R. Vanier, J. Org. Chem., 42(1977) 1817.

65 F.G. Bordwell and J.E. Bartmess, J. Org. Chem., 43(1978)3101; F.G. Bordwell, J.E. Bartmess and J.A. Hautala, ibid., 3107,3113; F.G. Bordwell and J. A. Hautala, ibid., 3116.

66 F.G. Bordwell and F. J. Cornforth, J. Org. Chem., 43(1978)1763.

67 M.I. Terekhova, E.S. Petrov, S.P. Mesyats and A.I. Shatenshtein, Zh. Obshch. Khim., 45(1975)1529.

68 E.S. Petrov, M.I. Terekhova, A.I. Shatenshtein, R.G. Mirskov, N.P. Ivanova and M.G. Voronkov, Izv. Akad. Nauk SSSR, Ser. Khim (1975)2351.

69 T.I. Lebedeva, E.S. Petrov, M.I. Terekhova and A.I. Shatenshtein, Dokl. Akad. Nauk SSSR, 225 (1975)357.

70 E.S. Petrov, E.N. Tsvetkov, S.P. Mesyants, A.I. Shatenshtein and M.I. Kabachnik, Izv. Akad. Nauk SSSR, Ser. Khim. (1976)782.

71 S.P. Mesyats, E.N. Tsvetkov, E.S. Petrov, M. I. Terekhova, A.I. Shatenshtein and M.I. Kabochnik, Izv. Akad. Nauk SSSR, Ser. Khim. (1974)2489; S.P. Mesyats, E.N. Tsvetkov, E.S. Petrov, N.N. Shalganova, T.M. Shcherbina, A.I. Shatenshtein and M.I. Kabachnik, Izv. Akad. Nauk SSSR, Ser. Khim. (1974)2497; E.S. Petrov, E.N. Tsvetkov, M.I. Terekhova, R.A. Malevannaya, A.I. Shatenshtein and M.I. Kabachnik, Izv. Akad. Nauk SSSR, Ser. Khim, (1976)534; E.S. Petrov, E.N. Tsvetkov, S.P. Mesyats, A.I. Shatenshtein and M.I. Kabachnik, Izv. Akad. Nauk SSSR, Ser. Khim. (1976) 782.

72 I.G. Faleev, Yu.I. Belokon and V.M. Belikov, Izv. Akad. Nauk SSSR, Ser. Khim. (1970)73.

73 R. Breslow, Pure Appl. Chem. 40(1974)493, and references cited therein; R. Breslow and R. Goodin, J. Am. Chem. Soc., 98(1976) 6076.

74 K.P. Butin, I.P. Beletskaya and O.A. Reutov, Elektrokhim., 2(1966) 635; O.A. Reutov, K.P. Butin and I.P. Beletskaya, Bull. Inst. Politeh, Iasi, II, 16(1970)33.

75 For example, see B.J. Wakefield, The Chemistry of Organolithium Compounds, Pergamon Press, Oxford, 1974.

76 J. Smid in Ions and Ion Pairs in Organic Reactions, M. Szwarc, Ed., Vol. 1, Wiley-Interscience, New York, 1972, p. 85.

77 J.B. Conant and G.W. Wheland, J. Am. Chem. Soc., 54(1932)1212.

78 W.K. McEwen, J. Am. Chem. Soc., 58(1936)1124.

79 A. Streitwieser, Jr. and D.M.E. Reuben, J.Am. Chem. Soc., 93 (1971)1794.

80 D.E. Applequist and D.F. O'Brien, J. Am. Chem. Soc., 85(1963)743.

81 R.M. Salinger and R.E. Dessy, Tetrahedron Letters, 11(1963)729.

82 D.J. Schaeffer, Chem. Commun., (1970)1043.

83 A. Streitwieser, Jr., W.M. Padgett, II, and I. Schwager, J. Phys. Chem., 68(1964)2922.

84 A. Streitwieser, Jr., C.J. Chang and W.B. Hollyhead, J. Am. Chem. Soc., 89(1967)63.

85 A. Streitwieser, Jr., C.J. Chang, W.B. Hollyhead and J.R. Murdoch, J. Am. Chem. Soc., 94(1972)5288.

86 A. Streitwieser, Jr., and F. Guibé, J. Am. Chem. Soc., 100(1978) 4532.

380

87   (a) G. Häfelinger and A. Streitwieser, Jr., Chem. Ber., 101(1968)
     657; (b) G. Häfelinger and A. Streitwieser, Jr., Chem. Ber., 101
     (1968)672; (c) G. Häfelinger and A. Streitwieser, Jr., Chem. Ber.
     101(1968)2785.
88   A. Streitwieser, Jr., P.J. Scannon and H.M. Niemeyer, J.Am. Chem.
     Soc., 94(1972)7936.
89   A. Streitwieser, Jr., and P.J. Scannon, J. Am. Chem. Soc., 95(197
     6273.
90   R. Kuhn and D. Rewicki, Justus Liebigs. Ann. Chem., 690(1965)50.
91   A. Streitwieser, Jr. and L.L. Nebenzahl, J. Org. Chem., 43(1978)
     598.
92   R. Filler and C-S Wang, Chem. Commun., (1968)287.
93   F. Guibé, unpublished results.
94   A. Streitwieser, Jr., and J.I. Brauman, J. Am. Chem. Soc., 85
     (1963)2633.
95   E.R. Vorpagel, unpublished results.
96   A. Streitwieser, Jr., C.M. Berke and K. Robbers, J. Am. Chem. Soc
     100(1978)8271.
97   E. Juaristi and A. Streitwieser, Jr., J. Org. Chem., 43(1978)2704
98   A. Streitwiesr, Jr., S.Q. Bryant, S. Alexandratos and E. Juaristi
     unpublished.
99   A. Streitwiesr, Jr., M.R. Granger, F. Mares and R.A. Wolf, J. Am.
     Chem. Soc., 95(1973)4257.
100 A. Streitwieser, Jr., L.L. Nebenzahl, P.J. Scannon and H.M.
     Niemeyer, J. Am. Chem. Soc., submitted.
101 S.P. Ewing, Dissertation, Univ. of Calif., Berkeley, 1974.
102 A. Streitwieser, Jr. and S.P. Ewing, J. Am. Chem. Soc., 97(1975)
     190.
103 A. Streitwieser, Jr., D. Holtz, G.R. Ziegler, J.O. Stoffer,
     M.L. Brokaw and F. Guibé, J. Am. Chem. Soc., 98(1976)5229.
104 E.S. Petrov, M.I. Terekhova and A.I. Shatenshtein, Zh. Obshch.
     Khim., 44(1974)1118.
105 E.S. Petrov, M.I. Terekhova, A.I. Shatenshtein, B.A. Trofimov,
     R.G. Mirskov and M.G. Voronkov, Dokl. Akad. Nauk SSSR, 211(1973)
106 T.I. Lebedeva, E.S. Petrov, M.I. Terekhova, and A.I. Shatenshtein,
     Dokl. Akad. Nauk SSSR, 225(1975)357.
107 T.I. Lebedeva, E.S. Petrov and A.I. Shatenshtein, Zh. Org. Khim.,
     13(1977)905.
108 E.S. Petrov, M.I. Terekhova and A.I. Shatenshtein, Org. React.
     Tartu 7(1970)1234.

109   A.J. Kresge and A.C. Lin, J. Chem. Soc., Chem. Comm., (1973)761.

110   A.J. Kresge, Accts. Chem. Res. 8(1975)354.

111   A. Streitwieser, Jr., and C.C.C. Shen, Tetrahedron Letters,
      No. 4 (1979)327.

112   E.S. Petrov, M.I. Terekhova, T.I. Lebedova, V.M. Basmanova and
      A.I. Shatenshtein, Zh. Obshch. Khim. 48(1978)616.

113   D.H. McDaniel and H.C. Brown, J. Org. Chem. 23(1958)420.

114   V.M. Vlasov, G.G. Yakobson, E.S. Petrov and A.I. Shatenshtein,
      J. Fluorine Chem. 9(1977)321.

115   J.E. Williams, Jr. and A. Streitwieser, Jr., J. Am. Chem. Soc.,
      97(1975)2634.

116   For two examples see: A. Streitwieser, Jr. and J.E. Williams, Jr.
      J. Am. Chem. Soc., 97(1975)191; J-M. Lehn and G. Wipff, J. Am.
      Chem. Soc., 98(1976)7498.

117   S. Bradamante, A. Mangia and G. Pagani, Tetrahedron Letters (1970)
      3381; J. Chem. Soc. B (1971) 545; G. Gaviraghi and G. Pagani,
      J. Chem. Soc. Perkin Trans 2, (1973)50; G. Pagani, J. Chem. Soc.
      Perkin Trans. 2, (1973)1184; (1974)1389.

118   S. Gau and S. Marques, J. Am. Chem. Soc., 98(1976)1538.

SUBJECT INDEX

FC